The Dictionary of Birds in color

The Dictionary of
BIRDS
in color

BRUCE CAMPBELL

Photographs from
ARDEA PHOTOGRAPHICS
London
and Aquila Photographics
David Attenborough
Biofotos
Bruce Coleman Ltd
Nicole Duplaix-Hall
Robert Harding Associates
Bobby Tulloch

NEW YORK

© 1974 by Bruce Campbell

This edition published in USA 1983
by Exeter Books
Distributed by Bookthrift
Exeter is a trademark of Simon & Schuster
Bookthrift is a registered trademark of Simon & Schuster
New York, New York

ISBN 0 671 05999 8

Printed in Hong Kong

Contents

Introduction

Birds, it can be argued, might have become the highest form of life upon earth. But to defy gravity so effortlessly demanded too drastic a stream-lining and jettisoning of cerebral ballast. It was left to a small group of terrestrial mammals to evolve the only reasoning species so far capable of observing and recording all other animals and plants. But civilised man's view remains largely subjective, conceivably at fault in many respects. When an ornithological expedition was seeking a very rare bird somewhere in Africa, its leader showed a village headman the most realistic representation of the sought-for species by a western artist. After looking at it for a time in puzzlement, the headman turned the drawing upside down.

By relying on the camera's rather than the human eye, this dictionary attempts to show as objective a representation as possible of a thousand species of birds; a further number are described in text alone. Between them they constitute about an eighth of the known kinds of living birds, believed to total about 8,650, out of some 51,000 species in the subphylum of vertebrate animals, which also includes the jawless (e.g. lampreys), cartilaginous (e.g. sharks and rays) and bony fishes (e.g. herring), the amphibia (e.g. frogs and newts), reptiles (e.g. snakes, lizards, turtles, crocodiles) and mammals, of which there are only about 4,250 species. The world total of insects is about a million, with many species being discovered every year, while no one would dare compute the number of other invertebrate animals.

Birds and mammals are the only two classes of warm-blooded vertebrates, able therefore to survive in greater climatic extremes than the reptiles and amphibians; but each has evolved a numerically dominant order of species generally small in size and most successful in dense vegetation: the passerine (sparrow-like) or perching birds, numbering over 5,000 species; and the rodents with over 1,700. At the top of the numerical pyramid each class has a comparatively few large predators living on land; both have relatively few fish-eating, sea-living species; but some of these, until man's fatal influence intervened, numbered millions of individuals; the reader can amuse himself by drawing other parallels, for example between the palatable waterfowl and game-birds and the ungulate mammals.

The few thousand kinds of bird that surround us today are the relics of a vast array of predecessors, estimated at anywhere between half a million and a million and a half species. Indeed, some authorities insist that the heyday of the birds was in Pleistocene times, down to 250,000 years ago, before the Ice Ages wreaked their havoc, and that we are now witnesses of their slow decline, at least in terms of species.

All the same, birds manage to occupy or visit every part of the biosphere except the depths of ocean. An alpine chough has been recorded at 8,200 metres (nearly 27,000 feet) on Everest, and migrant birds commonly fly at up to 7,000 metres or 21,000 feet. At the other extreme, the divers or loons and the Long-tailed Duck or Oldsquaw are credited with dives down to 60 metres (200 feet) and the ability to stay under water for up to three minutes. Some seabirds spend almost their whole lives outside the breeding season in the air; indeed, frigate birds only exceptionally settle on the water. Other seabirds spend most of their time miles offshore, while the Emperor Penguin, which nests on the antarctic ice, never touches land. Few birds burrow vertically downward more than a metre or so, but laterally they may inhabit tunnels up to 4 metres in length, like those artificially made to protect the rare Bermuda Cahow from its Tropicbird nest-rival.

A geographical consideration of bird distribution might start with areas having extreme conditions, like the great mountain ranges of south-central Asia, where a variety of beautiful pheasants and allied species are found to the limits of tree growth; higher up are their more distant relatives the Snowcocks and the unique Snow Partridge, *Lerwa*. The altitudinal level of bird life falls with latitude, but another group of game birds, the ptarmigan, with their feathered feet and snow-burrowing adaptations, can survive as residents in the arctic in a quite different way to the penguins on their southern ice floes.

The deserts also support some birds, especially larks and sand-grouse, though the Sahara can be the graveyard of some of the millions of migrants that annually overfly it. Another sort of desert, the man-scape of megalopolis, has its bird inhabitants, though the disappearance of horse traffic has probably reduced the number of House or English Sparrows in city centres, and many civic bodies look askance at the Feral Pigeons which see in tall and ornamental buildings replicas of the sea cliffs and mountain crags from which their remote ancestors came.

Bird life increases progressively from the polar regions, the great deserts of the world and the huge conurbations. Sometimes it is transient, a brief but multitudinous occupation during the short northern summer of perpetual daylight when there is a chance to raise a brood quickly on the suddenly abundant plant and small animal life. The rains bring a similar situation to tropical desert fringes and savannahs, but the suburbs of temperate zone cities tend to have a more stable and resident population, rich in individuals if not in species and sure of commensal food supply from man. Perhaps one of the loudest dawn choruses, competing with the perpetual traffic, is that of many Blackbirds and fewer Song Thrushes in the parks of inner London. Central Park, New York, on the other hand, is famous for its visitors on passage.

The land masses of the world were first divided in 1858 into zoo-geographical regions by P. L. Sclater, a leading British ornithologist; today we recognise six main regions, each with a distinctive fauna of breeding birds, though receiving large numbers of winter and passage visitors from other regions. The *Palaearctic* region (sometimes regarded as a sub-region of an *Holarctic* region) covers all Europe, Mediterranean Africa and most of Asia down to the great mountain chains; in Alaska it meets the other component of the Holarctic, the *Nearctic* region, which stretches down North America to Mexico. There is a zone of blending between the Palaearctic and the *Oriental* region, which latter covers the Indian sub-continent, south-east Asia and many of its islands, to meet the *Australasian* region in another blending zone round the Celebes. Here is the famous Wallace's Line, called after the co-discoverer of natural selection, A. R. Wallace, which passes between the islands of Bali and Lombok, noted for their distinct faunas. New Zealand constitutes a sub-region of the Australian region. The *Ethiopian*, with a Madagascan sub-region, meets the Palaearctic in a broad blending zone across the Saharan and Arabian deserts. Finally, the *Neotropical* region marches with the Nearctic region in Mexico. The Antarctic and the oceanic island groups are often regarded as outside the regions.

In terms of 'richness' the regions may be placed in this order: Neotropical (with 25 indigenous families and nearly 3,000 breeding species), Ethiopian, Australasian, Oriental and Holarctic (Palaearctic and Nearctic). The last, containing the north temperate zone, is where the scientific study of nature began, with the fewest species on which to work. Paradoxically, therefore, we know at present most about the few hundred breeding birds of this great region and least about the teeming bird life of South America.

Each of these major faunal regions contains a variety of terrains, and the novice bird-watcher, in whatever part of the world he finds himself, may well prefer an ecological to a purely systematic approach when getting on terms with the birds. The two are often related: woodpeckers are found in forests or on their edges, ducks in the wetlands, and bustards on open plains or their equivalent. There is also the fascination of seeing how the different 'niches' are filled in each habitat. In woodland, for example, there is a series of horizontal layers or zones: the field, herb or ground layer; the shrub layer (sometimes more than one); the trunks and lower parts of the main branches; and the canopy or crowns of the trees. Each presents certain opportunities for birds to exploit for food, as song or display perches, roosting places, nesting sites, or the source of nest materials. In the course of time each species has claimed the niches it needs, and competition will occur only if there is, say, a shortage of nest-sites for birds with similar requirements, or if there is only one drinking or bathing place in a pool or stream. The species in each community may be drawn from quite different groups or there may be several close relatives, like the titmice in European forests. The result is a mosaic of bird life in a mosaic of vegetation.

The Faunal Regions

1. PALAEARCTIC (with acknowledgements to R. Meinertzhagen and K. H. Voous)

The region covers that part of the Old World subjected to arctic conditions during the ice ages which ended about 10,000 years ago. Not all of it, however, was under ice and there were many centres whence bird life could recolonise as the climate improved. Today, working southward from the polar ice-cap, the main habitats are the tundra, a frozen or, in summer, largely water-logged swamp or bog with a short season of arctic flora among the mosses and lichens; the taiga or coniferous forest zone, studded with lakes often of great size; the mixed and deciduous or broad-leaved forest, originally dominating the lowlands but giving way to areas of moor and heath, to alpine mountain zones running usually from east to west; and to the savannah or steppe, now largely cultivated in western Europe and merging into desert in central Asia and elsewhere; round the Mediterranean there is the much denuded zone of aromatic scrub (macchia or maquis). The whole region is traversed by river valleys, often as in China highly cultivated, but also with riverine forest, marshes and wet grass-

Map of zoogeographical regions

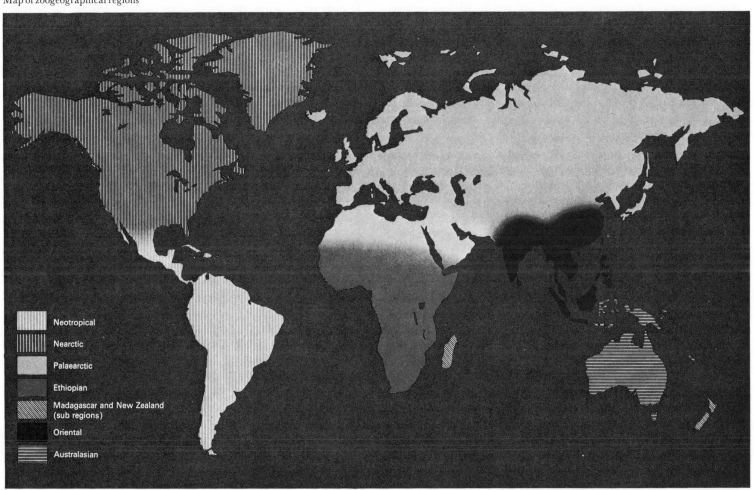

Neotropical

Nearctic

Palaearctic

Ethiopian

Madagascar and New Zealand (sub regions)

Oriental

Australasian

land. The northern and western coasts are noted for their rocky islands and headlands.

The characteristic bird-life of the *tundra* is a mixture of hardy residents, ptarmigan and a few birds of prey, and an abundant temporary breeding population of waterfowl, waders, gulls and terns, a few passerine birds associated with open country like the pipits and buntings, and an élite of predators. The *taiga*, on the other hand, is dominated by perching birds: seed-eating finches like the crossbills and grosbeaks, insect-eating tits and woodpeckers, and predators like the Ural and Hawk Owls. It is from the taiga, with high numbers and no food, irruptions of Crossbills, Waxwings and other species spread southward in late summer.

Transitional between tundra and taiga are zones of birch and bog where hardy warblers and other northern passerines breed alongside the waders. Southward the taiga shades into the main broadleaved forest of which oak is the characteristic tree and the acorn-eating Jay the typical bird. The bird communities are dominated by perching species, mostly song-birds *(Oscines)*, but including woodpeckers, owls, hawks and pigeons. It is this group which has spread out into the cultivated landscape of so much of the western Palaearctic, especially the great lowland stretching from France to the Urals; this is a form of steppe with its own birds, of which the Rook is a good example. Another vaster area of broad-leaved woodland once covered south-east Asia, parts of China and Japan; laughing thrushes and a variety of pheasants are typical inhabitants.

The mountain ranges rise out of the forests, with rather a sparse bird life in the west (Wallcreeper and Alpine Accentor are examples), but the great mountainous areas centred on Tibet carry a much richer fauna, typified by monal pheasants and partridges, passerines like rosefinches, redstarts, rock thrushes and choughs, and an aberrant avocet, the Ibisbill of high level lakes. At sea level the scrub woods round the Mediterranean have suffered from centuries of browsing, but are still the habitat of elusive warblers; they give way to arid areas and deserts stretching north-east to Mongolia, characterised by rock partridges, chats and wheatears, and by some penetration from the Ethiopian region.

But it is the cliffs and offshore islands of the Palaearctic with their wealth of seabirds – auks, gulls, terns, petrels and shearwaters, gannet and cormorants – that are one of the chief glories of the region, posing great problems of conservation in face of increasing pollution of the ocean.

2. NEARCTIC (with acknowledgements to Ernst Mayr)

The habitats of this region are comparable to those of the Palaearctic, with the geographical difference that the mountain ranges of North America run north and south, while those of Eurasia run mainly east and west. They therefore constitute a barrier to the advance of both plants and animals, while the American configuration allows the penetration of tongues of habitat with associated birds. Thus both tundra and taiga extend southward along the mountain ranges while the Rufous Hummingbird actually breeds northward to Alaska.

The taiga or 'Canadian conifer forest' is gradually replaced by a deciduous forest belt in areas of high rainfall, with species of oak prominent as in the Palaearctic. But the mid-west of the continent is characterised by its prairies, stretching north into Canada and merging southward with increasingly arid areas until the true desert is reached in the south-west of the region, where Mexico is substantially the broad frontier belt with the Neotropical region. The habitat pattern is variegated by the Great Lakes, by many great river systems with their associated wetlands, and by coastal cliffs and islands, especially in the far north-east and along the north-western coast.

The bird life of each major zone is characteristic, with relatively little overlap. The tundra and far northern species closely resemble those of the Palaearctic, but some, like the Snow Goose, and Canada Goose (now introduced to Europe) and several waders, are exclusively Nearctic. Three species, Great Northern Diver or Common Loon, Barrow's Goldeneye and Harlequin Duck, are found in Palaearctic Iceland and the diver, a regular winter visitor to Europe, has now bred in Scotland. Outstanding in the muskeg zone, where conifers and tundra meet, is the Whooping Crane, one of the world's rarest birds; at the other end of the size scale, many species of New World wood warblers breed in the forests. Summer visitors like the cranes and most of the breeding species, provide much excitement in spring and autumn on their passage through the bird-watching belt of the USA.

Found in a variety of habitats, the wrens are considered to be of Nearctic origin, though the Winter Wren of North America is also the Common Wren of Eurasia. Other indigenous families of the mixed or broadleaved forest belt, which as in the Palaearctic is now much diversified by cultivations and buildings, are the mocking birds or mimic thrushes, vireos and bunting-like American sparrows, which include a number of open country and even prairie and desert species. Several kinds of grouse are typical prairie birds and so are the meadowlarks, which are icterids and not larks in the Old World sense. The Roadrunner, related to the cuckoos, is an obvious inhabitant of the arid country in the south of the region.

The great ranges of the North American continent, of which the Rocky Mountains and Sierra Nevada are the most notable, and the intervening deserts and semi-deserts confine a number of species to the coastal areas of California. In the mountains to the south of the state the last remnant of the California Condor just survives; at the other extreme of size several hummingbirds occur as breeding species at high altitudes, where they may meet the all-brown Dipper that haunts the fast-flowing streams like its Old World counterpart.

The islands of the north-east Atlantic coast have much the same wealth of seabirds as throng the cliffs on the European side; but the Pacific coast boasts some distinctive auks; the nest of one, Kittlitz's Murrelet, has only quite recently been discovered high in the mountains of Alaska.

3. NEOTROPICAL (with acknowledgements to Ernst Mayr and C. C. Olrog)

Alfred Russel Wallace, quoted by Professor Mayr, described this region as 'distinguished from all the other great Zoological divisions of the globe by the small proportion of its surface covered by deserts, by the large proportion of its lowlands, and by the altogether unequalled extent and luxuriance of its tropical forests'. How long the last claim can stand, with the rapid and ruthless felling of this priceless resource, is open to question. Mayr also points out that the Andes, extending through 80° of latitude, are the greatest mountain range in the world, and the Amazon its greatest river.

These factors are reflected in a very rich but surprisingly uniform bird fauna; the lack of latitudinal barriers east of the Andes has allowed colonisation almost throughout the continent by tropical and sub-tropical species. On the other hand, the temperate zone is small in area, though it has some characteristic birds, like the little family of seedsnipe. Unique elements in South American bird life are the Hoatzin, Sun Bittern and Oilbird, and there are several very small endemic families, like the rheas and trumpeters. In contrast are the numerous hummingbirds (320 species) and such typical groups as the tinamous, puff birds, jacamars and toucans. Overshadowing these numerically are three large groupings of passerines, some 800 species strong, which dominate the sub-order Clamatores or Tyranni. This abundance reflects niches in the diversity of the tropical and sub-tropical forests, as compared with coniferous or temperate broad-leaved woodland.

But Mayr points out that few Neotropical birds have ventured into the Nearctic although, even before the Panama land bridge appeared, there were convenient island 'stepping stones'. Northern species, however, have not been slow to move south, some a very a very long time ago, like the tanagers, cardinals, honeycreepers and troupials. Then came the guans, quails, pigeons, jays and thrushes, followed by wrens, vireos, wood warblers and motmots. Most surprising are the arrivals of the holarctic Shorelark (Horned Lark) and Short-eared Owl, presumably along the Rockies and the Andes, and Mayr's view is that parrots made their way to the Nearctic by means of the Bering Straits.

Some water birds, in which the region as in all else is rich, have colonised it quite recently; other widespread groups have been established long enough to have evolved native species like the Andean torrent ducks and the peculiar Coscoroba Swan.

Most of the West Indian birds come from Central America, which has a very mixed bird fauna, but have been in the islands long enough for unique types to appear such as the family of todies and the Palm Chat. The majority of the Caribbean wild life is very much at risk today due to injudicious introductions like the mongoose, and to property development regardless of nature and amenity.

The seabird colonies of the Neotropical include the famous islands off the Peruvian coast where centuries of droppings (guano) from Guanay Cormorants produced most valuable deposits of fertiliser; there are other islands of great ornithological interest and their fauna is immortalised in R. C. Murphy's massive *Oceanic Birds of South America*, 1936. The Falkland Islands with their kelp geese also fall in the region but most important of all is the Galapagos group, some 600 miles west of Ecuador in the Pacific, where an invasion of supposedly South American finches has led to the classic model of species formation, an inspiration to every generation of zoologists since Charles Darwin first pondered their origins. The islands have other unique birds, like the Flightless Cormorant, Swallow-tailed Gull, Galapagos Albatross, and the most northerly breeding colony of penguins.

Central and South America, like Africa south of the Sahara, form a great reception area, in their case for birds breeding in the Nearctic. These include many water birds – some ducks and herons but many more almost cosmopolitan waders or shorebirds, gulls and terns – birds of prey, and millions of passerines, so that, during the northern winter, over half the bird species in the world will be represented in the Neotropical region. Nor are all its secrets given up; native species new to science are still being discovered at the rate of about one a year.

4. ETHIOPIAN (with acknowledgements to J. P. Chapin and R. E. Moreau)

The region covers Africa south of the Sahara, which forms a broad zone of blending with the Palaearctic; it includes the very important sub-regional fauna of Madagascar and the Mascarene Islands. The Ethiopian total of about 1,500 breeding species is only about half that of the Neotropical but contains great diversity and several endemic families.

R. E. Moreau emphasises a distinction within the region between the bird life of the evergreen rain forest, which covers much of Africa along the Equator, and all other habitats. There is also a considerable difference between the lowland and montane areas in both major ecological divisions of the region.

As the rain is of Atlantic origin, the equatorial forest declines eastward across the Continent. In its virgin state, with tall trunks limbless for perhaps 50 metres, it is not as hospitable a habitat as man creates by his cultivations or nature by the fall of a giant tree or the passage of a stream with consequent multiplying of the vegetation layers. The main birds of the forest floor are relatives of the game birds, thrushes and babblers; the curious 'bald crows' or rockfowl of West Africa are now considered to be 'way-out' babblers. Moreau lists many more groups in the upper layers of the forest: cuckoos, touracos, trogons, hornbills, barbets, starlings and weavers of the same family *Ploceidae* that embraces the House Sparrow. Flycatchers and warblers occur at all levels, and bulbuls in the undergrowth.

The rain forest is sandwiched between two zones characterised by a varying admixture of perennial grasses and deciduous trees, the products of a long dry season and a short wet period. Large areas of sparse leguminous *Brachystegia* woodland are found in the southern belt; at the other extreme is the savannah with only scattered trees, adapted to survive frequent burning in the dry season. The trees may form 'gallery forest' along drainage channels and, as many of them bear fruit, they are important to bird life. On the other hand the dense grass in the wet season makes penetration by birds difficult and it is not surprising that the very small *Cisticola* warblers are typical inhabitants, with seed-eating weavers of the ploceid and estrildid families. In what Moreau calls semi-arid zones the vegetation is reduced to thorny scrub and annual herbs. These zones are along the southern fringe of the Sahara, in the north-east of the region and in South-West Africa. Typical ground birds are coursers, bustards and larks.

Above about 1,700 metres or 5,000 feet there is a pronounced change in both plants and animals in what Moreau calls montane areas. These include the Cameroon Mountain in West Africa, the Abyssinian plateau and Kenya highlands, isolated peaks like Kilimanjaro (over 6,000 metres or nearly 20,000 feet high), and the central ranges of Ruwenzori and Kivu. Remarkably, several of these widely-separated mountains have many species of bird in common, even with 1,000 miles of the Congo basin between them, and must have been linked during the last ice age. (The whole question is discussed in detail in Moreau's *The Bird Faunas of Africa and its Islands*, 1966).

Although few families of birds seem to have originated in the Ethiopian region, it is notable for the unique Secretary Bird, Hamerkop, and Ostrich (since its extinction in Asia), and for the guineafowl, mousebirds or colies, touracos and wood hoopoes, while other not exclusively African groups such as barbets, shrikes and helmet shrikes are strongly represented. Though perhaps not so remarkable as in some other regions, the seabird colonies of Africa include the much studied (and threatened) Ascension Island.

Like the Neotropical region, the Ethiopian receives millions of birds during the northern winter. Moreau has calculated that about a third of all Palaearctic species, including some from north-east Asia, are winter residents and may, like the European Swallow, reach the southernmost parts of the continent.

Madagascar and the Mascarene Islands, sometimes called the Malagasy region, are full of evolutionary interest and problems. Most of Madagascar's 240,000 square miles are covered by wooded savannah, with a block of wet evergreen forest in the east and an arid south-western area; but there is little truly montane habitat. The distinctive mammals like the lemurs are well-known, but Madagascar is also the home of several small endemic bird groups: the mesites, rather like the rails or crakes, the asities, primitive perching birds, the vanga shrikes, the cuckoo rollers and the ground roller; indeed, a third of all the island's bird species are found nowhere else. Madagascar was also the home of the extinct giant Elephant Bird, while the Mascarene islands have suffered many extinctions, demonstrably at man's hands: the Dodo and the solitaires are the most famous. The Seychelles, to which much attention has been given in recent years, have not only important seabird colonies but several of the world's rarest land birds: a kestrel, *Falco area;* owl, *Otus insularis;* paradise fly-catcher, *Terpsiphone corvina;* magpie robin, *Copsychus sechellarum;* warbler, *Bebrornis sechellensis* and fody (weaver bird), *Foudia sechellarum.*

5. ORIENTAL (with acknowledgements to Salim Ali)

Much of the boundary between this and the Palaearctic is provided by the great east-west mountain chains from the Hindu Kush to the Himalaya and its eastern extensions. In the south-west the valley of the Indus and to the east the Yangtze Kiang mark the approximate limits. The large islands of Taiwan and Hainan are included and most of the groups to the south-east: Indonesia, the Philippines and Borneo. The boundary with Australasia was first defined by Wallace's line between Bali and Lombok, Borneo and Celebes. Huxley altered this to put the Philippines in Australasia, but the present line, modified from that first suggested by Weber in 1902, is farther east again. More strikingly than other inter-regional frontiers this one shows how abruptly the range of some groups can end, for example the barbets on Bali and the Australian honeyeaters and cockatoos on Lombok.

Salim Ali favours three sub-regional divisions. The 'Indo-Chinese' and 'Indo-Malayan' are predominantly areas of humid tropical and sub-tropical forest, but the first inclines both for plants and animals to the Palaearctic, the second to the Australasian. 'Indo-China' then includes the southern slopes of the Himalaya up to 3,000-4,000 metres (9,000 to 12,000 feet), grading into a montane habitat, as well as the richly vegetated mainland countries and islands to the east. 'Indo-Malaya', lying mainly 10° on either side of the equator, is almost entirely tropical and lacks both the Palaearctic links of 'Indo-China' and the Ethiopian association of the 'Indian' sub-region, which is roughly the same as the geographical sub-continent (including Ceylon), south of the Himalayan foothills. But within it Salim Ali distinguishes a 'south-western province', which is a tropical zone with resemblances to the other two sub-regions, possessing the Crimson-backed Woodpecker, Great Hornbill and other sedentary species also found in Malaya, Burma and the eastern Himalaya 1,000 to 1,500 miles away. It has been suggested that the Himalaya was once connected by way of the Satpura Mountains and Western Ghats with Kerala and Ceylon, which has not received as many species as the mainland; vultures of the genus *Gyps* are also absent from the island.

In the larger division of the Indian sub-region are arid and near-desert areas, where species with Ethiopian connections, like the apparently extinct courser *Rhinoptilus bitorquatus,* are to be found.

The Oriental region as a whole is noted for the strong representation of the pheasant family, 42 out of 48 species; and no less than eight genera are endemic to it. These include the peacocks and argus pheasants as well as the Jungle Fowl, ancestor of all domestic breeds. Other groups like the tragopans and monals are found at higher altitudes. The Western, Blyth's and Cabot's Tragopans, Sclater's and the Chinese Monals are now great rarities, Swinhoe's and the Mikado Pheasants are confined to Taiwan; the first has been bred in captivity in Britain and birds have been released in its native habitat. Several genera of smaller birds are peculiar to the region; Salim Ali lists the *Harpactes* trogons, *Nyctiornis* bee-eaters, *Psittacus* and *Loriculus* parrots, *Acridotheres* and *Gracula* starlings and the *Pericrocotes* cuckoo-shrikes.

The Philippines have some remarkable indigenous birds, including the very rare Monkey-eating Eagle, the Great Scops Owl and several pigeons and doves. The various smaller island groups attract colonies of seabirds, with some terns of cosmopolitan range, but the region is not so noted in this respect as the other five.

Like the Neotropical and Ethiopian, the Oriental is the home of many species during the northern winter. Then the jheels of India fill with water fowl and their banks are thronged with waders. The small passerine visitors are less obvious, but leaf warblers *Phylloscopus* of which many species occur, pose field problems for the growing number of Indian ornithologists.

6. AUSTRALASIAN (with acknowledgements to D. L. Serventy and B. B. Roberts)

This region, with its far-flung sub-regions of New Zealand and Antarctica (which some authorities consider should be treated separately outwith the 'classical' six regions of Sclater), has many curious features, due to its relatively long separation geologically from the rest of the world's land masses. Also partly due to this and unlike the other three regions wholly or mainly within the southern hemisphere, it is visited by comparatively few wintering species, except by waders, from the north.

The Australian and Asian land-masses have probably been apart since the early Tertiary 60 or 70 million years ago and New Zealand from Australia even longer, if indeed they were ever connected. This means, as Dr Serventy points out, a terrestrial separation since before the evolution of modern birds. But, according to Mayr, all the indications from a study of the bird life of both regions is that the Australasian derived from the Oriental. Infiltration evidently took place over a long period by way of island links, so that the present day birds of the region show many differences from their assumed ancestors. 'The later immigrants,' writes Serventy, 'show progressively closer relationship with Palaeo-tropical (Old World Tropical) and Palaearctic forms, and most of the widespread families are represented. The process of colonisation is still going on'. But Hawaiian birds, as might be expected, appear to be both Neotropical and Australasian in origins.

Continental Australia is geographically and climatically distinct from the other main land-masses of the region. Both New Guinea and New Zealand are mountainous and forest-covered, one with tropical and the other with sub-tropical and temperate vegetation. In contrast, Australia is like a huge shallow saucer with some of the world's most extreme desert conditions at the centre, becoming progressively more benign towards the rim, where there are even some humid areas with associated forest, for example in north Queensland.

Although some have not reached Australia and others, like the flamingos, died out, most Old World groups arrived and are now fitted to the diverse habitats. Secondary differentiation has meant the emergence of some endemic families showing little trace of their affinities; among them Serventy lists the Emu and cassowaries in open country, and woodland or scrub dwellers such as the megapodes, many parrots (including, of course, the 'budgie'), frogmouths, lyrebirds, scrub birds, wood swallows, honeyeaters (some of which have invaded extra-regional Hawaii), bower birds, magpie larks and 'magpies'; names which typify Australia to laymen as well as to ornithologists. More recent arrivals show their relationships clearly: quails, rails, grebes, cranes, *Accipiter* hawks, kingfishers, white-eyes, crows; even the Clamorous Reed Warbler and Richard's Pipit (known locally as the Australian or New Zealand Pipit) unaltered as to species. The Cattle Egret is the newest arrival as part of a remarkable expansion that has taken it also across the Atlantic from Africa.

In spite of its notable lack of fresh water compared with other land-masses, Australia is well off for water birds, with some unusual species like the Brolga crane, Magpie Goose (which has no webs between its toes), very rare Cape Barren Goose, and the philatelic Black Swan.

New Guinea is so famous as the main home of birds of paradise that its other specialities like the cassowaries and the crowned pigeons, giants of their order, are less regarded. This is one of the few areas of the world where new discoveries are still likely.

New Zealand has suffered enormous changes in habitat during the short period of European domination, though the last moas vanished in Maori times. Much of the primeval forest has been replaced by northern hemisphere conifers and, considering the size of the country, introductions both of mammals and birds – mostly European 'garden' species – has been on a scale unequalled elsewhere in the world. Nevertheless some remarkable natives survive, of which the rediscovered flightless rail, the Takahe, is mainly known to ornithologists while the Kiwi has become the national emblem. The Kakapo or Owl Parrot is now very rare and the Huia, in which the bills of male and female were differently shaped and had different functions, is presumed extinct. It was one of the wattlebirds; these include the Saddleback and Kokako and are considered by C. A. Fleming to show the nearest approach to that adaptive radiation which makes the Galapagos finches and Hawaiian honeycreepers of outstanding evolutionary interest.

Hawaii, an oceanic group outside the region, is also the home of the Nene, another goose with poorly developed webs to its feet, and one of the very few examples of a species successfully reinforced, in its native crater habitat, by stock bred in captivity thousands of miles away.

The South Island of New Zealand is the home of great seabird colonies, including both penguins and albatrosses; so are many of the archipelagoes and small islands, which may be regarded as extra-regional. As W. H. Drury has pointed out, in contrast to the land-masses of the north temperate and arctic zones, the south temperate and subantarctic are characterised by scattered island groups, populated by relatively few species of seabird but often in enormous numbers. B. B. Roberts can claim only forty breeding species for the whole antarctic zone, all seabirds: penguins, petrels; skuas, gulls and terns; shags; and sheathbills.

Origins and Species

The sections on the great zoogeographical regions of the world have indicated summarily that certain groups of birds are believed to have originated in one region rather than another. But what does 'originate' imply and what were the ancestors of these birds? Unfortunately the avian skeleton does not survive well and the fossil record is most imperfect; but it is generally accepted that the first birds evolved from reptiles; that is to say, through many generations over vast periods of time and by the process of natural selection, transition from a scale-covered four-footed reptile to a two-footed winged and feathered bird was achieved.

The spur to evolution was the appearance of a niche or ecological place for this new creature to occupy most efficiently, and progress towards it was made by the action of minute variations in the inheritance of each generation which conferred equally minute advantages.

Fortunately, there is the vital testimony of the magpie-sized *Archaeopteryx*, which lived about 140 million years ago and of which three individual remains have been found in Jurassic limestone in Germany, one as recently as 1956. Unequivocally a bird, it yet exemplifies a sort of half way stage in the long sequence of changes. It had a long tail with twenty free vertebrae, a short sacrum with only six vertebrae, free metacarpal bones in the hand,

Archaeopteryx. An artist's reconstruction
By courtesy of the American Museum of Natural History.

with claws on the fingers, teeth with alternative socket replacement and a simple brain with a small cerebellum, control centre for muscular co-ordination. Its bird-like features were a covering of true feathers, and their arrangement as primary and secondary flight feathers or remiges on the hand and the ulna; fusion of the collar bones into a wishbone; fusion of certain small bones in the foot, which had an opposable big toe for gripping branches.

Archaeopteryx's ancestor is considered to have been one of the small Pseudosuchian group of reptiles, which flourished about 200 million years ago and whose fossils have been found in the Lower Trias both in Europe and South Africa. The suggestion is that these animals took to living in trees, feeding on insects; so sight became more important, the sense of smell less so, and this gave advantage to bigger-eyed, larger brained variations. They then began to jump from branch to branch, and this developed into gliding with the consequent evolution of wings to replace the forelegs; but *Archaeopteryx* still had to climb upwards by means of its clawed fingers, vestiges of which are found in some existing birds, notably the young of the South American Hoatzin.

Remains of some dozens of kinds of bird are claimed from the Cretaceous or Chalk system, 70 to 135 million years ago. Almost all of them are water birds, whose skeletons stood a better chance of surviving in layers of sediment. *Icthyornis*, a tern-like bird, had a fully developed keel to the breastbone, so between its appearance and that of *Archaeopteryx* the full power of flight had been evolved, though the intermediate fossil evidence may never be found. The other remarkable feature of these Cretaceous birds is that some, like *Hesperornis*, the often illustrated six-foot long diver-like bird, had already lost the power of flight again and with it the carina or keel to the sternum.

For a long time it was believed that the existing or recently extinct ratite or flat-breasted birds, like the Ostrich, Emu, moas and elephant birds, were descended from forms that never had functional wings. But there are now strong anatomical grounds for thinking that all flightless birds show a secondary evolution, having surrendered the advantages of flight for increased size and great mobility over the ground – Ostriches are in effect two-legged plains game – or because, as on many islands, even as large as New Zealand's components, there were no enemies from whom escape by flight was necessary. They had yet to reckon with man and his 'best friends'! Incidentally, loss of flight for this reason confirms the importance which modern behaviour students attach to the influence of the predator in determining the actions and even the anatomy of potential prey animals.

Family 112 *Menuridae* LYREBIRDS Sexes differ
One of 2 families in the 3rd suboscine sub-order *Menurae*, this consists of two species found in south-eastern Australia. The Superb Lyrebird, *Menura superba*, the country's national bird, has somewhat over-shadowed the rarer and less obtrusive Albert's Lyrebird, *M. alberti*. Superficially like pheasants with which, as with birds of paradise, they were at times confused, lyrebirds are the largest suboscine passerines, having several anatomical peculiarities connected with the voice box and breastbone. They belong to sub-tropical forest, feeding on the ground on small animal life and nesting in winter when it is most abundant. The remarkable tail is the male adornment; with this and an astonishing repertoire of specific and mimicked notes, he conducts his displays on up to ten clearings in his large territory, taking no part in hatching and rearing the single chick.

Family 113 *Atrichornithidae* SCRUB BIRDS
Sexes differ
Most nearly related to the lyrebirds and therefore placed in the same sub-order are the 2 scrub birds, the 6½ ins Rufous, *Atrichornis rufescens*, of south-eastern Australia, and the 8 ins Noisy, *A. clamosus*, believed extinct and rediscovered in 1961 in one small area of Western Australia. Alone among passerines, their collarbones are not fused to form a wishbone and scrub birds are therefore very poor fliers. Their name indicates their habitat, in which observation is very difficult, but they appear to behave like miniature lyrebirds, fleet-footed and with a surprising and loud repertoire.

Family 114 *Alaudidae* LARKS
Sexes usually alike
Appropriately the oscine or song-bird sub-order is headed by a family renowned for beautiful voices. Some 75 species in 15 genera are recognised, 50 of them occurring in Africa and only 1, the holarctic Horned or Shore Lark, *Eremophila alpestris*, in America; 1 also reaches Australia and 1, New Guinea, but there are a number in both Europe and Asia. The larks are a remarkably uniform family, distinguished by the scaled and rounded back to the shank and by the very long hind claw, a sign of their running gait; the voice box also has special, rather primitive features. Larks are the passerines of open habits, from beaches and deserts to cultivated land, showing neat plumage adaptations to different backgrounds. But the predominantly African bush larks of the large genus *Mirafra* regularly perch. Some of these build domed nests instead of the typical simple open cup. The diet is varied, both vegetable and animal, and the famous songs are delivered most effectively in flight.

Family 115 *Hirundinidae* SWALLOWS and MARTINS
Sexes usually alike
One of the best known and relatively uniform passerine families, found almost all over the world except New Zealand (stragglers only), Antarctica and some other large islands. Nearly 80 species, from 5 to 9 ins long, are divided into 19 genera, some of doubtful validity. The anatomical feature of complete bronchial rings is not obvious; but the forked tails, pointed 9-primaried wings, small bills with wide bristle-edged gapes, evolved as aerial bagnets for insects, and usually glossy upper plumage can cause confusion only with the even more aerially adapted swifts (Family 79). Swallows and martins are summer visitors to the temperate zones, performing their long and well publicised migrations by day and feeding on the wing. Although swallows can perch, their weak feet having strong claws, they only land to collect material for their mud nests. Other species take over cavities or burrow in banks, but the Swallow, *Hirundo rustica*, and its near relatives now site their nests almost entirely on human artefacts. The large, monotypic African River Martin, *Pseudochelidon eurystomina*, is put in a separate subfamily because of its peculiar bronchial structure; it is extremely gregarious.

Family 116 *Motacillidae* PIPITS and WAGTAILS
Sexes alike (pipits), differ (wagtails)
Although with 9 instead of 10 primaries and cosmopolitan in range, the 50 odd species (in 4 to 6 genera) of this family are about as different in appearance and habits from the previous one as is possible among passerines. But they show superficial resemblances to the larks, being also adapted to open habitats, where they run, walk or fly after insect prey. They are mostly about sparrow size. The pipits, over 30 of them in the genus *Anthus*, have generally streaked plumages and their longish tails show white outer feathers. They have sharp straight bills and strong legs with notably long hind claws, most developed in the African long-claws *Macronyx*, whose bright yellow underparts and black necklace shows classic convergence with the American meadowlarks (Family 141). The wagtails, all in *Motacilla* except for the rather aberrant Asian Forest Wagtail, *Dendromanthus indicus*, are brighter than most pipits, often associated with water and include one species, the 'Yellow' *M. flava*, with most striking subspecific differentiation, indicated by the ♂ head plumage. One race nests in extreme north-western North America, where 2 pipits have also penetrated. At the other extreme Richard's Pipit, *Anthus novaeseelandiae*, reaches New Zealand, but the heartlands of the family are Eurasia, to which some members are summer visitors, and Africa. Like larks they build open nests, and pipits have well developed songs, often uttered in flight.

Family 117 *Campephagidae* CUCKOO SHRIKES and MINIVETS Sexes generally differ
Superficial characteristics govern the twofold English name of one group in this family of 70 species, now divided into 9 genera, and distributed primarily in the forests of the Old World tropics, extending to Australia. Size ranges from sparrow to pigeon; tails and pointed wings are longish; the rather broad bills are sometimes covered by bristles but the interesting feature of most species is the dense, loose plumage of feathers with stiff-pointed shafts on the lower back and rump: these are easily shed, possibly as a protective device. The cuckoo shrikes, typical genus *Campephaga*, are generally rather dull-coloured; some larger species have a distinctive wing-lifting display accompanied by loud calls. The 10 minivets *Pericrocotus* are sparrow-sized, with graduated tails and bright male plumages of red and black. The family as a whole is insectivorous, tree-living and open-nesting; the aberrant Ground Cuckoo Shrike of Australia, *Pteropodocys maxima*, is a bird of open country, but nests high in trees.

Family 118 *Pycnonotidae* BULBULS
Sexes alike, females sometimes smaller
Another Old World, primarily tropical family, its eastward range ending at Wallace's Line, only bridged by recent introductions to Australia. The 120 species are split into 15 genera, of which 10 are endemic to Africa and Madagascar and 2 to Asia. The widely distributed type genus *Pycnonotus* contains 50 species. Bulbuls, sparrow to thrush sized, are generally dull-plumaged except for bright patches, e.g. on cheek or vent, with rather long tails and short ineffective wings. Feet also are weak, bills straight and bristle-based; the dense back plumage recalls the cuckoo shrikes. Many species are crested, but the most distinctive feature is the patch of hair-like feathers at the nape. Originally forest birds, some bulbuls have spread into secondary and cultivated habitats close to man, enjoyed for their songs, as by Omar Khayyam, and active behaviour; others remain very secretive. They are primarily fruit-eaters and build open nests.

Family 119 *Irenidae* LEAFBIRDS Sexes differ
An Oriental Asian forest family, brightly coloured relatives of the bulbuls, with which they share many features, including the 'hairy' patch on the nape. The 8 leafbirds *Chloropsis* are about 8 ins long, generally greenish, with rather curved pointed bills and fruit-eating habits. The 4 little ioras *Aegithina* are more insectivorous, with relatively longer legs and bills; the males have rather striking aerial displays and a non-breeding plumage. The 2 fairy bluebirds *Irena* are starling-sized; 1 species is endemic to the Philippines, the other more widely distributed in south-east Asia, where the small, fruit-eating flocks are often conspicuous.

Family 120 *Laniidae* SHRIKES
Sexes usually alike
One classification of these predatory passerines defines 74 species in 4 subfamilies. Shrikes are primarily Old World birds of open woodland and scrub; they do not occur in Australia or the Pacific islands, and only 2 species (1 endemic) inhabit North America. In general they are from 7 ins to a foot long, with longish round or graduated tails, rather pointed wings, strong legs and claws, and powerful hooked and notched bills with which they do their killing. The type subfamily *Laniinae*, with 25 members, includes the migratory North Temperate species, characterised by black, white and grey in the plumage and often with a mask, and by the habit of building up larders of prey, from insects to small mammals. They are both conspicuous and secretive, with rudimentary songs, and build open nests. As well as *Lanius* the monotypic *Corvinella* and *Urolestes* are included. The bush shrikes *Malaconotinae* are all African and include 'duetting' species like the Brubru, *Nilaus afer*, the curious puffbacks *Dryoscopus*, and a possible interloper, *Lanioturdus torquatus*. The helmet shrikes *Prionopinae* – also African – have black and white plumages and are distinguished by the caruncles of skin round their eyes and by their striking crests. Finally, the monotypic *Pityriasinae*, whose sole representative is the Borneo Bristlehead, *Pityriasis gymnocephala*, which may not be a shrike at all, partly because of the uncharacteristic bill.

Family 121 *Vangidae* VANGA SHRIKES
Sexes alike or differ
A Madagascan family of rather brightly coloured forest birds, 5 ins to a foot long, presumed to be descended from an immigrant shrike ancestor, but now diversified into 12 species in 8 genera, 6 of them monotypic. They resemble true shrikes in many anatomical respects, but their bills show modifications, especially the enormous proboscis of the Helmetbird, *Aerocharis prevostii*. Vangas are gregarious and insectivorous rather than solitary and predatory, and are noisy on the move. They build open nests but little is known of their breeding biology.

Family 122 *Bombycillidae* WAXWINGS, SILKY FLYCATCHERS, HYPOCOLIUS Sexes alike or differ
A composite family of Northern Hemisphere, gregarious, medium-sized, fruit-eating passerines, whose relationship is somewhat tenuous, though the three subfamilies have similar anatomy, soft plumage, a tendency to crests and a tree-living habit. The (Bohemian) Waxwing, *Bombycilla garrulus*, is a holarctic conifer bird and classic irruption species; the Cedar, *B. cedrorum*, is North American and the Japanese, *B. japonica*, is confined to eastern Asia. The 4 Central American silky flycatchers are *Phainopepla nitens*, *Phainoptila melanoxantha* and 2 species of *Ptilogonys*, all about 7½ ins long; they are so little known as to have no English names and range from Panama to central California. The Grey Hypocolius, *Hypocolius ampelinus*, sole member of its subfamily and genus, is found in the valleys of the Tigris and Euphrates, irrupting like the Waxwing to north-western India and occasionally to north-east Africa.

Family 123 *Dulidae* PALM CHAT Sexes alike
Sometimes regarded as another monotypic subfamily in the *Bombycillidae* the Palm Chat, *Dulus dominicus*, of Hispaniola, is a gregarious, fruit-eating species with communal nesting habits.

Family 124 *Cinclidae* DIPPERS Sexes alike
The 4 similar species in the single genus are the Dipper, *Cinclus cinclus*, of Europe, western Asia (including high levels in the Himalayas) and North Africa; the Brown, *C. pallasii*, of northern Asia and Japan, the western North American, *C. mexicanus*, also brown all over, and the White-headed, *C. leucocephalus*, of the Andes. Dippers look like thrush-sized wrens, with their strong legs, short uptilted tails and round bodies and are probably closely related, even sharing a musty smell. They are the only truly aquatic passerines, yet have no webbed feet or obvious specialisation except for an operculum to the nostrils and effective eyelids. But they can swim, dive and move about under water in all directions, using wings and feet. They are all insectivorous, sedentary and solitary (except perhaps for

roosting), with attractive warbling songs; they build domed nests like wrens.

Family 125 *Troglodytidae* WRENS Sexes alike

The 60 species are divided into 12 to 14 genera and range in distribution from the Zapata Wren, *Ferminia cerverai*, confined to one marsh in Cuba, to the holarctic (Winter) Wren, *Troglodytes troglodytes*, found over much of Eurasia and into North Africa as well as North America. All other wrens are American, with most genera and species in the tropics. Wrens are remarkably uniform, 4 to 8 ins long, with brown, black-streaked plumage, tails usually short and uptilted, rather long-shanked strong legs and thin, slightly curved probing bills. Both sexes may sing and some tropical species are duettists. They are insectivorous, and build external domed nests or occupy cavities; several species are polygamous, the males building a number of 'cock's nests'. Solitary by day, wrens may collect in large numbers to roost. They are found in habitats of all kinds, from tropical forests to marshes (*Cistothorus* species), coasts, mountains and deserts, like the large Cactus Wren, *Campylorhynchus bruneicapillus*.

Family 126 *Mimidae* MOCKINGBIRDS or MIMIC THRUSHES Sexes alike

The 34 species of this all-American family of wooded country and scrub are divided into 13 genera, 9 of them monotypic. They appear to be intermediate between the wrens and the true thrushes in size and characteristics. Some have long tails but carry them uptilted like wrens; most of them have curved probing bills. But they build open thrush-like nests. Plumages, with few exceptions, e.g. the colourful Blue and Blue and White Mockingbirds, *Melanotis caerulescens* and *M. hypoleucus*, are shades of brown and grey. So the birds make up for it by their loud songs, containing mimic phrases or notes. The type genus *Mimus* has 9 species, distributed over the whole range of the family from Canada to Argentina, though the Galapagos super-species is put in its own genus as *Nesomimus trifasciatus*. Another islander is the Thrasher, *Mimodes graysoni*, of Socorro off the west coast of Mexico. There are 10 species of typical thrashers *Toxostoma* in North America; some appear to be evolving towards a totally ground-living habit.

Family 127 *Prunellidae* ACCENTORS Sexes alike

This family of a single genus *Prunella* and 12 species is almost exclusively Palaearctic, associated with conifer forests, secondary growth, mountain scrub and higher slopes, up to 17,000 ft in the Himalayas. Accentors are sparrow-sized or larger, rather inconspicuously plumaged in browns streaked with black or grey, have strong legs, pointed insectivorous bills but the crop and muscular gizzard of seedeaters; in fact, they feed mainly on insects in summer, on fruits and seeds in winter, all taken on or near the ground. They have simple, melodious songs, and build cup nests with blue eggs.

Family 128 *Muscicapidae*

This huge agglomeration of formerly separate families, totalling between them about 1,000 species, is best treated under the subfamilies as now recognised.

Turdinae THRUSHES, CHATS, ROBINS
Sexes alike or differ
Over 300 species in 45 genera are distributed all over the world, reaching New Zealand by introduction. They are rather unspecialised, small to medium-sized song birds, with 10 primary flight feathers (as throughout the whole family), tails short to long, straight bills and rictal bristles (usually the sign of an insect diet) and strong legs and feet for a life spent much on the ground. They build mainly open nests though some use holes. Above all they include some of the world's best songsters. The type genus *Turdus* (about 60 species) has the largest kinds, with its centre in Eurasia and Africa but members also in both Americas; several have colonised remote islands. Other genera are the Nearctic bluebirds, *Sialis* and thrushes, *Hylocichlas*, the mainly Neotropical *Catharus* and *Myadestes* (solitaires, best of tropical songsters) and the monotypic Wren Thrush, *Zeledonia coronata*. Genera of smaller birds include *Oenanthe* wheatears, several chats (e.g. *Saxicola*), *Luscinia* nightingales and bluethroats, *Phoenicurus* redstarts, and the Robin, *Erithacus rubecula*,

whose name has caused confusion all over the world, applied to all sorts of red-breasted birds.

Timaliinae BABBLERS, WREN TIT
Sexes alike or differ slightly
A very large Old World (including Australia) grouping, to which the monotypic North American Wren Tit, *Chaemia fasciata*, is attached. Babblers have relatively longer tails than thrushes and brighter plumages, but feebler, rounded wings and spend most of their time in cover on or near the ground; they unite in small flocks or parties with other species outside the breeding season. They are both insectivorous and vegetarian, build both open and covered nests and their young do not have a spotted first plumage. They include some fine song birds. The 5 tribes (in addition to the *Chamaeini* above) are the jungle babblers of the Ethiopian and Oriental regions, of dull plumage and secretive habits, divided into 5 genera. The scimitar and wren babblers are insectivorous, ground-living birds with 11 genera and 28 species, extending to New Guinea and Australia. The tit babblers are 6 genera and 35 species of small birds with a Madagascan genus *Neomixis* the jerys. The 140 song babblers in 17 genera are the largest tribe, distributed throughout Africa and southern Asia and including the brighter plumaged, tree-living forms. The Arrow-marked Babbler, *Turdoides jardineii*, is one of the 26 species in its genus, whereas the laughing thrushes *Garrulax* number 50, with some fine songsters. Finally there are the 2 large West African rockfowl, the Grey-necked *Picathartes gymnocephalus* and White-necked *P. oreas*, with bare heads and other aberrant characters.

Cinclosomatinae RAIL BABBLERS Sexes alike or differ
The bird giving its name to this composite group, the Rail Babbler, *Eupetes macrocerus*, is the only species occurring in Malaysia, the rest being found in Australia and New Guinea, primarily living on or near the ground in forest or scrub. They have long shanks, broad tails, densely feathered backs and rather small heads and bills. But they vary a great deal between some 10 small genera, of which the scrub robins, *Drymodes*, and quail thrushes, *Cinclosoma*, are rather thrush-like. The New Guinea logrunners, *Orthonyx*, are characterised by very large feet.

Paradoxornithinae PARROTBILLS
Sexes alike or differ
This subfamily contains about 20 species in the type genus *Paradoxornis* and the monotypic *Conostoma* (the Himalayan *C. oemodium* is about a foot long) and *Panurus*, represented by the Bearded Tit or Reedling *P. biarmicus*, which is Palaearctic. Most of the *Paradoxornis* species are found in the Oriental region, excluding Malaya, and are notable for their short, compressed, convex, usually yellowish bills; they are mostly robust, thick plumaged forest and woodland birds, insectivorous and vegetarian, frequently seen in small flocks. The smaller species tend to be the more brightly coloured. They build open nests but not much is known about the breeding biology of most of them.

Polioptilinae GNATCATCHERS Sexes differ slightly
A dozen species of small New World (Canada to Mexico and Bahamas) insect-eating birds, most closely related to the Old World warblers, grey above and pale below, with long, constantly moving tails, found mostly in or near wetlands. There are 8 *Polioptila* species and 4 in the genera *Microbates* and *Ramphocaenus*, known as 'gnat wrens'.

Sylviinae OLD WORLD WARBLERS
Sexes alike or differ
Some 300 species in about 30 genera are contained in this subfamily; they are overwhelmingly Eurasian or African, the northern members being migratory. Two kinglets, *Regulus*, and 1 leaf warbler, *Phylloscopus*, reach North America; about 20 species breed in Australia and the Fernbird, *Bowdleria punctata*, of New Zealand is also included. Warblers are typically slim, dull plumaged above, lighter below, rather elegant long-tailed little birds, insectivorous and fruit-eating, working their way through thick vegetation in canopy, scrub or grassland and building dainty cups or substantial domed nests. Many have fine songs, often delivered in flight, as by the 70 members of the largest genus *Cisticola*, the

primarily African grass warblers. Other important genera are *Sylvia*, 'true' warblers, *Phylloscopus*, the often puzzling little green leaf warblers, *Acrocephalus*, reed warblers, *Locustella*, grasshopper warblers, and *Cettia* including the tuneful Japanese Bush Warbler, *C. diphone*. The several tropical genera include the tailor birds, *Orthotomus*, which sew leaves together to hold their nests, and the wren warblers, *Prinia*. The kinglets, and 2 Asian tit warblers *Leptopoecile* are also included.

Malurinae AUSTRALIAN WREN WARBLERS
Sexes alike or differ
Another 'assemblage' of some 80 species in over 20 genera, found in Australia, New Guinea and New Zealand. They are generally small insectivorous birds resembling the *Sylviinae* but *Malurus* includes some brilliantly coloured species, hence the names 'superb warbler' and 'fairy wren'. Most species are tree-living, building domed nests which are frequently parasitised by cuckoos. Aberrant in various respects are the emu wrens, *Stipiturus*, with only 6 modified tail feathers, the Spinifex Bird, *Eremiornis carteri*, the *Ephthianura* 'chats' and the pipit-like song larks, *Cinclorhamphus*.

Muscicapinae FLYCATCHERS Sexes alike or differ
A very large Old World subfamily, extending to Australia and New Zealand (the fantails *Rhipidura*) in distribution and convergent in habits with the tyrant flycatchers of America (Family 108). Several hundred species are divided into tens of genera. The typical Palaearctic genera *Muscicapa* and *Ficedula* are small, weak-footed, essentially perching birds whose broad bills and rictal bristles proclaim their 'trade'. They are migratory, cavity-nesting and have spotted juveniles like the thrushes. Very different are the strikingly plumaged, very long-tailed paradise flycatchers, *Terpsiphone*, with their neat open nests. These and the puffbacks, *Batis*, wattle eyes, *Platysteira* and *Diaphorophyia* of Asia, *Arses* of New Guinea and *Zeocephus* of the Philippines have colourful fleshy eye rings. *Bradornis* of Africa contains the largest species, shrike-like in hunting habits; *Abrornis* is no larger than a kinglet. Most flycatchers are solitary but the *Newtonia* species of Madagascar form flocks to search the foliage. The diversity within the subfamily is almost as wide as in the whole order.

Pachycephalinae THICKHEADS or WHISTLERS
Sexes usually alike
A subfamily of robust flycatchers from Australia, New Guinea and the islands of south-east Asia; they have a number of popular Australian names. In size from sparrow to jay, whistlers are often yellow and green. mixed with black and reddish; wattles are exceptional, but some species are crested. Juveniles are sometimes spotted. *Pachycephala* is by far the largest of the genera. Nests may be open or well-hidden; the Australian Crested Bellbird, *Oreica gutturalis*, garnishes the rim with paralysed caterpillars. Most species have pleasant call notes and the pairs of some sing duets; hence apparently the name whistler.

Family 129 *Paridae* TITMICE
Sexes may differ slightly
The family may be considered in 3 subfamilies, of which the typical *Parinae* contains 43 of the 65 species; its main strength lies in the Palaearctic, but some are found in Africa to the very south and in North America. Tits are small (3 to 8 ins long) very active, tree-living birds, with moderately long tails, round bodies, rather rounded wings and powerful, somewhat conical bills with which they break nuts and penetrate bark. Yellow, blue and grey-green on the body, with black caps and white cheeks, are plumage characteristics. Most species nest in holes and form communal flocks after breeding, searching the foliage for insects and nuts, which several northern species store. The *Aegithalinae* or long-tailed tits consist of 8 species, counting the 2 tiny North American bush tits *Psaltriparus*. This group builds elaborate domed nests. *Remizinae*, the penduline tits, have finer bills and are found more in open wooded country than the forest-loving Parus tits, and the Penduline Tit, *R. pendulinus*. is associated with water. There are 6 *Anthoscopus* species in Africa and in North America the monotypic Verdin, *Auriparus flaviceps*, inhabiting sem-desert. The subfamily is noted for its durable penduline nests.

Family 130 *Sittidae* NUTHATCHES
Sexes alike or differ
Closely related to the tits are the typically Holarctic nuthatches *Sitta*, 18 species out of 31 in the family. They are stout-bodied birds from tit to woodpecker size (*S. magna*, the Giant Nuthatch of mountainous southern Asia) with strong legs and claws and rather long straight bills with which to probe bark, chip wood and hammer nuts. They do not use their tails, which are short and soft, to support themselves against trunks, but rely on their claws; they also climb head downwards. The Eurasian species use mud to reduce the entrance to the hole nest and the 2 rock-haunting species build mud frontages to their chosen cavities. Only the Nuthatch, *S. europaea*, enters North Africa; there are 4 species in North America. The Wallcreeper, *Tichodroma muraria*, is an aberrant Eurasian monotype, to which the Afro-Asian Spotted Creeper, *Salpornis spilonotus*, may be related. The two creepers, *Rhabdornis*, live in the Philippines, several treerunners, *Sitella*, more colourful than *Sitta*, in Australia and New Guinea, also the home of the Wonder Treerunner, *Daphoenositta miranda*. But Madagascar has the most aberrant species, *Hypositta corallirostris*, which may be not a nuthatch at all.

Family 131 *Certhiidae* TREECREEPERS Sexes alike
This Old World family of 5 species reverses the position of the wrens, 1 having penetrated America as far south as Nicaragua, where it meets the convergent woodcreepers (Family 100). Treecreepers are slender little birds, mottled brown above and white below, with long claws and thin, curved probing bills. Like woodpeckers they support themselves against tree trunks on stiff tail feathers, which are moulted from the outermost inwards. They hunt by spiralling round a trunk, then fly down to the base of the next; sometimes they 'back-pedal' with fluttering wings or even move head downwards; their prey is almost entirely invertebrate and they often link up with tit flocks when foraging. They nest in crevices. The Treecreeper or Brown Creeper, *Certhia familiaris*, is the Holarctic species. In Eurasian deciduous woodland it is replaced by the Short-toed, *C. brachydactyla*, which also penetrates north-west Africa. The distribution of the other 3 species, *C. himalayana*, *C. discors* and *C. nipalensis* is primarily the Himalayan foothills.

Family 132 *Climacteridae* AUSTRALIAN TREECREEPERS Sexes differ slightly
This small group of 6 or 9 mainly east Australian species has been placed in both the 2 previous families, but has claims to be considered on its own. About 6 ins long, these birds are more strikingly plumaged than the Eurasian treecreepers, with a coloured wing bar and striped underparts. They have longer legs and toes, prominent curved claws and a long curved bill, but their tail feathers are soft, not adapted as supports. They live in a variety of wooded habitats, haunting tree trunks like *Certhia* but do not join mixed flocks. They nest in tree holes.

Family 133 *Dicaeidae* FLOWERPECKERS
Sexes alike or differ
The majority of the 55 species in this Oriental and Australian family are in the genera *Prionochilus* and *Dicaeum*. They are small birds with short, stumpy tails and partially serrated, variably shaped bills, some rather tit-like, some long and curved; the tip of the tongue is semi-tubular. Plumages range from the drab (with sexes alike) to species with brightly coloured males. Two *Dicaeum* species reach the Palaearctic; but the Philippines have 13, of which 11 are endemic and New Guinea has 11 endemics, including 3 monotypic genera *Oreocharis*, *Paramythia* and *Rhamphocharis*. The 7 small, 'snub-nosed' pardalotes *Pardalotus* range from New Guinea to Tasmania; the name refers to the generally spotted plumage pattern. Flowerpeckers inhabit forests and secondary growth, including bamboo clumps and gardens. They feed on fruit, nectar and insects; several species, e.g. *Dicaeum hirundinaceum*, concentrate on mistle-toe berries and are responsible for their dissemination, some birds scraping the seeds off their bills and on to fresh hosts, and others evacuating them fairly rapidly through a specially adapted stomach.

Family 134 *Nectariniidae* SUNBIRDS
Sexes differ in sunbirds, alike in spiderhunters
This large Old World family, counterpart to the hummingbirds, has been variously arranged but now numbers over 100 species in relatively few genera, of which the more important are *Nectarinia*, *Cinnyris*, *Aethopyga* and *Anthreptes*. While over half the species live in Africa, the range extends via Palestine to India, south-east Asia, the Pacific islands and (1 species) to Australia. In size from about 3 to 8 ins long, sunbirds are generally larger than hummingbirds and much less diversified as to tails and bills. They drink nectar both directly and by piercing the tubular corollas of large flowers, and usually perch to do so, though they can hover. They have specialised tongues, partly tubular and forked at the tip. In striking metallic colours male sunbirds can match the hummingbirds; they also have a duller non-breeding plumage and females are usually, though not always, much drabber. They are generally solitary but several, of different species, may visit the same flowers. They are also mainly sedentary, but some show quite extensive seasonal movements. The domed or purse nests of plant fibres and cobwebs are often conspicuous; some species of *Cinnyris* and *Chalcomitra* associate with social insects (Hymenoptera) and spiders when nesting. The 9 spiderhunters *Arachnothera* of the Oriental region form rather a distinct group, generally larger with duller plumages alike in both sexes; most of them feed only on invertebrates.

Family 135 *Zosteropidae* WHITE-EYES Sexes alike
A family noted for uniform plumages in which yellow-green, grey, brown and white are predominant. Some authorities would put all 85 species in the genus *Zosterops*; others allot 62, with 23 in 11 other genera. White-eyes are found throughout the Ethiopian, Oriental and Australasian regions, mainly in the tropics and inhabiting wooded country of all kinds, including gardens, but not dense forest. Most are about 4 ins long and nearly all show the white orbital ring of feathers that gives the name. They have 9 functional primaries on their rounded wings, and short rather curved bills with which they pierce fruit, removing the inside with bristle-tipped tongues; they also feed on nectar and insects. Their songs are not notable. They are highly gregarious and this is believed to account for their success, though apparently weak fliers, in colonising remote islands not reached by other passerines. They reached New Zealand naturally about 1850 but were introduced to Hawaii and elsewhere. They build open nests and have a remarkably short ($10\frac{1}{2}$ days) incubation period; the young may leave the nest with part of the head still featherless.

Family 136 *Meliphagidae* HONEYEATERS, SUGARBIRDS Sexes alike or differ
Unlike the white-eyes, this is a very diverse family of 167 species divided into 38 genera, 14 of them monotypic, and primarily Australasian in distribution, though 1 or 2 species have penetrated the Oriental and even to the Palaearctic region. Size and structure show enormous diversity, but all species have long semi-tubular, cleft, bristle-tipped tongues adapted to nectar-feeding. Bills are of diverse lengths and shapes. Plumages are on the whole dull, with a tendency to bare patches, lobes and wattles on the head; some dimorphic *Myzomela* species are brilliantly coloured. Habits are also very variable, though all species are tree-living and nearly all build their nests off the ground. Honeyeaters are gregarious, nomadic and have a looping flight. Besides nectar, they take insects and fruit, but they have an important role as pollinators of many Australian trees and shrubs, which are adapted for bird visitors, just as the honeyeaters' tongues and digestive systems have been reciprocally evolved. Some species have good songs, sometimes uttered in flight, while those of the New Zealand Tui, *Prosthemadera novaeseelandiae*, and Bellbird, *Anthornis melonura*, are famous. The 2 sugarbirds *Promerops* are found in South Africa and attached to the family by virtue of similar tongue and intestinal structure; they are long-tailed with long curved bills.

Family 137 *Emberizidae* BUNTINGS, TANAGERS, HONEYCREEPERS Sexes alike or differ
This is a somewhat controversial grouping, best treated in its 5 subfamilies.

Emberizinae: a subfamily of New World origin, with about 160 species in 50 genera. Predominantly small (sparrow-sized – hence the American name for many species) brown birds with streaked plumages above and a tendency to white outer tail feathers, but with exceptions like the Towhees, *Pipilo* and Juncos, *Junco*. Some 37 *Emberiza* buntings have colonised the Old World (Palaearctic and Ethiopian) while the Crested Bunting, *Melophus lathami*, is found in the Oriental. The Snow, *Plectrophenax nivalis*, and Lapland Bunting or Longspur, *Calcarius lapponicus*, are Holarctic. Buntings are open country birds with strong feet and generally blunt seed-eating bills; migratory species have longer wings than sedentary forms. They build mainly on the ground. The head patterns of the males are often diagnostic.

Pyrrhuloxiinae: 'Cardinal-Grosbeaks': a New World group with 11 genera. Primarily tropical with some migratory North American breeding species. Most species nest in trees. The subfamily includes some of the most colourful species, e.g. the Indigo, *Passerina cyanea*, and Painted Bunting, *P. ciris*.

Thraupinae: the tanagers are another New World group of some 200 species, smallish (4 to 8 ins) birds of woodland but not dense forest. Some are brilliantly plumaged, but poor songsters. They feed mainly on fruits and some insects. The small euphonia, *Tanagra*, species disseminate mistle-toe by their partiality to its berries. The South American Plush-capped Finch, *Catamblyrhynchus diadema*, is one aberrant; another is the Swallow Tanager, *Tersina viridis*, which is given its own subfamily – *Tersinae;* it nests in burrows.

Coerebinae: the Honeycreepers do not look much like the other subfamilies and their modified tongues approach those of the *Meliphagidae* (Family 136). They are another Neotropical nectar-feeding group, with which are included the flowerpeckers *Diglossa* and the Bananaquit, *Coereba flaveola*. They are generally rather small birds with long thin curved bills and brilliantly coloured males, though the flowerpeckers are dull. They are sedentary, gregarious, forest-edge birds, working the canopy; the Bananaquit has become closely associated with man. Most build open nests in forks of trees or bushes.

Family 138 *Parulidae* AMERICAN OR WOOD WARBLERS Sexes usually differ
The taxonomic position of this important New World family has varied, but it is generally agreed to be somewhere close to the tanagers (Family 137, subfamily *Thraupinae*), certainly nowhere near the Old World warblers (Family 128, subfamily *Sylviinae*), unless the aberrant Olive Warbler, *Peucedramus taeniatus*, really belongs there. Few of the 113 species, arranged in 26 genera, are more than 6 ins long; about half of them breed only in North America and the West Indies; the rest are tropical or widely distributed. They are found in a variety of habitats but are primarily tree-living. The northern breeding species are migratory and, while recognisable in their spring plumages, pose problems of identification when they return south drably feathered in autumn. Yellow, orange, black and white are favourite colours, but some species, especially in the tropics, show red. Many are insectivorous, with rictal bristles and bills appropriately flattened for aerial capture; others are fruit and berry eaters. They build nests, usually open, from ground level to 60 ft in trees; the Ovenbird, *Seiurus aurocapillus*, makes a large domed structure on the ground.

Family 139 *Drepanididae* HAWAIIAN HONEYCREEPERS Sexes alike or differ
A small family of 22 species (9 of them recently extinct) in 9 genera, 4 of them monotypic, and one of the classic examples of adaptive radiation from a common ancestor into species with, for example, specialised bills ranging from the short, cross-bill of the Akepa, *Loxops coccinea*, to the very long curved probe of the Kauai Akialoa, *Hemignathus wilsoni*, or the stubby, parrot or finch-like organ of the Palila, *Psittirostra bailleui*. Honeycreepers are 4 to 8 ins long, males usually bigger

than females. Plumages are very varied: green, yellow, red and black. The crested, *Palmeria dolei,* is grey and red. Habits are solitary or gregarious, songs not remarkable and nests open. All members of the family have a musky smell, one indication of their common ancestor. Their survival under modern conditions is one of the serious problems of conservation.

Family 140 *Vireonidae* VIREOS, SHRIKE VIREOS, PEPPERSHRIKES Sexes alike

Another New World family with 1 vestigial and 9 functional primary feathers. Considered by some to be most closely related to the previous family, the 40 odd species in the subfamily *Vireoninae* are much more uniform in plumage, grey-green above, yellow and white below. They are 4 to 7 ins long, with typical perching feet and claws and short rather hooked bills. They live mainly in open woodland, sometimes in the tree canopy and build delicate nests slung between twigs. About 20 species in the genus *Vireo* include those nesting in North America – and therefore migratory – of which the Red-eyed, *V. olivaceus,* Yellow-throated, *V. flavifrons* and White-eyed, *V. griseus,* are very well known, the first for its persistent, monotonous summer-long song. The neotropical genus *Hylophilus* consists of 15 greenlets, smaller and even more uniform than the typical vireos; 3 species are found north of Panama. The Neotropical subfamily *Vireolaniinae* contains the Chestnut-sided Shrike Vireo, *Vireolanius melitophrys,* larger than the vireos and a hunter of big insects, and 2 or 3 species of *Smaragdolanius* which are smaller and little known, living high in the forest canopy. The *Cyclarhinae* consists of the 2 strongly-built pepper shrikes, *Cyclarhis gujanensis* and *C. nigrirostris,* predators on large insects and living in the middle storeys of the forest.

Family 141 *Icteridae* ICTERIDS Sexes usually differ

About 90 species are included in this heterogeneous family of 9 primaried New World passerines, related to the *Emberizidae* (Family 137). They have conical, usually straight, unnotched bills, and lack rictal bristles; there is also a propensity to black plumage. Apart from these points, there is great diversity in size (6 to 21 ins), plumage, length of tail and habits. Diet varies through a range of plants and small animals. The strength of the family is in tropical forest but members are found in all sorts of habitats and latitudes: the Rusty Blackbird, *Euphagus carolinus,* breeds within the Arctic Circle and another 'northerner', the Bobolink, *Dolichonyx oryzivorus,* migrates in winter to the south of Argentina. The tropical species, on the other hand, are mainly sedentary. The meadowlarks *Sturnella* are scattered and solitary; the grackles *Cassidex* and some blackbirds *Agelaius* are immensely social, not only for nesting, but form huge multi-specific roosts. The nests of Bobolink and meadowlarks are simple cups in the grass, whereas the orioles, of the genus *Icterus,* among others, build elaborate hanging nests, often in colonies. The cowbirds, especially the Brown-headed, *Molothrus ater,* are brood parasites on a range of species, including their own relatives.

Family 142 *Fringillidae* FINCHES
Sexes usually differ

There has been much taxonomic debate about the relationship of the seed-eating passerines (see *Emberizidae* Family 137). Three subfamilies are included here, united by 12 tail feathers, 9 primaries and normally a stout conical bill suited for breaking seeds or even nuts. The *Fringillinae* consist only of the Chaffinch, *Fringilla coelebs,* the very restricted Canary Islands Chaffinch, *F. teydea,* and the Brambling, *F. montifringilla,* all Palaearctic. They lack a crop, have for seed-eaters relatively fine bills and feed insects to their young in open nests. To the *Carduelinae* are ascribed 122 species in a number of genera, many monotypic and including the little-known Asian Przevalski's Rosefinch *Urocynchramus pylzowi,* which has a functional tenth primary. The strength of the group (68 species in 21 genera) lies in the Palaearctic, but there are 30 species in 9 genera in the Ethiopian region and 25 species in 8 genera are recorded in the New World, where 2 genera are endemic. Included in the subfamily are the whole range of finches from the large (and very large-billed) grosbeaks (*Coccothraustes, Eophona, Hesperiphona, Mycerobas*), crossbills (*Loxia*), rosefinches (*Carpodacus,* 20 species) and goldfinches (*Acanthis, Carduelis, Spinus*). The third subfamily is the remarkable Darwin's finches *Geospizinae,* 13 species in 3 genera in the Galapagos and one monotypic genus in the Cocos. They show classic adaptive radiation from a finch ancestor. There are minor differences, e.g. in plumage and size, but it is the specialisation of the bills to take different foods which is so striking.

Family 143 *Estrildidae* WEAVER FINCHES and VIDUINE WHYDAHS Sexes differ

Another family of seed-eaters with taxonomic problems. The waxbills, grassfinches and mannikins comprise some 108 species in 15 genera, all in southern parts of the Old World, including Australasia They are mostly very small and differ from the ploceid weavers (Family 144) in their untidy nests, white eggs and remarkable patterning of palate and tongue in the young. These mature very quickly and may breed at a few months, much more precociously than the ploceids. They have a great variety of courtship displays. The waxbills, tribe *Estrildini,* have about 10 genera confined to Africa, 2 Oriental avadavats and the Sydney Waxbill, *Estrilda temporalis,* which may not be closely related. There is a good deal of adaptive radiation in the tribe, as reflected in bill shapes. The grassfinches *Erythurini* are mostly Australian; they show some beautiful plumages and include some well-known cagebirds. The mannikins *Amadini* show less plumage variation but are geographically spread over south-east Asia, including India and Ceylon, Australasia and Africa, where the genus *Lonchura* occurs. Although the relationship is doubtful, the 11 species of whydahs or widow birds in the genus *Vidua* are included here. They are all Ethiopian, living socially on the savannahs in mixed flocks and laying their eggs in waxbills' nests. Their young counterfeit the mouth pattern of their hosts and their juvenile plumages. Male whydahs in breeding plumage are noted for their elongated central tail feathers.

Family 144 *Ploceidae* WEAVERS and SPARROWS
Sexes alike or differ

The last of these complicated families of mainly Old World seed-eaters may be divided into 3 subfamilies. In general they are larger than estrildids (size range linnet to thrush) with 12 tail-feathers, a reduced tenth primary and the expected strong bills. They build covered nests, sometimes communally, and their young do not have coloured mouth patterns. There are only 2 buffalo weavers *Bubalornithinae,* the largest (10 ins long) members of the family, the Black, *Bubalornis albirostris,* and White-headed, *Dinemellia dinemelli,* the first being polygamous. Both forage on the ground in parties for a varied diet. The 'true' weavers *Ploceinae* comprise about 90 species, predominantly African, with 5 in south-east Asia and India. Red and yellow are characteristic plumage tints, especially in the genus *Ploceus* (57 species) and *Malimbus* (10 species), which are tree-living groups, noted for their complex nests with protective devices e.g. tunnels, sites over water, association with wasps, and exceptionally variable egg colours. The diochs *Quelea,* fodies *Foudia,* and bishops (with the 'non-viduine' whydahs) *Euplectes* are distinguished by brilliant male plumages and, frequently, long tails. There are also the monotypic genera *Amblyospiza, Neospiza* (only 2 specimens known) and parasitic *Anomalospiza.* The diochs and bishops build in grass and the fodies in trees; their nests are not so well protected as the ploceines' and their eggs are more uniform. Male bishops and whydahs are noted for their long tails, the most extreme being that of the Sakabula, *Euplectes progne,* which is 20 ins long. These birds of open habitats tend to be strongly territorial, with remarkable displays. The Old World sparrows *Passerinae* include the 8 African sparrow weavers in 4 genera of generally brown-plumaged open country birds, of which the Black-billed, *Plocepasser mahali,* is the most widespread; the Sociable Weaver, *Philetarius socius,* builds the most remarkable communal nest. There are 2 African scaly weavers *Sporopipes frontalis* and *S. squamifrons,* dry-country colonial birds. The northern groups of the *Passerinae* include the 7 snow finches *Montifringilla,* 6 confined to Asia where they are some of the highest breeding species. The 4 rock sparrows *Petronia* have 1 African and 1 species found in India; of the other 2 southern Palaearctic species, one reaches Europe. Finally there are the *Passer* sparrows which include the almost ubiquitous (partly due to introductions) House Sparrow, *P. domesticus;* at least 8 species are more or less commensal with man.

Family 145 *Sturnidae* STARLINGS, MYNAHS, OXPECKERS Sexes more or less alike

The 110 species of this Old World family are split into 25 genera and are most numerous in India and south-east Asia, though also well represented in Africa. Only 1 species reaches Australia though the genus *Aplonis* is well-known in Polynesia. There are a few Palaearctic species, of which the Starling, *Sturnus vulgaris,* (a too successful colonist of North America after introduction) and irruptive Rosy Pastor, *S. roseus,* are the best known. Starlings are medium to large (7 to 17 ins) strongly built, long-legged, long-billed highly gregarious passerines, with poor songs but some excellent mimics; black predominates in the plumage, which may also be iridescent. Some species have wattles, lappets or bristly feathers as head ornaments. Starlings tend to be omnivorous and the Wattled, *Creatophora cinerea,* is a considerable predator on locust swarms in Africa. Starlings build open or cavity nests and the Celebes Starling, *Scissirostrum dubium,* excavates a hole, having a woodpecker-like bill and stiff tail-feathers. The 2 African oxpeckers *Buphagus,* with their specialised ecology dependent on large mammals, are included in the family.

Family 146 *Oriolidae* OLD WORLD ORIOLES
Sexes differ

A homogeneous family of some 30 mainly tropical Old World species, in size from starling to jay, with long pointed wings, longish tails, curved bills and a tendency to black and gold in male plumages. They are tree-living, feeding on invertebrates and fruit, usually in evergreen forest, and build hammock nests in forked branches. The beautiful fluting song is well developed in the Golden, *Oriolus oriolus,* which, like the E Asian Black-naped, *O. chinensis,* penetrates the Palaearctic as a summer visitor. Several species have evolved on small islands, e.g. Sao Tomé (Guinea) and the Moluccas, while the Kinkimavo, *Tylas,* of Madagascar may be an aberrant oriole. The 4 fig birds *Sphecotheres* are primarily Australasian; they have bare skin around their eyes and build flimsier nests than *Oriolus.*

Family 147 *Dicruridae* DRONGOS
Sexes differ somewhat

Another family of Old World tropical passerines, starling to jay sized excluding the long variable tail of 10 to 12 feathers, most spectacularly developed in the Asian Giant Racket-tailed Drongo, *Dicrurus paradiseus,* also an accomplished mimic. Apart from the monotypic Mountain Drongo, *Chaetorhynchus papuensis,* of New Guinea, all other species are *Dicrurus,* with generally metallic black plumages. A number sport crests of various shapes, rictal bristles are prominent and the iris is often red. Most variation is shown by the Asian species, several of which penetrate to the Palaearctic. The long-winged, strong-billed drongos are solitary and notably aggressive; the King Crow, *D. macrocercus,* of India recalls the Kingbird of North America (Family 108). Drongos attack birds of prey fiercely, but they allow other species to nest in their vicinity; their own nests are rather shallow hanging cradles. They feed primarily on insects and small vertebrates.

Family 148 *Callaeidae* WATTLEBIRDS
Sexes more or less alike

A small New Zealand family of 2 living and 1 recently extinct species, for which various relationships have been suggested. All three have paired wattles of unknown function drooping from their gapes; their long tails show projecting feather shafts, they have long first primaries on their rounded wings, strong feet with long hind claws, and generally black plumage except for the bright wattles. They live in the primitive forest, in pairs or flocks, feeding on the ground or travelling from branch to branch without sustained flight. The Huia, *Heteralocha acutirostris,* largest of the three (19 to 21 ins) and last seen in 1907, was famous for the difference between the male and female bills. The male's shorter organ picked out grubs from decayed trees while the female's long flexible probe entered borings in harder wood. The starling-sized Saddleback, *Creadon carunculatus*, has separate races on North and South Islands, as has the Kokako or Wattled Crow, *Callaeus cinerea*, 17 to 18 ins, said to be the finest native song bird.

Family 149 *Grallinidae* MAGPIE LARKS or MUDNEST BUILDERS Sexes alike or differ

A small Australian family of 4 rather diverse species, having in common their habit of building mud cup-nests on trees near water. The strikingly black and white Magpie Lark or Mudlark, *Grallina cyanoleuca*, starling-sized, hunts invertebrate food on the ground, is pugnacious against passing birds of prey and pairs for life, though large flocks have been reported outside the breeding season. Little is known about the smaller *G. bruijni* of New Guinea. The Apostlebird, *Struthidea cinerea*, gets its name from its small flocks of about 12. The larger White-winged Chough, *Corcorax melanor-hamphus*, is also a bird of south-east Australian open woodland. Both species nest communally in groups of up to 20, each female contributing probably 2 eggs.

Family 150 *Artamidae* WOOD SWALLOWS or SHRIKES Sexes usually alike

A principally Australian family with a single genus *Artamus* of 10 to 15 species, from 5 to 8 ins long, the only passerines with powder-down patches. The species radiate from Australia to the islands of south-west Asia, one reaching India and western China. Wood swallows are rather stocky, short-tailed birds with long pointed wings; their slightly curved pointed bills have wide gapes. The soft plumage is predominantly of grey, brown, black and white. They fly rather like slow-beating swallows but can also glide, the larger species spiralling in up-currents, for they are birds of open country rather than dense woods and dart after insects like flycatchers. They will attack passing predators, uttering harsh calls, and may be found in small parties, huddled on a branch, or roosting in much larger numbers. They build shallow cup nests high up on the base of a branch or other projection.

Family 151 *Cracticidae* SONG SHRIKES Sexes alike

Another small but diverse Australian family, fairly closely related to the crows; they have been given a number of English names. Ranging from 10 ins to 2 ft in length, these are strongly built birds with large heads and powerful, usually hooked bills; legs are strong and shanks rather long; plumages are often black or black and white. All species fly well and most are noisy, gregarious and tree-living. Only two currawongs, the Pied, *Strepera graculina*, and Grey, *S. versicolor*, are now

recognised, both having several rather variable races. They have a mixed diet, including small vertebrates, flock in winter but breed separately, building open nests in trees, as do the other two genera. There are 2 (or 3) species of bell magpie, *Gymnorhina*, covering most of Australia between them. Both black- and white-backed forms of *G. tibicen* have been introduced to New Zealand. The Western, *G. dorsalis*, lives, apparently promiscuously, in groups of varying sex composition on communally defended territories. The 6 or 7 butcherbirds *Cracticus* show convergence with the shrikes (*Laniidae* Family 120), even to the extent of establishing larders of prey. The Pied, *C. nigrogularis*, is considered to be one of the world's best song birds. Two species are confined to New Guinea.

Family 152 *Ptilinorhynchidae* BOWER BIRDS Sexes generally differ

Another and very famous Australasian family, confined to New Guinea and northern Australia. The 19 species range from thrush to crow size; they are forest birds with short shanks and strong perching feet, short, sometimes curved or even hooked bills. Wings and tails are also short but they fly strongly and spend little time on the ground except when displaying; nests are built often high in trees. The catbirds, subfamily *Ailuroedi-nae*, do not build bowers. The Green, *Ailuroedus crassi-rostris*, and White-throated, *A. buccoides*, have 'normal' passerine displays. The male Stagemaker or Tooth-billed Catbird, *Scenopoeetes dentirostris*, of Queensland, however, clears a space on the forest floor and covers it each morning with fresh leaves, cut with its specialised bill. He then perches above and advertises his stage. There are three groups of typical bower birds *Ptilino-rhynchinae* according to their constructions: the plat-form builders *Archboldia*; the maypole builders, *Priono-dura* and *Amblyornis*; and the avenue makers *Ptilino-rhynchus*, *Chlamydera* and *Sericulus*. The members of the first two groups, except for the Golden or Newton's Bower Bird, *Prionodura newtoniana*, are confined to the New Guinea rain forests and little is known about their displays. The avenue makers are also found in Austra-lia and their behaviour has been watched. The function of the bower, built early in the season, is apparently to attract the female to the already sexually advanced male. The male, whose plumage is often brilliant, dis-plays to the female but without approaching her until she is ready to mate, a state coinciding with the onset of insect life needed to rear the brood which she does by herself. The painting activities of the Regent, *Sericulus chrysocephalus*, and Satin Bower Birds, *Ptilinorhynchus violaceus*, using respectively bark and leaves to apply the mixture of charcoal, fruit pulp, wood and saliva to the bower are two more proved examples of tool-using by birds like the probe used by the Galapagos Wood-pecker Finch, *Camarhynchus pallidus*.

Family 153 *Paradisaeidae* BIRDS OF PARADISE Sexes alike or differ widely

Some 40 species are recognised in this, perhaps the most spectacular bird family of all, with its centre in New Guinea and adjacent islands, e.g. the Arus; there are a few – the most studied – species in northern Australia and 2 in the Moluccas, the large Paradise Crow, *Lyco-corax pyrrhopterus*, silky black and brown-winged, and the smaller Standardwing, *Semioptera wallacei*, with long plumes at the 'wrists' of the wings. The occurrence of natural hybrids even across generic boundaries is believed to indicate the origin of the fantastic male plumages and displays for which the family is famous: they are a device to prevent too much interbreeding between promiscuous and polygamous birds. But some species do not show sexual dimorphism and are not polygamous, the males assisting in rearing the brood, e.g. the large, wattled Moluccan Bird of Paradise, *Macgregoria pulchra*, and the glossy manu-codes *Manucodia* and *Phonygammus*. Those species with most bizarre plumages and displays are the polygam-ous ones. Displays may be solitary or communal, on the ground or in trees, where, for example, the Emper-or Bird of Paradise, *Paradisaea guilielmi*, hangs upside-down on his perch. The bulky nest built of sticks is placed in a tree, but the clutch is relatively small, being of only one or two eggs.

Family 154 *Corvidae* CROWS, MAGPIES, JAYS Sexes alike

The last and perhaps 'most evolved' of all bird families is 100 species strong, nearly world-wide and contains the largest of all passerines, the Holarctic Raven, *Corvus corax*, over 2 ft long. The smallest jays are about a foot long, but all the family is characterised by stout bodies, strong feet and legs, the shanks scaled in front and smooth behind, powerful slightly hooked bills with bristles covering the nostrils, and rather broad unspecialised but effective wings for flapping and soaring. Many species are omnivorous and all build stick nests on trees, rocks or in holes. Crows have colonised some islands but not New Zealand and others in the Pacific. Jays are strongly represented in northern South America but not in its temperate zone, while only typical crows have crossed the Sahara. Re-markable distribution patterns are shown by the Azure-winged Magpie, *Cyanopica cyanus*, (Spain and north-east Asia, but nowhere between) and the Scrub Jay, *Aphelocoma coerulescens*, found on the west coasts of North America and in Florida. Crows may be solitary or gregarious, or a mixture of both; they are found in all types of habitat, including the 'manscape' and the success of many of them as human commensals is considered by our conceited species to be proof of their intelligence.

41
Pelecanus onocrotalus
Old World White Pelican

42
Sula bassana
Gannet

43
Sula leucogaster
Brown Booby

44
Sula nebouxii
Blue-footed Booby

45
Sula sula
Red-footed Booby

46
Nannopterum harrisi ♂
Galapagos Cormorant

47
Phalacrocorax africanus 🔟
Long-tailed Shag

48
Phalacrocorax atriceps
Blue-eyed Shag

49
Phalacrocorax bougainvillii
Guanay

50
Phalacrocorax carbo ◯
Cormorant

51
Phalacrocorax varius
Pied Cormorant

52
Anhinga anhinga
Darter

53
Fregata magnificens ♂
Magnificent Frigate bird

41

54
Ardea cinerea
Grey Heron

55
Ardea goliath
Goliath Heron

56
Bubulcus ibis
Cattle Egret

57
Cochlearius cochlearius
Boatbill

58
Egretta alba
Great White Heron OR
Common Egret

43

140
Buteo lineatus
Red-Shouldered Hawk

141
Chelictinia riocourii
Swallow-tailed Kite

142
Circaetus cinereus
Brown Harrier OR
Snake Eagle

143
Circus approximans ♂
Swamp Hawk

144
Circus ranivorus
African Marsh Harrier

145
Elanus caeruleus
Black-shouldered Kite

146
Gypaetus barbatus
Lammergeier

147
Gypohierax angolensis
Palm-nut Vulture

148
Gyps africanus
African White-backed Vulture

149
Gyps bengalensis
Indian White-backed Vulture

150
Haliaeetus albicilla
White-tailed Eagle

151
Haliaeetus leucogaster
White Breasted Sea Eagle

152
Haliaeetus vocifer
African Fish Eagle

153
Haliastur sphenurus
Whistling Eagle OR Kite

154
Heterospizias meridionalis
Savannah Hawk

155
Hieratus pennatus
Booted Eagle

156
Lophoaetus occipitalis
Long-crested Hawk Eagle

157
Melierax canorus
Pale chanting Goshawk

158
Milvus migrans aegyptius
Yellow-billed Kite

59

159
Neophron percnopterus
Egyptian Vulture

160
Pandion haliaetus
Osprey

161
Polemaetus bellicosus ♀♂
Martial Eagle

162
Polyboroides typus
African Harrier Hawk

163
Sarcogyps calvus
Asian King Vulture

164
Stephanoetus coronatus
Crowned Eagle

165
Terathopius ecaudatus
Bateleur

166
Trigonoceps occipitalis
White-headed Vulture

230
Notornis mantelli
Takahe

231
Porphyrio porphyrio
Purple Gallinule

232
Porphyrula martinica
American Purple Gallinule

233
Porzana carolina ♂
Sora Rail

234
Porzana plumbea
Spotless Crake OR
Putoto

235
Rallina tricolor
Red-necked Rail

236
Rallus longirostris
Clapper Rail

237
Rallus owstoni
Guam Rail

238
Psophia leucoptera
Pale-winged Trumpeter

239
Rhynochetus jubatus
Kagu

240
Eurypyga helias
Sun Bittern

241
Cariama cristata
Red-legged Seriema

242
Choriotis kori
Kori Bustard

243
Eupodotis australis
Australian Bustard

244
Eupodotis senegalensis ♂
White-bellied Bustard

245
Lissotis melanogaster ♂
Black-bellied Bustard

246
Otis tarda ♀
Great Bustard

247
Otis tetrax ♀
Little Bustard

77

248
Actophilornis africana
African Jacana OR
Lily Trotter

249
Irediparra gallinacea ♀♂
Lotus Bird OR
Australian Jacana

250
Jacana spinosa
Wattled OR
South America Jacana

251
Microparra capensis
Lesser Jacana

252
Rostratula benghalensis ♀
Painted Snipe

253
Haematopus moquini
African Black Oyster Catcher

276
Calidris alba ♂
Sanderling

277
Calidris alpina ○
Dunlin OR
Red-backed Sandpiper

278
Calidris canutus ⬗
Knot

279
Calidris ferruginea ○
Curlew Sandpiper

280
Calidris fusciollis ♀○
White-rumped Sandpiper

281
Calidris maritima ⬗
Purple Sandpiper

282
Calidris temminckii ○
Temminck's Stint

283
Catoptrophorus semipalmatus
Willet

284
Gallinago nigripennis ○
African Snipe

285
Limicola falcinellus ○
Broad-billed Sandpiper

286
Limnodromus scolopaceus ◐
Long-billed Dowitcher

287
Limosa limosa ○
Black-tailed Godwit

288
Micropalma himantopus ◯
Stilt Sandpiper

289
Numenius arquata ◯
Curlew

290
Numenius phaeopus ◯
Whimbrel

291
Philohela minor ♀◯
American Woodcock

292
Philomachus pugnax ♂◯
Ruff

293
Scolopax rusticola ♀◯
Eurasian Woodcock

294
Tringa brevipes ♂
Grey-tailed OR
Siberian Tattler

295
Tringa erythropus ♂
Spotted Redshank

296
Tringa glareola ♂
Wood Sandpiper

297
Tringa hypoleucos ○
Common Sandpiper

298
Tringa stagnatilis ⬗
Marsh Sandpiper

299
Tringa totanus ○
Redshank

300
Tringytes subruficollis
Buff-breasted Sandpiper

301
Himantopus himantopus ♂○
Black-winged OR
Black-necked Stilt

302
Recurvirostra avosetta ○
Avocet

303
Phalaropus fulicarius ♀○
Grey OR
Red Phalarope

304
Phalaropus lobatus ♀○
Red-necked Phalarope

305
Dromas ardeola
Crab Plover

306
Burhinus bistriatus
Double-striped
Stone Curlew

307
Burhinus capensis ○
Spotted Thick-knee

308
Burhinus oedicnemus ○
Stone Curlew

339
Sterna sumatrana ◯
Black-naped Tern

340
Thalasseus elegans ◯
Elegant Tern

341
Xema sabini ◯
Sabine's Gull

342
Rynchops nigra ◯
Black Skimmer

343
Alca torda ◯
Razorbill

344
Cepphus grylle ◯
Black Guillemot

345
Fratercula arctica ◯
Atlantic Puffin

346
Uria aalge
Common Guillemot
OR
Murre

COLUMBIFORMES

347
Eremialector decoratus ♂
Black-faced Sandgrouse

348
Eremialector quadricinctus ♀♂
Four-banded Sandgrouse

349
Pterocles exustus ♂
Chestnut-bellied Sandgrouse

350
Caloenas nicobarica ♂
Nicobar Dove

351
Chalcophaps indica ♂
Emerald Dove

352
Claravis pretiosa ♂
Blue Ground Dove

353
Columba albitorques ◯
White-collared Pigeon

354
Columba arquatrix
Olive Pigeon

355
Columba guinea ◯
Speckled OR Cape Rock Pigeon

356
Columba livia
Rock Dove

357
Columba oenas ♂
Stock Dove

358
Columba palumbus
Wood Pigeon

359
Columbina passerina ♀
Common Ground Dove

360
Gallicolumba luzonica
Luzon Bleeding Heart

361
Geopelia cuneata ○
Diamond Dove

428
Piaya cayana
Squirrel OR
Chestnut Cuckoo

STRIGIFORMES

429
Tyto alba ♀♂
Barn Owl

430
Tyto tenebricosa
Sooty Owl

431
Aegolius acadicus
Saw-whet Owl

432
Aegolius funereus
Tengmalm's, Boreal
OR
Richardson's Owl

433
Asio capensis
African Marsh Owl

434
Asio flammeus
Short-eared Owl

435
Asio otus
Long-eared Owl

436
Athene noctua
Little Owl

437
Bubo africanus
Spotted Eagle Owl

438
Bubo bubo
Eagle Owl

439
Bubo ketupu
Malaysian Fish Owl

440
Bubo lacteus
Giant Eagle Owl

441
Bubo virginianus
Great Horned Owl

442
Ciccaba woodfordii
African Wood Owl

443
Micrathene whitneyi
Elf Owl

444
Ninox novaeseelandiae
Morepork, Spotted
OR
Boobook Owl

445
Nyctaea scandiaca ♀
Snowy Owl

446
Otus asio
Screech Owl

447
Otus leucotis
White-faced Owl

448
Otus scops
Scops Owl

449
Speotyto cunicularia
Burrowing Owl

514
Buceros bicornis ♀
Great OR
Great Pied Hornbill

515
Bucorvus abyssinicus ♂
Abyssinian Ground Hornbill

516
Bucorvus leadbeateri ♂
Ground Hornbill

517
Tockus alboterminatus
Crowned Hornbill

518
Tockus deckeni ♂
Van der Decken's Hornbill

131

519
Tockus erythrorhynchus
Red-billed Hornbill

520
Tockus flavirostris
Yellow-billed Hornbill

521
Tockus nasutus ♂
Grey Hornbill

PICIFORMES

522
Galbula ruficauda
Rufous-tailed Jacamar

523
Bucco macrodactylus
Chestnut-capped Puffbird

524
Malacoptila panamensis
White-whiskered Puffbird OR
Softwing

525
Eubucco bourcierii ♀
Red-headed Barbet

526
Lybius leucomelas
Pied Barbet

527
Lybius torquatus
Black-collared Barbet

528
Pogoniulus bilineatus
Golden-rumped Tinkerbird

529
Pogoniulus chrysoconus
Yellow-fronted Tinkerbird

530
Trachyphonus darnaudii
D'Arnaud's Barbet

531
Trachyphonus erythrocephalus
Red and Yellow Barbet

532
Trachyphonus vaillantii
Crested OR
Levaillant's Barbet

533
Indicator minor
Lesser Honeyguide

534
Aulacorhynchus caeruleogularis
Blue-throated Toucanet

535
Aulacorhynchus prasinus
Emerald Toucanet

536
Pteroglossus pluricinctus
Many-banded Araçari

537
Campethera abingoni
Golden-tailed Woodpecker

538
Campethera bennettii ♂
Bennett's Woodpecker

135

607
Lullula arborea
Wood Lark

608
Mirafra africana
Bush Lark

609
Delichon urbica
House Martin

610
Hirundo abyssinica
Striped Swallow

611
Hirundo albigularis
White-throated Swallow

612
Hirundo cucullata
Larger Striped Swallow

613
Hirundo daurica
Red-rumped Swallow

614
Hirundo dimidiata
Pearl-breasted Swallow

615
Hirundo fuligula
African Rock Martin

616
Hirundo rupestris
Crag Martin

617
Hirundo rustica
Barn Swallow

618
Hirundo senegalensis
Mosque Swallow

619
Hirundo smithii ♂
Wire-tailed Swallow

620
Progne subis ♀
Purple Martin

621
Riparia paludicola
African Sand Martin

622
Tachycineta bicolor
Tree Swallow

623
Anthus cervinus ♀
Red-throated Pipit

624
Anthus leucophrys
Plain-backed Pipit

625
Anthus novaeseelandiae
Richard's Pipit

626
Anthus pratensis + ♂ Cuculus canorus
Meadow Pipit + Common Cuckoo

627
Anthus trivialis ♂♀
Tree Pipit

628
Macronyx ameliae ♂
Rosy-breasted Longclaw

629
Macronyx capensis ♂
Orange-throated Longclaw

630
Macronyx croceus
Yellow-throated Longclaw

631
Motacilla aguimp
African Pied Wagtail

632
Motacilla alba ♀
White Wagtail

633
Motacilla cinerea ♀
Grey Wagtail

702
Thamnolaea cinnamomeiventris ♂
Cliff Chat

703
Thamnolaea coronata ♂
White-crowned Cliff Chat
OR Snowy-crowned Robin

704
Turdus iliacus
Redwing

705
Turdus libonyanus
Kurrichane Thrush

706
Turdus merula ♂
Blackbird

707
Turdus migratorius ♂
American Robin

708
Turdus olivaceus
Olive Thrush

709
Turdus viscivorus
Mistle Thrush

710
Garrulax caerulatus
Grey-sided Laughing Thrush

711
Leiothrix argentauris ♀
Silver-eared Mesia

712
Leiothrix lutea
Pekin Robin

713
Parisoma subcaeruleum
Common Tit Babbler

714
Pomatorhinus erythrogenys
Rusty-cheeked Scimitar Babbler

715
Pomatostomus superciliosus ♀
White-browed Babbler

716
Turdoides jardinei
Arrow-marked Babbler

717
Cinclosoma castanotum
Chestnut Quail Thrush

718
Cinclosoma cinnamomeum ♂
Cinnamon Quail Thrush

719
Orthonyx spaldingi ♀
Northern Logrunner

720
Psophodes olivaceus
Eastern Whipbird

721
Panurus biarmicus ♀
Bearded Tit OR Reedling

722
Polioptila caerulea
Blue-grey Gnatcatcher

723
Ramphocaenus melanurus
Long-billed Gnat Wren

724
Acrocephalus palustris
Marsh Warbler

725
Acrocephalus schoenobaenus ♀♂
Sedge Warbler

726
Acrocephalus stentoreus
Clamorous Reed Warbler

727
Apalis thoracica
Bar-throated Apalis

171

799
Terpsiphone viridis ♂
African Paradise Flycatcher

800
Pachycephala pectoralis ♂
Golden Whistler

801
Aegithalos caudatus
Long-tailed Tit

802
Parus atricapillus
Black-capped Chickadee

803
Parus caeruleus
Blue Tit

804
Parus cristatus
Crested Tit

805
Parus major
Great Tit

806
Parus montanus
Willow Tit

807
Parus niger ♂
Southern Black Tit

808
Parus palustris
Marsh Tit

809
Remiz pendulinus
Penduline Tit

810
Sitta canadensis ♂
Red-breasted Nuthatch

811
Sitta europaea
Nuthatch

812
Sitta neumayer
Rock Nuthatch

813
Certhia familiaris
Treecreeper

814
Climacteris picumnus
Australian Brown Treecreeper

815
Dicaeum hirundinaceum ♀
Mistletoe Bird

816
Pardalotus melanocephalus
Black-headed Pardalote

817
Pardalotus punctatus ♂
Spotted Pardalote

818
Pardalotus striatus
Yellow-tipped Pardalote

819
Arachnothera magna
Streaked Spiderhunter

820
Chalcomitra senegalensis ♂
Scarlet-chested Sunbird

821
Cinnyris chalybeus ♂
Lesser OR
Southern Double-collared
Sunbird

822
Cinnyris talatala ♀
White-bellied Sunbird

823
Cinnyris venustus ♂
Variable Sunbird

824
Cyanomitra verticalis ♂
Green-headed Sunbird

189

874
Saltator atripennis
Black-winged Saltator

875
Chlorochrysa phoenicotis
Glistening Green Tanager

876
Iridosornis rufivertex
Golden-crowned Tanager

877
Piranga rubra ♂
Summer Tanager

878
Ramphocelus icteronotus ♂
Yellow-rumped Tanager

879
Ramphocelus nigrogularis ♂
Masked Crimson Tanager

880
Tanagra laniirostris ♂
Thick-billed Euphonia

881
Tangara cyanoptera ♂
Black-headed Tanager

882
Tangara gyrola
Blue-rumped Green Tanager

883
Tangara nigroviridis
Black and Green Tanager

884
Thraupis episcopus ♂
Blue-grey Tanager

885
Tersina viridis ♂
Swallow Tanager

886
Coereba flaveola
Bananaquit

887
Cyanerpes caeruleus ♀♂
Yellow-legged Honeycreeper

888
Dacnis lineata ♂
Black-faced Dacnis

889
Diglossa caerulescens ♂
Bluish Flowerpecker

890
Basileuterus rufifrons
Rufous-capped Warbler

891
Dendroica dominica ♂
Yellow-throated Warbler

892
Dendroica magnoliae ⬤
Magnolia Warbler

893
Dendroica petechia ♂
Yellow Warbler

894
Helmitheros vermivorus
Worm-eating Warbler

895
Icteria virens
Yellow-breasted Chat

896
Mniotilta varia ♂
Black and White Warbler

897
Myioborus miniatus
Slate-throated Redstart

898
Myioborus ornatus
Golden-fronted Redstart

899
Seiurus auricapillus
Ovenbird

900
Setophaga ruticilla ♂
American Redstart

901
Vermivora celata
Orange-crowned Warbler

902
Wilsonia canadensis ♂
Canada Warbler

903
Wilsonia pusilla ♂
Wilson's Warbler

904
Cyclarhis gujanensis
Rufous-browed Peppershrike

905

Hylophilus ochraceiceps
Tawnv-crowned Greenlet

906
Vireo griseus
White-eyed Vireo

907
Agelaius xanthomus
Yellow-shouldered Blackbird

908
Cacicus cela
Yellow-rumped Cacique

909
Gymnomystax mexicanus
Oriole Blackbird

910
Icterus galbula ♀
Baltimore Oriole

911
Molothrus ater ♂ ♀
Brown-headed Cowbird

912
Quiscalus niger ♂
Greater Antillean Grackle

913
Quiscalus quiscala ♂
Purple Grackle

914
Sturnella magna ♂
Eastern Meadowlark

915
Acanthis cannabina ♂
Linnet

916
Acanthis flammea ♀
Redpoll

917
Atlapetes semirufus
Ochre-breasted Brush Finch

918
Carduelis carduelis
Eurasian Goldfinch

919
Carduelis chloris ♂
Greenfinch

920
Carpodacus mexicanus ♂
House Finch

980
Creadion carunculatus
Saddleback

981
Grallina cyanoleuca ♂
Magpie Lark

982
Artamus leucorhynchus
White-breasted Wood Swallow

983
Cracticus torquatus ♂
Grey Butcherbird

984
Gymnorhina tibicen ♂♂
Australian Magpie

985
Strepera graculina
Pied Currawong

986
Chlamydera maculata ♂
Spotted Bower Bird

987
Prionodura newtoniana ♂
Newton's Bower Bird

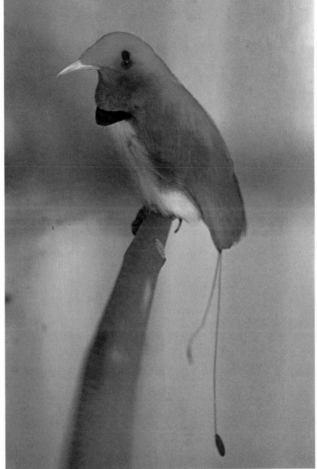

988
Ptilinorhynchus violaceus ♂
Satin Bower Bird

989
Astrapia stephaniae ♀
Princess Stephanie's Bird of
Paradise

990
Cicinnurus regius ♂
King Bird of Paradise

991
Epimachus meyeri ♀
Sickle-billed Bird of Paradise

992
Paradisaea raggiana ♂
Count Raggi's Bird of Paradise

993
Aphelocoma caerulescens
Scrub Jay

994
Aphelocoma ultramarina
Mexican Jay

995
Cissa chinensis
Hunting Cissa

996
Corvultur albicollis
White-necked Raven

997
Corvus corax
Raven

998
Corvus corone cornix
Carrion Crow

999
Corvus frugilegus
Rook

222

1000
Corvus monedula
Jackdaw

1001
Corvus ossifragus
Fish crow

1002
Cyanocitta stelleri
Steller's Jay

1003
Cyanocorax yncas
Green Jay

1004
Cyanopica cyanus
Azure-winged Magpie

BLACK-THROATED
  DIVER see **Gavia arctica**
  TROGON see **Trogon rufus**

BLACK-WINGED
  ORIOLE see under **Oriolus larvatus**
  PRATINCOLE see under **Glareola pratincola**
  RED BISHOP see under **Euplectes orix**
  SALTATOR see **Saltator atripennis**
  STILT see **Himantopus himantopus**

BLEEDING HEART, LUZON see **Gallicolumba luzonica**

BLUE
  CHAFFINCH see under **Fringilla coelebs**
  CRANE see **Anthropoides paradisaea**
  GROUND DOVE see **Claravis pretiosa**
  GROUSE see **Dendragapus obscurus**
  HERON, LITTLE see **Florida caerulea**
  PENGUIN, LITTLE see **Eudyptes minor**
  ROCK THRUSH see **Monticola solitarius**
  TIT see **Parus caeruleus**
  TOURACO, GREAT see **Corythaeola cristata**
  WREN see **Malurus cyaneus**
  WREN, BANDED see under **Malurus callainus**

BLUE AND WHITE FLYCATCHER see **Cyanoptila cyanomelana**

BLUE AND YELLOW MACAW see **Ara ararauna**

BLUE-BILLED DUCK see **Oxyura australis**

BLUEBIRD,
  EASTERN see **Sialia sialis**
  FAIRY see **Irena puella**
  WESTERN see under **Peucedramus taeniatus**

BLUE-CHEEKED
  AMAZON PARROT see **Amazonia brasiliensis**
  BEE-EATER see **Merops superciliosus**

BLUE-CROWNED MOTMOT see **Momotus momota**

BLUE-EARED GLOSSY STARLING see **Lamprocolius chalybeus**

BLUE-EYED SHAG see **Phalacrocorax atriceps**

BLUE-FACED HONEY-EATER see **Entomyzon cyanotus**

BLUE-FOOTED BOOBY see **Sula nebouxii**

BLUE-GREY
  GNATCATCHER see **Polioptila caerulea**
  TANAGER see **Thraupis episcopus**

BLUE-HEADED AMAZON PARROT see **Amazonia brasiliensis**

BLUE-NAPED
  FRUIT DOVE see **Ptilinopus melanospila**
  MOUSEBIRD see **Colius macrouros**

BLUE-SPOTTED WOOD DOVE see under **Turtur abyssinicus**

BLUE-SPOTTED WOOD DOVE BLACK-BILLED see **Turtur abyssinicus**

BLUE-TAILED PITTA see **Pitta guajana**

BLUETAIL, RED-FLANKED see **Tarsiger cyanurus**

BLUETHROAT see **Luscinia svecica**

BLUE-THROATED
  HUMMINGBIRD see **Lampornis clemenciae**
  SYLPH see **Lampornis clemenciae**
  TOUCANET see **Aulacorhynchus caeruleogularis**

BLUE-WINGED PITTA see **Pitta brachyura**

BLUISH FLOWERPECKER see **Diglossa caerulescens**

BOATBILL see **Cochlearius cochlearius**

BOBOLINK see **Dolichonyx oryzivorus**

BOBWHITE see **Colinus virginianus**

Bocagia minuta see **Tchagra minuta**

BOKMAKIERIE see **Malaconotus zeylonus**

BOHEMIAN WAXWING see **Bombycilla garrulus**

Bombycilla cedrorum *Bombycillidae*
CEDAR WAXWING   7¼ ins
Nearctic: breeds from Cape Breton Is, Quebec, Ontario, British Columbia S to Georgia, New Mexico, California; winters S to W Indies, Panama. Habitat open, scattered trees, e.g. in swamps, orchards, rather than continuous woodland like *B. garrulus*. Very similar to *B. garrulus* but under tail coverts white, no white and yellow wing markings, white round black mask more pronounced. Juvenile resembles *B. garrulus* with prominent pale 'eyebrow'. Habits, voice, feeding also similar, flocks staying together most of year. Breeds variably, late June into August, building relatively large nest of plant material 6 to 35 ft up on lateral branch of broadleaved or coniferous tree. 4 to 6 grey-blue eggs, spotted black and brown. **659**

Bombycilla garrulus *Bombycillidae*
(BOHEMIAN) WAXWING   8 ins
Holarctic: across northern Eurasia from 20°E in Scandinavia, mainly between 60° and 70°N to Sea of Okhotsk; Kamtchatka; replaced N Manchuria, Sakhalin, Japan by very similar *B. japonica*. Breeds N America mainly down W side from Alaska to N Idaho; irregular migrant usually into temperate zone to about 35°N, e.g. Asia Minor, S California. Habitat: often dense coniferous and mixed woodland and their edges, wintering woodland parks, gardens, even into cities. Upperparts, including prominent crest, vinaceous brown; rump, short tail grey with subterminal black, yellow tip; flight feathers greyish-black to black with white and yellow tips; shafts of tail feathers and secondaries may have red 'waxy' tips; eyestripe, bib black; underparts pale vinaceous shading to deep sienna under tail coverts; legs black, bill mainly black, eyes dark brown. ♀ greyer, wing and tail markings less bright and no waxy red; juvenile duller, underparts streaked. Often perches high, but quite tame. Flight strong with long undulations; wings rattle when rising and descending. Gregarious in winter. Rather silent, usual call high, trilling *sirrr*, from which rather jumbled song develops. Agile in trees when feeding on berries; also hawks insects in air and feeds on ground; drinks freely. Breeds from mid June Lapland, ♀ and ♂ building nest of twigs, lichens *Cladonia, Usnea,* some grass or softer lining. 4 to 6 ashy-grey or pale blue eggs, spotted black or blackish brown over grey, incubated mainly ♀, fed by ♂, *c.* 14 days. **660**

Bombycilla japonica see under **B. garrulus**

BONAPARTE'S GULL see **Larus philadelphia**

BOOBOOK OWL see **Ninox novaeseelandiae**

BOOBY,
  BLUE-FOOTED see **Sula nebouxii**
  BROWN see **Sula leucogaster**
  RED-FOOTED see **Sula sula**

BOOTED EAGLE see **Hieraetus pennatus**

BOREAL OWL see **Aegolius funereus**

BORNEO BRISTLEHEAD see **Pityriasis gymnocephala**

Bostrychia carunculata *Threskiornithidae*
WATTLED IBIS   *c.* 32 ins
Ethiopia and Eritrea; resident in swamps and high moorland. Upperparts dull iridescent green, underparts brown, washed green; white wing-bar distinguishes from other ibises. Face feathered but wattle hangs from throat. Usually in flocks of 50 to 100, roosting in ravines. Harsh call *haa*, with loud raucous roars as flock takes off. Diet: snakes, frogs, mice, insects. Breeds April or July in Ethiopia; nest of sticks with finer lining of grass and bark, in trees, or bushes on cliffs. 2 rough shelled white eggs, other details much as Hadada Ibis, *Hagedashia hagedash*. **79**

BOUBOU see **Laniarius ferrugineus**

Bowdleria punctata *Muscicapidae: Sylviinae*
FERNBIRD   7 ins
Confined to New Zealand and neighbouring islands; separate races Stewart (*B. p. stewartiana*), Codfish (*wilsoni*) and Snares Islands (*caudata*); now mainly in swamps, undeveloped land (*pakihi*) and ferny scrub. Upperparts, flanks warm brown, streaked darker; forehead, forecrown chestnut; feathers of longish tail look spiny due to disconnected barbs; underparts white, spotted dark brown throat, breast. Flies with trailing tail seldom more than 50 yds, remaining hidden in foliage, though Snares race often in open, feeding in penguin colonies and floor of *Olearia* forest. Insectivorous: variety taken to young. Call: low note followed by sharp metallic one; also soft *click*; contact calls between pair: *plik* and *coot*. Breeds September to February; nest deep in vegetation from ground level to *c.* 4 ft above water, neatly woven cup of plant stems, lined feathers, built ♀ and ♂. 2 or 3 white or pinkish eggs heavily marked brown and purplish, usually at big end, incubated by ♀ and ♂ 12½ days. Young, fed both parents, fly 12-13 days (M. F. Soper). 2 broods on Snares I (E. F. Stead).

BOWER BIRD,
  GOLDEN see **Prionodura newtoniana**
  NEWTON'S see **Prionodura newtoniana**
  SATIN see **Ptilinorhynchus violaceus**
  SPOTTED see **Chlamydera maculata**

Brachyrhamphus brevirostris *Alcidae*
KITTLITZ'S MURRELET   9 ins
Holarctic: from arctic E Siberia, Kamtchatka to Aleutians and Alaska (Cape Lisburne, Glacier Bay); winters Aleutians, Kamtchatka to Japan. Habitat: breeds rocky mountain slopes above tree line; otherwise coastal waters. Upperparts slaty grey, streaked buff; flight feathers very dark grey; outer tail feathers white; throat, breast, flanks mottled buff and grey; belly white, feathers edged sooty grey; very short legs and bill dark; eyes very dark brown. Winter; crown, upperparts dark slate; underparts, cheeks, white; white bar between wing and back. Short bill and nearly complete dark band on breast help distinguish from Marbled Murrelet, *B. marmoratus*. Habits little studied; feeds small crustaceans, other invertebrates. Breeds bare lichened rock, blending with plumage; single yellowish or light olive green egg, evenly marked brown.

Brachyrhamphus marmoratus see under **B. brevirostris**

Bradornis pallidus *Muscicapidae: Muscicapinae*
PALE FLYCATCHER   6-7 ins
Ethiopian: several races cover most of region; resident savannah woodland, acacia bush, coastal scrub, grazed pastures, maize fields, gardens. Upperparts, including cheeks, breast, grey-brown, wings darker; underparts pale brown shading to white on throat, centre belly, flanks tinged buff. Legs, bill black, eyes very dark brown. Juvenile streaked and spotted. Larger, stouter than Spotted Flycatcher, *Muscicapa striata*, and less conspicuous than most flycatchers, taking much of food from ground: spiders, termites, flies, moths. Often perches motionless on low boughs. Calls: *chirp* or *churr*; rasping *tsek* of alarm; occasional warbling twitter of 6 to 7 notes as song. Breeds at or just before beginning of wet season, building neat but slight cup nest of rootlets in fork of tree or

bush. Usually 3 pale green eggs, marked reddish brown over violet. Family parties stay together a long time; some evidence that 'auxiliary adults' help parents rear brood. **775**

Bradypterus baboecalus *Muscicapidae: Sylviinae*
AFRICAN SEDGE or LITTLE RUSH WARBLER 6 ins
Ethiopian: throughout region, wherever suitable habitat (reedbeds, long swampy grass) occurs. Upperparts warm dusky brown; flight feathers edged paler; broad graduated tail; 'eyebrow', underparts pale buff with dusky streaks on side neck; legs grey, bill brown, eyes brown. Behaviour inquisitive, often perches at top of reeds. Flies with whirring or snapping wings. Song: jerky, unmelodious, like stick on revolving spokes; other calls include ventriloquial *thri*, croaking *crack, crack* . . . Feeds on insects, small molluscs. Breeding season varies over range; deep cup nest of coarse grass, lined fibres, built low in reeds. 2 to 4 green to pinkish white eggs, marked grey and variably spotted. **728**

Bradypterus sylvaticus *Muscicapidae: Sylviinae*
KNYSNA SCRUB WARBLER 5½-6 ins
Ethiopian; very local S Africa around Table Mountain and E Cape Province to coastal Natal. Resident in dense tangled scrub, e.g. bramble thickets on SE slopes Table Mountain, at forest edge. Upperparts, including wings, tail, light olivaceous brown; tail short, rounded; underparts paler, chin and throat whitish, mottled and streaked brown; belly whitish. Legs olive brown, bill pinkish brown, eyes dark hazel. Very skulking, identified mainly by fine song (August to December): series of high-pitched notes, followed by rapid lower notes merging into 'blurred trill' and ending in 'bubbling trill' (McLachlan and Liversidge). Breeds September, building bowl-shaped nest of dry leaves, grasses, with finer lining, off ground and below leaf canopy in thicket. 3 pinky-white eggs, finely marked red, incubated 19 days; young fly 13-14 days. **729**

BRAMBLING see **Fringilla montifringilla**

Branta canadensis *Anatidae*
CANADA GOOSE 36-40 (body 21-24) ins
Nearctic: 10 races spread across Alaska, Canada and northern USA, wintering S to coast of Gulf of Mexico; introduced in Europe. Habitat: swamps and around lakes and ponds with tree cover, also more open cultivated country; in winter greater tendency to frequent seashore. All races have black neck and head with white patch from chin to behind eyes; legs and bill dark, eyes dark brown. Body colour varies from dark brown of Vancouver Canada Goose, *B. c. occidentalis* to light brown-grey, with pale front, of Eastern Canada Goose *canadensis*, race now well established Britain. Flies in V formation on longer passages, gregarious outside breeding season, normally feeds by day on grass, with some animal food in summer, but may feed on water when breeding, upending like ducks; can dive when moulting or injured. Call: trumpeting honk. Nests, often in small colonies, in April on islands or sometimes sheltered marshes, making hollow in ground lined with grasses, reeds, down and feathers. Usually 5 or 6 near white eggs, incubated 28-29 days by ♀ guarded by ♂; young, flying at 6 weeks, are tended by ♀ with ♂ nearby. **103**

Branta leucopsis *Anatidae*
BARNACLE GOOSE 23-27 ins
W Palaearctic: breeds NE Greenland, Spitzbergen and Novaya Zemlya; winters Scotland, Ireland and coasts of Denmark, Germany and Netherlands. Mainly terrestrial, grazing at night on pastures and marshes near shore and sometimes on tidal flats; occasionally rests at sea. Shining black breast; neck and crown with creamy white face and forehead, upper body dark grey with black and white bars, underneath pale grey; tail, legs and small bill black, eyes dark chestnut. Flock, punctuated with squabbles between individuals, keeps to itself but less shy than other geese, feeds on vegetable matter such as leaves, seeds and grass; flies in V formation on longer passages. Call: repeated

shrill short barks. Nests late May to mid June in colonies often on face of cliff or sometimes on islands, laying 3 to 5 greyish white eggs in hollow, often used repeatedly, lined with down, droppings and a little moss. ♀ incubates, guarded by ♂, for 24-25 days; young fly after 7 weeks, tended by both parents. **104**

Branta sandvicensis *Anatidae*
NENE or HAWAIIAN GOOSE 23-26 ins
Confined to Hawaiian Is: Hawaii, Maui (reintroduced). Habitat: dry lava slopes and craters, only watered by rain pools; descends to *c.* 1,200 ft in winter. Body mottled brown, black and white; head, face, chin, back of neck black; cheeks, front of neck buff, feathers furrowed. Powerful, black legs, feet, toenails, only partially webbed; bill black; eyes very dark brown with white orbits. Aggressive in breeding season, vibrating furrowed neck feathers. Head-dipping in courtship, mates on land. In flocks after breeding, flighting between feeding and roosting places. Call: low moaning, hence *ne-ne*; raucous noises in courtship. Diet: plant leaves and stems, flowers, berries; 'plucks' seeds from grass, sedges (P. H. Baldwin). Breeds late October to February, ♀ building nest of plant debris, lined down, among rocks, and incubating 3 to 6 white to greenish eggs, *c.* 30 days. Young, attended both parents, fledge 10-12 weeks Hawaii. Classic example of 'dying' species revived by liberation of captive-bred stock in native habitat. **105**

BRAZILIAN TEAL see **Amazonetta brasiliensis**

BRISTLEHEAD, BORNEA see **Pityriasis gymnocephala**

BROADBILL, AFRICAN see **Smithornis capensis**

BROAD-BILLED
HUMMINGBIRD see **Cynanthus latirostris**
PRION see under **Pachyptila desolata**
SANDPIPER see **Limicola falcinellus**

BROADBILL,
GRAUER'S see **Pseudocalyptomena graueri**
GREEN see **Calyptomena viridis**

BROAD-TAILED PARADISE WHYDAH see under **Steganura paradisaea**

BROLGA see **Grus rubicundus**

BRONZE CUCKOO, HORSFIELD see under **Malurus leucopterus**

BRONZY SUNBIRD see **Nectarinia kilimensis**

BROWN
BOOBY see **Sula leucogaster**
CREEPER see **Certhia familiaris**
CUCKOO DOVE, LARGE see **Macropygia phasianella**
FLYCATCHER, AUSTRALIAN see **Microeca fascinans**
FLYCATCHER, EURASIAN see **Muscicapa latirostris**
HARRIER see **Circaetus cinereus**
HAWK see **Falco berigora**
KIWI see **Apteryx australis**
MESITE see **Mesitornis unicolor**
PARROT see **Poicephalus meyeri**
PELICAN see **Pelecanus occidentalis**
PIGEON see **Macropygia phasianella**
SONGLARK see **Cinclorhamphus cruralis**
THRASHER see **Toxostoma rufum**
TREECREEPER, AUSTRALIAN see **Climacteris picumnus**
WEEBILL see **Smicrornis brevirostris**
WOOD OWL, JAVAN see **Strix leptogrammica**
WOOD OWL, MALAYSIAN see **Strix leptogrammica**

BROWN-EARED
BULBUL see **Hypsipetes flavala**
PHEASANT see **Crossoptilon mantchuricum**

BROWN-HEADED
BUSH SHRIKE see **Tchagra australis**
COWBIRD see **Molothrus ater**

BRUBRU see **Nilaus afer**

BRUBRU, BLACK-BACKED see under **Nilaus afer**

BRUSH FINCH, OCHRE-BREASTED see **Atlapetes semirufus**

BRUSH WARBLER, SEYCHELLES see **Bebrornis sechellensis**

Bubo africanus *Strigidae*
SPOTTED EAGLE OWL 18½ ins
SE Palaearctic: S Arabia; Ethiopian: 2 races cover almost whole region; northern race *B. a. cinerascens* resident in variety of habitats; southern *africanus* in rocky country with steep, bush-clad ravines. Upperparts mottled grey, black and white, with white spots on mantle; flight feathers and tail broadly barred; ear tufts prominent; underparts from breast barred and flecked grey-brown; feathered legs barred dark and white; bill blackish horn, eyes yellow. Brownish phase also occurs; *cinerascens* has fine vermiculations on upperparts. Nocturnal; sleeping on ground during day; seen early morning on elevated perches. Hooting duets, ♂'s mournful-sounding *hu hu*, answered by ♀'s *hu hu hu*; clicking alarm 'call' probably with bill. Diet: mainly beetles, but some small birds, mammals and reptiles. Breeding season variable throughout range; makes scrape on overhung rock ledge, among roots of trees, occasionally large tree hole; sometimes old nest of other bird, head of *Borassus* palm; lays usually 2 white eggs. Incubation and fledging much as *B. bubo*. **437**

Bubo bubo *Strigidae*
EAGLE OWL *c.* 25-28 ins, ♀ larger than ♂
Palaearctic, Oriental, marginally Ethiopian: across Eurasia from Scandinavia and Iberia to Pacific, mainly between 30° and 60°N; also Indian subcontinent; N Africa into Sahara; resident in coniferous taiga, lowland and montane forests farther S; steep rocks in ravines, rocky islands, cliffs in sandy and stony deserts, ruins, sometimes reedbeds. Upperparts mottled blackish and tawny; wings and tail barred; underparts buff with fine wavy bars and bold streaks on breast; facial disc not marked but erectile ear tufts prominent; legs feathered, claws and bill black, eyes orange. Upright stance when perched, close to trunk. Noiseless flight, usually low and wavering but sometimes rises high; hunts in dusk, and in daylight in northern summer. Roosts in rocks or thick foliage. Calls: rather feeble *oo oo oo* and low *kreak kreak*; spits and snaps bill when alarmed; song loud, deep *boo hoo*, repeated at longish intervals and audible far; ♀ higher-pitched, duets with ♂. Wing-claps in display. Takes variety of mammals up to roe deer fawns, birds up to buzzards; reptiles, amphibians, even beetles. Breeds from March in Europe, in cavities and clefts, overhung ledges, old nests of other birds; pyramids in Egypt. 2 or 3 white eggs incubated by ♀ 34-36 days; ♂ brings food to her for young, who leave nest *c.* 5 weeks, before fledging. **438**

Bubo ketupu *Strigidae*
MALAYSIAN FISH OWL 18 ins
Oriental: Indo-China, Malaysia; resident in paddy field areas, river banks in primary forest, casuarina trees on shore (Borneo). Upperparts dark brown, mottled light brown with buff feather edges; light and dark bars on wings and tail; facial disc brown, finely streaked; ear tufts prominent; underparts buff, rather delicately streaked red-brown; bare legs greyish-white; bill black, yellower at cere, eyes lemon-yellow. Very much at home in water, taking fish, frogs, crustaceans and large water bugs. Call a melancholy repeated trill or whistle. Breeding season: young nearly full grown mid-February in Borneo. **439**

Bubo lacteus *Strigidae*
GIANT EAGLE OWL   25 ins
Ethiopian: almost whole region, except Congo Forests, SW tip S Africa. Resident in country with tall
timber but not continuous forest, e.g. acacia savannah.
Generally blackish grey, but dark colour phases occur;
underparts from head finely vermiculated grey-brown
and white; facial disc black-fringed, long ear tufts very
dark brown; legs feathered to claws, strong bill white,
eyes brown. Juvenile largely barred smoky grey.
Nocturnal; hooting 'song' a string of notes in ascending scale, of mournful quality to human ears. Clicks
bill when alarmed. Food: snakes, lizards, caterpillars;
birds up to guinea-fowl size; may attack poultry.
Breeding season variable throughout region; lays
usually 2 white eggs on decayed wood in hollow trees,
on platform of sticks in large fork, occasionally in old
nests, even old petrol drum. Incubation and fledging
much as *B. bubo*. **440**

Bubo virginianus *Strigidae*
GREAT HORNED OWL   18-23 ins
Nearctic and Neotropical: from arctic tree limit to
Straits of Magellan; not W Indies. Resident in
wooded country from dense forests to coastal mangrove swamps; not common in tropical lowlands.
Upperparts generally mottled brown, black and
white; facial disc chestnut, dark fringed above white
half-collar with vertical streaks; underparts barred
dark and light. Subarctic race may be almost white,
western race very pale, Labrador race very dark.
Feathered legs white, bill dark horn, eyes yellow.
Nocturnal; deep resonant hoot usually *hoo hoohoo hoo
hoo* (R. T. Peterson); also frightening shriek. ♂'s
courtship includes nodding, head rotation, bowing,
wing-clapping. Food: variety of mammals and birds
up to rabbits, grouse, poultry, quite often skunks; has
killed geese, turkeys. Breeds from January in USA, in
old nests of other birds, holes in large trees, rock
crevices. 2 to 4 white eggs incubated by ♀ *c.* 5 weeks;
young leave nest *c.* 30 days, before fledging. **441**

Bubulcus ibis *Ardeidae*
CATTLE EGRET   20 (of which neck and legs 9) ins
SW Palaearctic, Ethiopian, Oriental, quite recently
Australasian (partly introduced), Neotropical and Nearctic. Plumage generally white with seasonal pale
buff plumes on head and mantle. Legs mainly dark
brown; bill and eyes yellow – all variable seasonally.
Breeds in riparian and riverine woods and reedbeds;
otherwise in open, not necessarily wet, country where
parties accompany large wild or domestic mammals,
snapping up disturbed insects; also perch on backs to
remove parasites, and take frogs and lizards from
ground. Mutual displays at nest with croaking and
guttural notes; gregarious roosts in trees. Breeding
season varies with latitude: April to July in N. Forms
colonies often with other species in trees, bushes, reeds
or rocky islets; 4 to 6 pale blue eggs laid in nest of local
plant material and incubated for 21-24 days by ♀ and
♂, who also feed brood; young fly in *c.* 7 weeks. Two
broods in tropics. **56**

Bucco macrodactylus *Bucconidae*
CHESTNUT-CAPPED PUFFBIRD   5½ ins
Neotropical: S Venezuela W to Colombian Andes; S
to E Peru, W Amazonian Brazil, N Bolivia; resident in
forests. Upperparts to tail brown, speckled white and
golden-brown; crown chestnut, cheeks black, white
stripe below ear coverts; collar orange rufous; white
throat and upper breast traversed by broad black
underparts buffish, lightly barred dusky grey; thick
hooked bill. Solitary and difficult to observe: habits
generally as *Malacoptila panamensis*; largely insectivorous, excavating tunnel and nest chamber in
ground for 2 or 3 white eggs. **523**

Bucephala clangula see under **B. islandica**

Bucephala islandica *Anatidae*
BARROW'S GOLDENEYE   *c.* 18 ins
Nearctic, marginally Palaearctic: breeds Iceland, SW
Greenland, Labrador and mountains of W North
America S to central California; residents of Iceland
and Greenland winter S to coast, N American birds go

S as far as Long Island on Atlantic and San Francisco
on Pacific coast. Habitat: lakes and streams in mountains when breeding. ♂: head purplish blue, upperparts
black with large white patches on scapular and wing
coverts (but less white than Common Goldeneye,
B. clangula); underparts, neck and crescent markings
on face white. ♀: head brown, lower neck and underparts white with grey breast, flanks, thighs and vent;
upperparts mottled blackish and grey with white
patches on wing coverts. Legs, ♂ orange-yellow, ♀
brownish yellow; bill (shorter and higher than in *B.
clangula*), ♂ black, ♀ black with yellow patch, extensive
in N American birds; eyes, ♂ yellow, ♀ pale yellow.
Strong flyer, wings whistle in flight, usually in small
flocks, fairly tame; feeds on small aquatic animals and
sometimes pondweeds, may dive for up to 50 seconds
to turn over stones on bottom to expose food. Call:
hoarse croak and a vibrant mew. Semi-colonial, nests
in tree-holes, sometimes up to ½ mile from water; in
treeless regions such as Iceland uses cavities in or under
rocks, in stream banks or even walls. 8 to 12 pale green
eggs, incubated by ♀ *c.* 30 days. **106**

Buceros bicornis *Bucerotidae*
GREAT or GREAT PIED HORNBILL   *c.* 52 ins
Oriental: Western Ghats (India) from about Kandala
to S Travancore; Himalayas, up to *c.* 5,000 ft, from
Kumaon to Assam; Burma and through Malaysia to
Sumatra. Resident heavy evergreen forest. ♂: face,
back, underparts and wings (with double white bars)
black; neck, belly and tail coverts white; tail white
with broad black sub-terminal band; huge horn-
shaped bill under U-shaped casque. Legs greenish, bill
yellow with reddish tip and black on ridge below
casque (yellow with black front and back), eyes blood-
red. ♀: smaller, especially bill and casque; back of
casque red, eyes pearly white. Usually in pairs or
small parties; noisy laboured flight. Calls: deep,
harsh roars and croaks; characteristic loud reverber-
ating *tok*. Food: fruit, chiefly wild figs; also reptiles,
rodents, nestlings, large insects. Breeds March-April
onwards, earlier in S. 2 (sometimes 1) white eggs in
large unlined tree hollow, usually 60 ft or more up.
♀ walls up entrance from inside, using own faeces; fed
by ♂ through narrow slit; incubates *c.* 31 days, breaks
out when young *c.* 2 weeks old and usually rebuilds
wall. Both parents feed young. **514**

Bucorvus abyssinicus *Bucerotidae*
ABYSSINIAN GROUND HORNBILL   42 ins
Ethiopian: from Somalia down to Equator in Kenya,
E across to Guinea coast, keeping N of Congo forest
belt, in any kind of open country, bush, savannah, thin
woodland. All black except white primaries (conspicuous only in flight); bare skin round eye, upper
throat blue; lower throat, neck, red in ♂, blue in ♀;
bill has some red, casque open in front. Walk along
like stately turkeys in small parties picking up insects,
small reptiles, covering considerable distances, rarely
fly. Voice a deep grunting *oomp, oomp, oomp*. Nest in
holes in trees, rocks, not mudded up, eggs 1 to 3 dirty
white. Stick nests up trees have been recorded. **515**

Bucorvus leadbeateri *Bucerotidae*
GROUND HORNBILL   42 ins
Ethiopian: replaces preceding species to S, i.e. from
Equator in Kenya down to E Cape Province, W to
Angola, skirting Congo forests to NW Kalahari to SW.
Resembles *B. abyssinicus* in all respects except ♂ has all
red face and upper neck; bill blackish, casque closed.
516

BUDGERIGAR see **Melopsittacus undulatus**

BUFFALO WEAVER, WHITE-HEADED see
Dinemellia dinemelli

BUFF-BREASTED SANDPIPER see **Tryngites
subruficollis**

BUFF-CROWNED WOOD PARTRIDGE see
Dendrortyx leucophrys

BUFF-THROATED
  FOLIAGE GLEANER see under **Automolus
    leucophthalmus**
  WOODCREEPER see **Xiphorhynchus guttatus**

Bugeranus carunculatus see **Grus carunculatus**

BULBUL,
  ASHY see **Hypsipetes flavala**
  BLACK-EYED see **Pycnonotus barbatus**
  BROWN-EARED see **Hypsipetes flavala**
  CAPE see under **Pycnonotus nigricans**
  RED-EYED see **Pycnonotus nigricans**
  RED-VENTED see **Pycnonotus cafer**
  SOMBRE see **Andropadus importunus**
  WHITE-CHEEKED see under **Pycnonotus cafer**
  WHITE-VENTED see **Pycnonotus barbatus**

BULLFINCH see **Pyrrhula pyrrhula**

BULLY CANARY see under **Serinus albogularis**

BULN BULN see **Barnardius barnardi**

BUNTING,
  BLACK-HEADED see **Emberiza melanocephalus**
  CIRL see under **Emberiza cia**
  CORN see **Emberiza calandra**
  CRESTED see **Melophus lathami**
  GOLDEN-BREASTED see **Emberiza
    flaviventris**
  GREY-NECKED see under **Emberiza
    hortulana**
  LAPLAND see **Calcarius lapponicus**
  LAZULI see **Passerina amoena**
  PAINTED see **Passerina ciris**
  PINE see **Emberiza leucocephala**
  RAINBOW see **Passerina leclancheri**
  RED-HEADED see under **Emberiza
    melanocephalus**
  REED see **Emberiza schoeniclus**
  ROCK see **Emberiza cia**
  SNOW see **Plectrophenax nivalis**
  STRIOLATED see under **Melophus lathami**

Buphagus africanus *Sturnidae*
YELLOW-BILLED OXPECKER   *c.* 8½ ins
Ethiopian: Eritrea S (but not E Kenya, E Tanzania)
to S Africa (Zululand, Ovamboland); Angola. Resident in habitats of host animals; in Zambia: buffalo;
eland, kudu, roan antelopes; rhinoceros (R. I. G.
Attwell). Upperparts, including wings, tail, dark
earth brown; rump, upper tail coverts buff-brown;
throat, neck as upperparts; breast dusky, rest underparts buff-brown; legs black; bill, with broad base
lower mandible, yellow, tip red; eyes orange. Juvenile's bill yellow. Usually near game or large domestic
animals; perching on them in upright posture or
sidling all over them by means of sharp claws, searching for ticks; even displays and mates on host. Hides
on opposite side from observer. Several may collect on
one animal before flying off with rattling call; distinct
from hissing *kriss kriss*. May enlarge wounds on host;
also takes flies. Breeds during rains, e.g. October-
November S Africa, May-June Sudan; nest of straw,
grasses, lined fine grass, hair, feathers, in tree holes,
rock crevices, under eaves. 2 or 3 white or very pale
blue eggs, sometimes spotted chestnut, brown over
violet. Incubation, fledging probably as *B. erythrorhynchus;* young fed by 4 adults at one nest (R. J.
Dowsett). **964**

Buphagus erythrorhynchus *Sturnidae*
RED-BILLED OXPECKER   8-8½ ins
Ethiopian: E side of continent from Eritrea, Ethiopia,
southward to Botswana, S Africa (Transvaal, Natal);
resident savannah, forest edge, 4,600 to 8,500 ft
Kenya; favourite hosts Zambia: eland, kudu, roan,
sable antelopes; hippopotamus; rhinoceros (Attwell),
also buffalo, warthog. Closely resembles *B. africanus*
but upperparts pale ashy brown, uniform with rump;
bare facial area; legs blackish, bill red; eyes yellow to
red, orbits yellow. Juvenile sooty brown above. Habits
much as *B. africanus;* reputed to return to same
animal; defaecates clear of host (V. D. van Someren).

Chattering display usually on host's back. Roosts reedbeds, sometimes tree holes. Various calls: hissing *tsee; churrr; tzik tzik;* warning rattle; shrill twittering in flight. Fond of dustbathing. Food mainly ticks (*c.* 2,300 in 55 stomachs – R. E. Moreau); also flies and wound tissue of host. Occasionally seen to drink. Breeding variable within range: mainly during rains. Nest in crevice, tree hole, wall, under eaves; of plant debris, lined hair from living host. 3 to 5 bluish white to off-white eggs, rough shelled, marked shades of brown. Incubation 11-12 days; fledging 28-29 days. **965**

BURCHELL'S GLOSSY STARLING, see **Lamprotornis australis**

Burhinus bistriatus *Burhinidae*
DOUBLE-STRIPED STONE CURLEW   18 ins
Neotropical: Mexico, Costa Rica, Hispaniola S to NE Colombia, Venezuela, Guyana, N Brazil; resident in savannahs and open cultivated country. Resembles *B. oedicnemus:* upperparts streaked tawny and dark brown; broad white wing bar and bars on tail; black and white bands over eye; throat and underparts white; breast streaked buff; legs olive-green, bill black, eyes yellow. Habits and behaviour much as relatives; utters 'loud cackling notes'. Clutch 2 eggs and breeding details probably as relatives. **306**

Burhinus capensis *Burhinidae*
SPOTTED THICK-KNEE   *c.* 17 ins
Ethiopian: several races almost throughout region, except SW, in suitable habitat: dry open or bush veld, usually near water, e.g. rocky river beds; some local migration. Resembles Stone Curlew, *B. oedicnemus;* upperparts pale brown spotted and streaked black; wings show black tip with small white square and spot on coverts; neck, breast, flanks buff streaked black; legs yellow, bill black, large eyes yellow. Immature more heavily marked black. Crepuscular habits and behaviour much as Stone Curlew. Calls plaintive *tche-uuuu;* of Stone Curlew's call; also excited *pi pi pi pi.* Food largely insects. Breeding season variable throughout range. Lays 2 pale brown eggs marked dark brown and grey on flat ground or bare scrape; nesting details much as Stone Curlew, *B. bistriatus.* **307**

Burhinus magnirostris see under **Esacus magnirostris**

Burhinus oedicnemus *Burhinidae*
STONE CURLEW   *c.* 16 ins
Palaearctic, Oriental: broad band from SE England, Iberia and NW Africa (including Canary Islands) to Lake Balkash, Burma, Ceylon and Arabia. Northern birds migrate mainly to N Africa in winter. Habitat: open shingle, e.g. riverbeds, sand dunes and deserts, heaths, dry salt marshes, even cultivated land. Fairly uniform light brown, streaked and flecked dark brown, with paler throat and underparts; much of flight feathers black with white marks and two white bars across coverts; tail shows white crescent between black borders; legs pale yellow, bill blackish, base yellow, eyes yellow. Crepuscular, performing evening flights in flocks with eerie *cur-lew* calls. Usually runs with short steps, stopping to stand upright, sometimes bobbing head down, hind part up; frequently squats on tarsus. Feeds mainly by night on small land animals up to lizards and mice. Breeds from first half April in S Europe, making large, usually unlined scrape on bare ground. 2 rounded eggs, pale buff with dark brown and grey streaks, spots and scrawls, incubated by ♀ and ♂ 25-27 days; both tend young *c.* 6 weeks; sometimes a second brood. **308**

Burhinus vermiculatus *Burhinidae*
WATER DIKKOP or THICK-KNEE   15 ins
Ethiopian: several races S throughout region from Kenya; resident in neighbourhood of water: river beaches, banks and islets. Resembles Stone Curlew, *B. oedicnemus:* upperparts tone grey, barred and vermiculated black; black and white bars on shoulder of closed wing; primaries dark grey, coverts grey; underparts white but neck and breast streaked black, under tail coverts buff; legs greenish slate, bill black, base yellow, eyes pale green. More approachable than

relatives; associates locally with crocodiles, e.g. Murchison Falls, Uganda. Often in small parties, roosts in shade by day. Call rendered plaintive *kwa-lee-vee* cf Stone Curlew. Food largely insects. Breeding season variable throughout range. 2 buff eggs, heavily marked rich brown, chocolate and purple, laid in scrape on sandy shore or rocky islet. Incubation and fledging much as Stone Curlew. **309**

BURROWING OWL see **Speotyto cunicularia**

BUSH
  CHAT, RUFOUS see **Cercotrichas galactotes**
  LARK see **Mirafra africana**
  SHRIKE, BLACKCAP see **Tchagra minuta**
  SHRIKE, BLACK-HEADED see **Tchagra senegala**
  SHRIKE, FASCIATED see **Cymbilaimus lineatus**
  WARBLER, CHINESE see **Cettia diphone**
  WARBLER, SEYCHELLES see **Bebrornis sechellensis**
  WARBLER, SHORT-TAILED see **Cettia squameiceps**

BUSTARD,
  AUSTRALIAN see **Eupodotis australis**
  BLACK-BELLIED see **Lissotis melanogaster**
  DENHAM's see **Neotis denhami**
  GREAT see **Otis tarda**
  HARTLAUB's see **Lissotis hartlaubii**
  KORI see **Choriotis kori**
  LITTLE see **Otis tetrax**
  WHITE-BELLIED see **Eupodotis senegalensis**

BUTCHERBIRD,
  GREY see **Cracticus torquatus**
  PIED see under **Cracticus torquatus**
  SILVER-BACKED see under **Cracticus torquatus**

Buteo galapagoensis *Accipitridae*
GALAPAGOS HAWK   ♂: 18, ♀: 21 ins
Confined to Galapagos where sedentary but ranges over nine islands. Variable brown with crown darker than back; mantle feathers pale edged; tail silvery grey, barred black; under wing coverts black, but flight feathers with pale bars; underparts light, spotted brown, legs yellow, bill blackish, eyes brown. Immature variegated buff, white and black. Very noisy in breeding season, uttering series of short screams. Usually solitary or in pairs and family groups, perching on tree or lava ledge, then soaring up for display flights. Hunts varied prey, including young marine iguanas; takes edible human leavings and has little fear of man. Breeding season irregular. Nest, on ledge, low tree or ground, built up year after year, of sticks with finer linings. Lays 1 to 3 white eggs, incubated ♀ and ♂ 37-38 days. Young, fed at first mainly by ♂, fledged 50-60 days. Both periods longer than for other buzzards. ♀ often has two mates (Tjitte de Vries). **139**

Buteo lineatus *Accipitridae*
RED-SHOULDERED HAWK   20-22 ins
Nearctic: S Canada to S Florida and Central Mexico; northern birds migratory. Habitat moist or swampy woodlands, e.g. along river bottoms. Blackish brown above, streaked rufous, especially shoulders; tail black with white bars and tip; wings dark brown flecked white; throat white, flecked dark brown; breast rufous, becoming barred lighter brown on belly; whitish 'mirror' under wings in flight. Legs greenish yellow, cere yellow, bill black, eyes brown. Unobtrusive and sedentary in winter, becoming conspicuous in breeding season, uttering triple whistling scream and displaying in air. Food varied: small vertebrates and large insects, e.g. grasshoppers. Breeds from late January (Florida) to April (New England), building nest of sticks and debris in tall tree. 2 to 4 white eggs, marked shades of brown, incubated by ♀ and ♂ *c.* 4 weeks. Young, fed by ♀ and ♂, fly 5-6 weeks. **140**

BUZZARD,
  CRESTED HONEY see under **Pernis apivorus**
  HONEY see **Pernis apivorus**

Bycanistes subcylindricus *Bucerotidae*
BLACK AND WHITE CASQUED HORNBILL   30 ins
Ethiopian: W African rain-forest zone as far E as W Kenya, NW Tanzania. Genus contains some half dozen species of similar appearance, habits with overlapping ranges in heavily forested parts of region. All are heavily built black and white birds with very large casqued bills, feeding mainly on fruit, also insects and sometimes eggs and young of small birds. *B. subcylindricus* distinguishable by large white wing patch; lower belly, under tail coverts, ends of outer tail feathers all white, otherwise all black. Flight cumbersome, noisy, several rapid beats followed by long glide, often above canopy. Loud raucous voice, *rark rark rark.* Hole-nester, usually in high tree, sometimes rocks; entrance reduced to small slit by mud-plastering, through which ♀ fed by ♂ while incubating. Eggs 1 to 3, white.

CABOT'S TERN see **Sterna sandvicensis**

Cacatua roseicapilla or Kakatoe roseicapilla *Psittacidae.*
GALAH   14 ins
Continental Australia, except E and W coastal areas; open country, wooded savannah, dry plains, crop fields, up to 5,000 ft; local movements according to food supply. Variable: upperparts, wings, under tail coverts grey; scapulars and rump paler; forehead and crown pale pink; face, nape, underparts deep pink; tail light grey above, very dark underneath; legs grey, bill brown, eyes dark brown, facial skin red. Wheeling flight of flaps and glides; flocks of hundreds manoeuvre at dawn, dusk or during rain; rests during day, often biting off green twigs, chewing bark and rotten wood. Call: loud whistling screech of two syllables. Ground feeder on grass, clover and other seeds, locally damages crops; also roots, bulbs, shoots; tree seeds in drought; insects and their larvae. Gulps when drinking. ♂ displays to ♀ with crest raised and head movements. Breeds variably, mainly July to December in S, February to June in N following rains. Lines tree hole, locally rock crevice, near water with eucalypt leaves. 2 to 5 white eggs incubated by ♀ and ♂ *c.* 4 weeks; both feed young who fly 5-6 weeks; 2 broods in good seasons. **388**

Cacicus cela *Icteridae*
YELLOW-RUMPED CACIQUE   ♀: 9½; ♂: 11 (bill 1½) ins
Neotropical: Central and E Panama, Trinidad, Guyanas, Venezuela, E Colombia S to N Bolivia; Amazonian and E Brazil S to Bahia; Central and N Colombia; W Ecuador, NW Peru; resident open woodland, edge mangrove swamps, riverbanks, sea level to *c.* 4,500 ft; lowlands in Trinidad. Generally glossy black with narrow crest, but lower back, inner wing coverts, upper and under tail coverts bright golden or orange yellow according to race; basal half tail yellow, rest black; legs black, bill dusky green or yellowish to ivory according to race, eyes pale cobalt blue. Outstanding songster (both sexes), noisy in breeding colonies, often in solitary tree near house or in village or town. Food: insects, fruit. Breeds January to June Trinidad; ♀ builds tubular nest 1½ to 2 ft long, of grass, plant fibres, round chamber lined leaves, suspended from branch of tree. 2 elongated white, cream or greenish eggs variably marked dark umber over pale brown, lilac, incubated ♀ *c.* 12 days; fledging period similar. Sometimes evicted by tyrannid, Black-banded Petchary, *Legatus leucophaius.* **908**

CACIQUE, YELLOW-RUMPED see **Cacicus cela**

CACTUS WREN see **Campylorhynchus bruneicapillus**

Cairina moschata *Anatidae*
MUSCOVY DUCK   ♀: 26, ♂: 33 ins
Neotropical: Mexico, Central America, S America S to Peru and Uruguay. Ancestor of farmyard Muscovy Duck. Habitat: forest streams, ponds and marshes surrounded by woodlands. ♂: head, crest, neck and underparts brownish black; upperparts black with green gloss, wing coverts and axillaries white; bare black skin surrounded by small caruncles from bill to

eyes. ♀: smaller with much reduced bare face patch. Legs black, bill black with pale pink band near tip, eyes yellow-brown. Roosts and spends much of day perched in large trees; heavy slow flight; congregates in small flocks in dry season, feeds dawn and dusk on aquatic vegetation and small animals. ♂♂ polygamous and fight fiercely. Call: usually silent, ♂ hisses, ♀ gives weak quack. Nests in hollows of trees, old nests and large forks; lays 8 to 15 white eggs with greenish sheen, incubated *c.* 35 days. The domestic form is illustrated. **107**

Calamanthus campestris *Muscicapidae: Malurinae*
RUFOUS FIELD WREN *c.* 4¾ ins
Australia: W New South Wales, NW Victoria and southern S Australia W to Eyre Peninsula. Habitat: low scrub on open plains. Upperparts rufous-brown streaked black; crown, cheeks and rump more rufous; 'eyebrow' white; underparts whitish streaked dark brown; dark brownish tail with white tip. Legs and bill brown, eyes very pale yellow. Smaller and more rufous plumage than closely related Striated Field Wren, *C. fuliginosus*. Usually in pairs or small parties; shy, scuttles over ground; insectivorous. Call: lark-like, uttered from top of bush. Breeds after heavy rain in all seasons; globular nest with side entrance, in tuft of grass, underneath low bush or on bare patch of ground; of grass with feather lining; 3, sometimes 4, light brown eggs, darker and richer at larger end.

Calamanthus fuliginosus see under **C. campestris**

Calandrella cinerea *Alaudidae*
SHORT-TOED LARK 5½ ins
Palaearctic, Ethiopian; *c.* 14 races; breeds in belt 30°N to 45°N, Mongolia to Spain and N Africa; also S Africa up E side to Uganda, Ethiopia and SW Arabia; winters southern breeding range S to Sahara, Sudan and Central India. Habitat: open sandy or stony fields usually with very little vegetation. Upperparts pale brownish with broad dark streaks, less so on rump; underparts white with sandy-buff band across upper breast and dark mark on sides of breast. Some races more reddish. Legs pale brownish flesh, bill horn, eyes brown. Call: hard *chichirrp* recalling House Martin, *Delichon urbica*. Song stereotyped *tee-tsit-si-wee, tsi-wichoo*, especially in flight. Song-flight prolonged and undulates at *c.* 50 feet. Outside breeding season in large flocks. Food mainly seeds but also takes insects. Breeding season varies with race (Europe mid April to July). Nests on ground in deep cup rather sheltered. 3 to 5 usually yellowish finely freckled eggs, incubated by ♀ 11-13 days. Young leave nest *c.* 9 days and fly 7-10 days later. Usually 2 broods. **600**

Calcarius lapponicus *Emberizidae: Emberizinae*
LAPLAND BUNTING or LONGSPUR *c.* 6 ins
Holarctic: N coasts Eurasia from Norway to Arctic America and Greenland (not Iceland, Spitsbergen); migrates S to temperate zone for winter: NW Europe; SE Russia and across Asia. Breeds above or beyond tree line on high 'fjeld' (Norway) and moss tundra with creeping birch and crowberry *Empetrum;* winters steppes, rough grassland, stubbles near coast in Europe. ♂: upperparts brown streaked black, outer tail feathers white; crown to throat black, partly framed narrow white stripe which curves round to eye; nape chestnut; underparts whitish, flanks streaked black. Head pattern much obscured brown in winter, as ♀ all seasons. Legs, eyes dark brown, bill yellow tipped black. Normally runs but can hop. Perches hummocks in tundra, trees where available. Flight undulating. Joins winter flocks of other seed-eaters, Skylarks, *Alauda arvensis,* but generally rather wild. Breeding season calls: *teeleu* (anxiety), *teeuu, ticky-tick* (also on passage); sharp *zit,* explosive *peet-teu.* Song in display flight 'lively outpouring' (B. W. Tucker) like beginning of Skylark. ♂ flutters up to 40 ft, planes round, wings stretched, then sinks downward. Food: seeds of grasses and other plants, insects and their larvae in summer. Breeds end May onwards, ♀ building nest of grasses, moss, lined fine bents, hair, feathers, in hollow in ground or side of tussock. 4 to 6 greenish grey to olive brown eggs, heavily marked reddish brown and blackish, incubated mainly ♀, 13-14 days; both parents feed young, who leave nest 8-10 days. **852**

Calendula magnirostris see **Galerida magnirostris**

Calidris alba or Crocethia alba *Scolopacidae*
SANDERLING *c.* 8 ins
Holarctic: local on arctic coasts and islands; summer visitor for only 2 months, cosmopolitan in winter on sandy beaches to Argentina, S. Africa (rare), New Zealand, probably also inland Central Asia. Breeds stony lichen tundra with low vegetation, e.g. creeping willow. Summer: upperparts, including head, neck, upper breast, mottled light chestnut and black; wing pattern black with white wing bar; tail brown and blackish, edged white; underparts white; legs and bill black, eyes brown. Winter: upperparts pale grey, head whitish; black shoulder patch; underparts white. Juvenile mottled black and buff above with pale buff face and breast. Usually seen in parties, stout little birds running fast after retreating surge; fly with *twick twick* call. Churring note by ♂ on song flight. Eats mainly small insects in summer, otherwise small crustaceans, molluscs, gasteropods, beach insects. Breeds from mid or late June, making scrape on dry, rocky tundra. 4 dull greenish-olive eggs, sparsely marked brown and grey, incubated by ♀ and ♂ 23-24 days; ♀ and ♂ tend young, who fly in *c.* 2 weeks. **276**

Calidris alpina *Scolopacidae*
DUNLIN or RED-BACKED SANDPIPER 6¾-7½ ins
Holarctic: more or less circumpolar in temperate to arctic zones, farthest S in Britain, Ireland and Baltic; wintering mainly N temperate, not crossing Equator; coastal, estuarine and muddy lake shores. Breeds well vegetated damp areas, usually near pools, in low level or mountain tundra; coastal marshes and river valleys in temperate, moorland up to 3,000 ft in Britain. Summer: upperparts mottled chestnut and black; head brown, chin white, throat streaked; black patch on lower breast; wings brown and blackish with white bar; tail dark, white edged, black tipped; underparts white; legs dark olive; long, slightly curved bill black, eyes brown. Winter: upperparts and head grey-brown with black streaks; underparts white with dark patch on breast. Singly, in parties or huge flocks in winter, often mixing with other small waders and indulging in massed aerial evolutions. Usual call short nasal *tshripp,* expanded in spring to musical reeling mainly by ♂, who hovers lark-like in display flight; also *kwot kwot* of alarm when with young. Takes mainly small insects, their larvae and crustaceans when breeding; in winter also worms and snails. Breed from early May in S of range, making usually well hidden scrape in grass, moss, other low but thick cover. 4 bluish-green to buff eggs, spotted and spirally streaked red-brown and grey, incubated by ♀ and ♂ 21-22 days; both tend young, who fly *c.* 4 weeks. **277**

Calidris canutus *Scolopacidae*
KNOT *c.* 10 ins
Holarctic: discontinuous in arctic zone; summer visitor *c.* 2 months, wintering mainly N temperate muddy estuaries and coasts, but reaches Argentina, S Africa, New Zealand, exceptionally Macquarie 55°S. Breeds dry level stony tundra. Summer: upperparts black and chestnut, crown streaked black; head and underparts chestnut; wings with black tips, white bar; tail dark brown; legs olive brown, straight bill black, eyes brown. Winter: upperparts grey, underparts white, faintly streaked. Juvenile has grey-brown upperparts, breast buff. Flocks in winter like Dunlin, *C. alpina,* packing even closer. Winter call *knut* (hence name?) and whistling *twit-wit;* fluty 'song' by ♂ in display flight; *quee quee quee* of alarm with young. Food in summer insects, spiders, crustaceans, parts of tundra plants; mainly small marine animals in winter. Breeds from mid June Siberia, making scrape on rocky or stony tundra. 4 greenish to buff eggs, with small brown and grey spots, incubated by ♀ and ♂ 20-25 days. ♂ takes main share tending young, who fly *c.* 3 weeks. **278**

Calidris ferruginea *Scolopacidae*
CURLEW SANDPIPER *c.* 7½ ins
Palaearctic: arctic Siberia from Yenisei to Kolynin; summer visitor, wintering Mediterranean area, Ethiopian, Oriental and Australasian regions; sandy and muddy shores and creeks. Breeds low ground near rivers, tundra slopes. Summer (♂ brighter): upperparts mottled chestnut and black; face, neck underparts rich chestnut like Knot, *C. canutus*; wings grey-brown, white bar and black tips; rump white, tail blackish; under tail coverts white; legs olive-brown, long finely curved bill black, eyes black brown. Winter: upperparts dark grey-brown, face and underparts much as Dunlin, from which bill and white rump distinguish it. Juvenile has buff breast. Associates with Dunlin, *C. alpina,* on shore, looking taller and slimmer. Call soft chirrup; trilling song on breeding ground, where pairs or small parties chase each other; *wick wick wick* of alarm with young. Takes insects and their larvae in summer; otherwise small crustaceans, molluscs and worms. Breeds from *c.* 20 June semi-socially, making scrapes often on southerly slopes of tundra. ♀ and ♂ incubate 4 greenish to buff eggs, heavily marked dark brown and grey, and tend young, whole cycle taking *c.* 6 weeks. **279**

Calidris fuscicollis or Erolia fuscicollis *Scolopacidae*
WHITE-RUMPED SANDPIPER *c.* 7 ins
Nearctic: N coasts and islands of Alaska and Canada to S Baffin Is; summer visitor, migrating to S Argentina and Falkland Islands; winters mud flats, shores of fresh and salt lagoons, marshes. Breeds boggy tundra, shores of lakes and rivers. Summer: upperparts mottled rich brown and black; pale grey breast streaked and spotted black; wings pale with dark tips; rump white above black terminal bar to tail; underparts white, legs and bill dark, eyes black brown. Winter: upperparts grey-brown. Juvenile as summer adult. Resembles Dunlin, *C. alpina,* in habits. Sometimes crouches rather than flies. Call a squeaky *jeet;* also faint squeaky spring song in flight up to 60 ft. Diet mainly animal: worms, molluscs, insects, also crustaceans and leeches; some plant seeds. Breeds from second half June, making scrape, usually lined grass and willow leaves, in hummock on wet tundra. ♀ incubates 4 greenish or buff eggs, spotted and speckled tawny brown and grey and tends brood; ♂♂ collect in parties. **280**

Calidris maritima *Scolopacidae*
PURPLE SANDPIPER *c.* 8 ins
Holarctic: discontinuous in subarctic and arctic zones, but S to Kuriles in N Pacific, where regarded by some as separate species, Rock Sandpiper *C. ptilocnemus* Resident ice-free N Pacific, others winter temperate zone to 45°N; rocky coasts, frequently in harbours. Breeds often in cloud or mist cover on swampy tundra, bare mountain tops, islands off coast. Summer: upperparts dark brown with rufous margins to feathers on back, which has purplish sheen; wings dark with white bar; tail centrally dark with light edges; breast mottled brown extending to white underparts with dark flank marks; legs yellow, bill black-brown, base yellow, eyes brown. Upperparts much greyer in winter, legs duller. Associates with Turnstones, *Arenaria interpres*, in winter, allowing close approach before flying off silently or with low *weet-wit.* Other notes on breeding ground, where flight becomes erratic; 'song' loud trill in gliding flight; also raises and lowers wings in display on ground. Takes insects and their larvae, tundra herbage, including seeds and moss spores; crustaceans and gasteropods in winter. Breeds from mid-June, making scrape, lined with leaves, in moss and tundra plants. 4 eggs, greenish when fresh and marked dark brown and purple, incubated mainly by ♂ 21-22 days; he tends young who fly *c.* 3 weeks. **281**

Calidris
minuta see under **C. temminckii**
ptilocnemus see under **C. maritima**

Calidris temminckii *Scolopacidae*
TEMMINCK'S STINT *c.* 5½ ins
Palaearctic: subarctic (breeds sporadically Britain)

and arctic zones from Scandinavia to Bering Straits; summer visitor, wintering freshwater margins, mainly Ethiopian and Oriental regions. Breeds swampy areas of scrub and birch zone, often near grassy valleys. Summer: upperparts grey-brown with black-brown marks and rufous feather edges; wings with dark trailing edge and tips and narrow white bar; tail centrally dark with white edges; underparts from throat white; legs variable, bill and eyes very dark brown. Winter and juvenile greyer with grey-brown patch on breast. Haunts cover much more than Little Stint, *C. minuta,* towering into erratic flight like miniature snipe. Call high-pitched trilling titter; sings in moth-like display flight and on ground with wings raised. Takes mainly small insects and their larvae, picked off vegetation and mud. Breeds early June onwards, making well hidden scrape in moss and low cover. ♀ sometimes lays two clutches of 4 greenish-grey eggs, spotted evenly liver brown, incubating one herself, ♂ the other, 21-22 days. Each tends own brood, which fledge 2-2½ weeks. **282**

CALIFORNIA
GULL see **Larus californicus**
QUAIL see **Lophortyx californicus**

CALIFORNIAN CONDOR see **Gymnogyps californicus**

Callaeas cinerea *Callaeidae*
KOKAKO 15 ins
Confined to New Zealand; N Island race *C. c. wilsoni* quite widespread; S Island *cinerea* barely survives. Resident native forest. Generally dark bluish-grey, tinged olive brown from lower back and belly downward; flight and tail feathers blackish brown, tinged slaty; velvety black band over bill encircles dark brown eyes; wattles blue (*wilsoni*) or orange (*cinerea*); legs, bill black. Immature more generally tinged brown, wattles smaller, paler. Progresses by hopping up limbs and trunks, then gliding on to next tree, seldom flies far. Pairs remain together all year, taking mainly or entirely vegetable food: leaves, flowers, fruits, from outer branches of native trees; use feet like parrot when feeding. Calls various: quiet, repeated *took*, probably of alarm; low mewing; bell-like note followed by sharp *kik;* full song, audible at distance, 'two long rich organ notes' (Maning) followed by 3 short *pips*. Breeds November to March, ♀ and ♂ building platform of twigs, with finer material, rotten wood on top; cup of moss lined softly, e.g. tree-fern scales. Usually 3 pale brownish grey eggs, marked brown and purplish brown, incubated ♀ *c.* 25 days. ♂ helps feed young on fruit and leaves; they fly 27-28 days.

Callocephalon fimbriatum *Psittacidae*
GANG-GANG COCKATOO 13½ ins
Confined to SE Australia; habitat spring and summer dense montane forest up to 7,000 ft; comes into open, often round habitations, autumn and winter. ♂: dark grey with pale feather edges, head scarlet with large crest of separated brush-like feathers. ♀ has underparts barred brick-red and white, dark grey head with small dark crest. Legs grey, bill horn-grey, eyes dark brown. Juvenile like ♀ but crest red-tipped. Small flocks outside breeding season sit preening in tree-tops, calling wheezily, as also in silent, owl-like flight. Often takes off in short playful flight and returns to trees; but makes long flights over hills. Lands only to drink. Alarm call, prolonged rasping screech. Food: green seeds of wattle, acacia, eucalypts; berries in winter, e.g. of introduced hawthorn, pyracantha; holds food in left foot, standing on right. Breeds October to January, 60 to 70 ft up in tree hole enlarged by birds, usually near water. 2 or 3 white eggs incubated by ♀ and ♂ *c.* 28 days; young fly *c.* 7 weeks, fed by ♀ and ♂ further 4-6 weeks. **389**

Caloenas nicobarica *Columbidae*
NICOBAR DOVE *c.* 16 ins
Oriental, Australasian: smaller wooded islands and islets off larger land masses from Nicobars and Mergui Archipelago E to Philippines, New Guinea and Solomon Is; moves between islands. ♂: dark slate grey with glossy metallic blue-green and copper-bronze upperparts and short white tail; short feathers on head contrasting with long hair-like feathers that hang down from neck. ♀: slightly smaller, shorter neck hackles and greyer head, neck and breast. Legs purplish red with yellow-brown claws, fairly heavy bill and cere (smaller in ♀) dark grey, eyes pale brown. Adapted to poor light of forest floor where it feeds by flicking aside leaves with bill to expose seeds, fruits and small animals. Walks with wings drooping low at sides; flight swift and powerful. Call: occasionally short, deep but soft cooing. Breeds in colonies on islands, often several nests in a tree; single white egg on untidy twig platform in thick cover. **350**

Calonetta leucophrys or Anas leucophrys *Anatidae*
RINGED TEAL 14 ins
Neotropical: S Brazil, Uruguay, Paraguay, S Bolivia and NE Argentina. Habitat: open pools and lagoons in marshes, often near woodland. ♂: fairly decorative, top of head and hind neck black, breast pink with black spots, flanks grey; face, sides of head and throat creamy, mantle olive grey, scapulars chestnut-red, back, rump and tail black; wings black with white patch, secondaries green, tertiaries olive brown. ♀: pale with dark brown back and wings, top of head and hind neck, sides of head and throat white with brown markings; irregular brown spots on breast. Legs lilac pink, slender bill lead blue (duller in ♀), eyes brown. Flies and swims well, perches easily. Call: ♂, soft long whistle; ♀, short harsh quack. Nests late summer in tree holes; lays 5 to 8 white eggs, incubated *c.* 23 days. **108**

Caloperdix oculea *Phasianidae*
FERRUGINOUS WOOD PARTRIDGE 9-10½ ins
Oriental: SE Asia, SW Siam, Malaysia, Sumatra, Borneo. Sedentary in lowland bamboo jungle and secondary forest up to 3,000 ft; usually near streams. Back and tail black spotted and barred chestnut; wings olive brown marked black; head, neck, underparts reddish chestnut, crown darker, face and throat paler, short blackish stripe behind eye; mantle and sides black, barred white, belly whitish, flanks spotted black; legs dull greenish yellow, bill black-brown, eyes brown. Usually in bevies of 4 or 5. Duets: ♂ calls 8 or 9 times, accelerating up scale, breaking into *E-terang* 2 to 4 times; ♀ replies with long series of faster notes (T. H. Harrisson). Diet: insects, especially termites and beetles; berries, seeds, grasses. Breeding variable within range; December and January in Borneo. Nest a lined scrape or domed with hole at side (Borneo) sheltered by bush. 8 to 10 white eggs incubated probably by ♀.

Calypte anna *Trochilidae*
ANNA'S HUMMINGBIRD 4 ins
Nearctic: California, partly resident or moving locally to mountains in summer, coast in winter. Habitat: canyons, foothills, riverine woodland with oaks, scarcer in deserts and chaparral; now frequent in gardens and parks. ♂: upperparts iridescent dark green from nape to slightly forked tail; underparts white, flanks washed green; crown, face, throat rose red with lobes at sides of neck. ♀ has green head, white throat spotted dark green, often with traces rose red. Legs, bill, eyes dark. ♂ in display flies backward 'like helicopter', sings briefly, then rises *c.* 100 ft, dives down and up again in narrow U, with sharp *peek* from vibration of spread tail feathers. Feeding and alarm call *chick;* rattling *ztikl ztikl ztikl* when ♂ chases ♀; jumbled song from perch. Takes nectar and insects from flowers, insects and small spiders off leaves or in air; drinks tree sap and comes to sugar solutions; punctures soft fruits. Becomes torpid at night. Breeds from late December, ♀ building nest of plant materials, decorated lichens, often lined feathers, on twig, typically of oak, 3 to 30 ft. 2 white eggs incubated by ♀ 16 days; she feeds young who fly 21 days. 2 broods. **467**

Calypte costae *Trochilidae*
COSTA'S HUMMINGBIRD 3¼ ins
Nearctic: breeds from S Central California, S Nevada, SW Utah, to SW New Mexico, SE Arizona, S Lower California; winters mainly Lower California, W Sonora (Mexico). Habitat: dry foothills and desert slopes with sages, cacti, yuccas, mesquite and other shrubs; marginally into chaparral and canyon woodlands. ♂ as Anna's Hummingbird, *C. anna*, but purple (looking black in dull light) replaces rose red on head, gorget and side lobes; ♀ and immature lack this colour or have only traces. In display ♂ swoops down from up to 200 ft, passing close to tops of shrubs and climbing again slowly to complete U some 75-100 ft across; successive dives may be from different angles. Also dances in front of ♀ with spread gorget, throwing tail from side to side. Soft *chick* when feeding, and rattling calls in chases. Song 2 or 3 hissing *tss-tss-see;* drawn-out version of this in display flight one of highest bird sounds audible to man. Feeds on nectar and insects from tubular flowers; also catches insects and spiders in air or off leaves. Nest of mixed plant materials like other species but looser in texture than *C. anna;* outside decorated dry leaves or lichens; from 1 to 9 ft in shrub, often exposed to sun. ♀ incubates 2 white eggs 16 days, feeds young, who fledge 22 days. **468**

Calyptomena viridis *Eurylaimidae*
GREEN BROADBILL 6 ins.
Oriental: Burma, Malaysia, Indonesia to Borneo; resident in evergreen forest, sometimes thinner cover and near or distant from water. ♂: iridescent grass-green with black patches on head and three bars on wing; ♀ dull green without markings, green ring round eye; feet dull green with yellowish soles, deep bill, largely concealed by tight crest of feathers, black above, greenish below and at tip, edges yellow; eyes dark brown. Described as 'sluggish', remaining in tops of tall trees. Calls: *chai* repeated fast, and soft pleasant whistle (B. E. Smythies). Throat-fluffing, bill raising and gaping display by ♂. Feeds on fruit. Breeds February to April Burma, ♂ and ♀ building gourd-shaped nest of coarse vegetable fibres or dead bamboo leaves, hung by narrow neck from branch and with tail of material hanging down; entrance at side. Clutch: 2 or 3 creamy white eggs, tinged pale brown. Both parents incubate eggs and feed young. **556**

Camaroptera brevicaudata *Muscicapidae:Sylviinae*
GREY-BACKED CAMAROPTERA 4½ ins
Ethiopian: almost whole region, except Cape Province. Resident in varied habitats, from secondary forest growth to arid sandy country with few bushes. Upperparts dark grey, except 'panel' formed by golden green edges to wing feathers; paler greyish buff below; 'thighs' yellow; long legs yellowish brown; long bill horn; eyes brown. Some south-eastern races have green rump, tail. Feeds on ground, carrying short tail upright. In arid areas spends much time in deep shade. Nicknamed 'Bush goat' from low buzzing call; other calls include explosive alarm note, loud ringing *plick, plick*. Eats insects, spiders. Breeding season varies: October to April in Zaire; shorter in S. Domed nest of fine grass, spider webs built in bag of *c.* 6 leaves sewn together; probably mimics tailor-ant nest. 2 white eggs, spotted lilac, reddish brown. **731**

CAMAROPTERA, GREY-BACKED see **Camaroptera brevicaudata**

Campephaga sulphurata *Campephagidae*
BLACK CUCKOO SHRIKE 9 ins
Ethiopian: Sudan, Ethiopia, Somalia, to Angola, S Africa; resident wooded country from lowland scrub to forests. ♂: black all over, glossed bluish green, sometimes yellow shoulders; yellow gape wattles distinguish from drongos with which often associates. ♀: upperparts olive-brown with dusky bars; wings, tail edged yellow and white; underparts white barred black and yellow. Legs, bill black, eyes light brown. Juvenile resembles ♀. Usually in pairs in parties of other species, hunting through canopy, whence takes insects and larvae from foliage; also fruits and tree seeds; sometimes feeds on ground. Usually silent but has soft, low trill and *chup* call. Breeding season varies within range. Builds very small nest for its size, of plant materials in moss or lichen on bough or in fork. 2 pale greyish or yellowish green eggs, heavily marked shades of brown over lilac. **636**

Campethera abingoni *Picidae*
GOLDEN-TAILED WOODPECKER 7 ins
Ethiopian: one race in Senegal, across to Sudan, others in E and Central Africa from Somalia down to Natal, in most kinds of woodland at all altitudes. Olive-green above with paler green spots, bars; forehead to nape and sides of throat crimson; pale yellow below with black streaks; golden yellow tail. Usual woodpecker behaviour, hopping up trees supported on stumpy tail, undulating flight, loud laughing call. Feeds on ants, grubs; lays 2 or 3 round white eggs in tree-hole. **537**

Campethera bennettii *Picidae*
BENNETT'S WOODPECKER 7 ins
Ethiopian: S Zaire across to Tanzania, S to Natal, in dry thorn bush country. ♂: upperparts including wings dark green, barred and spotted lighter green and whitish; head to nape and moustachial stripe crimson; earcoverts, chin, throat white; rest of underparts pale yellow, spotted black on neck, breast, flanks; lower flanks sometimes barred; tail dusky yellow, barred darker and usually black-tipped. ♀'s forehead and crown black, spotted white; earcoverts, throat chocolate brown; moustachial stripe white, speckled black. Legs, bill dark grey, eyes red. Juvenile like ♀ but more spotted. Fast undulating flight. Deep, bell-like call unusual for woodpecker. Feeds on insects, especially ants. Breeds September to January, boring hole in dead tree, laying 3 white eggs. Habits very little studied. **538**

Campethera punctuligera *Picidae*
FINE SPOTTED WOODPECKER 7 ins
Ethiopian: Senegal, NE Zaire, S Sudan in well-wooded open country. Very similar to *C. abingoni*, but much more finely barred above and spotted below. Usual woodpecker habits, feeding on ground as well as in trees. Call a kestrel-like *kweeyu*. **539**

Campylopterus falcatus *Trochilidae*
LAZULINE SABREWING 4½ (bill nearly 1) ins
Neotropical: N Venezuela, Colombia; E Ecuador; resident forest and scrub from *c.* 4,500 to *c.* 9,500 ft. ♂: upperparts iridescent green, blue on crown; outer primaries with thickened bent shafts, resembling sabres; tail feathers chestnut, central pair with broad bronze-green tips; throat and breast iridescent dark violet blue shading to blue green on underparts. ♀ has upperparts and tail like ♂, throat iridescent blue, underparts grey. See *Aglaiocercus kingi* for general hummingbird habits and behaviour.

Campylorhamphus falcularius *Dendrocolaptidae*
BLACK-BILLED SCYTHEBILL 10 (bill 3) ins
Neotropical: Brazil, E Paraguay and Argentina; resident in forests. Mainly olivaceous brown, wings and tail rufous chestnut; underparts pale brown; yellow-brown streaks on sides of neck, upper mantle, breast; throat whitish; long curved bill dusky grey. Behaves like giant treecreeper, extracting insects, their larvae and eggs from tree trunks, also probing among clustered palm fruits and between stems of vines. Nests in tree hole, laying probably 2 or 3 eggs. **558**

Campylorhynchus bruneicapillus *Troglodytidae*
CACTUS WREN 8 ins
Nearctic, marginally Neotropical: Central Texas, S Utah, S California to Central Mexico; resident cactus desert, mesquite, arid scrublands. Back brown flecked black and white, long tail greyish brown, barred darker, white spots outer edge; wings grey-brown heavily barred; crown chestnut, prominent white 'eyebrow' stretching to nape; cheeks, chin mainly white, underparts pale, upper breast densely spotted black, thinning out on belly. Legs flesh-brown, slightly curved bill horn-coloured, eyes brown. Tail not usually cocked up as shorter-tailed wrens. Flies low over ground. Call monotonous, 'unbirdlike' (R. T. Peterson) *chuh chuh chuh chuh* on one pitch, but gaining in rapidity. Mainly insectivorous. Breeds April onwards, building large purse-shaped nest of grasses and twigs, lined feathers, fur, in cactus or thorny bush, usually quite low. 4 or 5 creamy white eggs, thickly spotted pale reddish brown. 2 or 3 broods. **664**

Campylorhynchus griseus *Troglodytidae*
SPOTTED or BICOLOURED WREN 7-8½ ins
Neotropical: W Guyana, Venezuela S of Orinoco and adjacent Brazil, lowlands of Colombia; Magdalena Valley; resident forest edge, clearings, semi-arid scrub, savannah, sea level to 4,500 ft. Black rufous; unbarred wings blackish, also tail with outer feathers more or less barred and tipped white; crown, nape, ear coverts dark brown; 'eyebrow' and underparts white. Large Magdalena Valley race has back brownish black, wings edged rufous, all but central tail feathers white towards ends, with narrow black tips. Habits generally as other wrens; mainly insectivorous; both sexes sing. 2 or 3 eggs, fledging period up to 18 days. **665**

Capito niger *Capitonidae*
BLACK-SPOTTED BARBET 6½ ins
Neotropical: Venezuela S of Orinoco, Colombia E of Andes to Peru, Bolivia; W Amazonian Brazil; resident tropical rain forest, swampy woodlands, secondary growth. ♂: upperparts to tail black with yellow bar across wing coverts and yellow suffusion of crown; forehead and large patch on throat red; underparts bright yellow with dark crescents on flanks and lower belly; legs, powerful bill black, eyes dark brown. ♀ has throat, breast, flanks heavily spotted dark brown; underwings and undertail brown. Keeps high in trees, sometimes clinging to bark like nuthatch; flight straight, not undulating. Diet: berries and other fruits; large insects. Excavates nest hole in tree, also taking woodpecker holes, up to 20 ft. 2 white eggs incubated by ♀ and ♂, who both tend young.

Caprimulgus indicus *Caprimulgidae*
MIGRATORY or JUNGLE NIGHTJAR 11 ins
E Palaearctic and Oriental: breeds E Siberia, Japan, southward to Burma, Indian subcontinent and Ceylon; winters S E Asia. Habitat in S of range higher afforested hills. Upperparts marbled and mottled with browns and blacks and grey vermiculations; oval white throat patch, breast grey; belly buff, barred brown. ♂ has white patches on first 4 primaries (rufous in ♀) and subterminal white bands on first 4 outer tail feathers. Feet flesh-brown, bill pinkish brown with black bristles, eyes dark brown. Nocturnal, taking flying ants and termites, grasshoppers, locusts, beetles, small wasps. Can run for short distances. Call: *tuc tuc tuc* repeated rapidly; less rapid *chuckoo chuckoo chuckoo*, repeated 3 to 14 times, fading into expiring whistle. Indian race also calls *uk-krukroo*, repeated every 2 seconds. Breeds February onwards in subcontinent, laying 2 eggs on ground, usually on slope and shaded. Those of Himalayan race white, marbled grey; Indian race: pale cream to warm buff, marked blackish and reddish brown. Incubation by ♀ and ♂ 16-17 days. **459**

Caprimulgus pectoralis *Caprimulgidae*
DUSKY NIGHTJAR 9 ins
Ethiopian: several races cover almost whole region; resident in wooded areas, including plantations of introduced pines and eucalypts in S Africa. ♂: generally warm brown and black, with wine-red wash, also on breast; broad brown collar on hindneck; white spots on first 4 primaries; apical third of 2 outermost tail feathers white; eye brown. ♀: wing spots washed buff, less white on tail. Nocturnal, resting on ground or lengthwise on branch by day. Hawks insects by night from special perch. Musical call, uttered perched across branch towards dusk or moonlit nights, varies throughout range; one form: *fwey wey wiriu*, third syllable descending and drawn out. Breeds August-November S Africa, laying 2 buffish or pinkish-white eggs, marked rufous or purple with underlying grey, on ground, often shaded by bush. Incubation and fledging much as other *Caprimulgus* species. **460**

Caprimulgus vociferus *Caprimulgidae*
WHIP-POOR-WILL 9-10 ins
Nearctic and Neotropical: breeds SE Canada, from Central Saskatchewan to Nova Scotia, E USA to NE Texas; also mountains S Arizona, New Mexico to Honduras; migratory in N of range, wintering from lowlands of Central S Carolina, Gulf of Florida, to Costa Rica. Habitat woodland near open country. Beautifully mottled and blending plumage characteristic of nightjars: browns, greys, black and buff. Pale stripe from bill over eye bounds black face and throat, which is divided by broader white stripe; short rounded wing-tips barred dark brown and rufous; tail, white-edged in ♂, projects well beyond folded wings. Eye, dark brown, reflects red in light. Insistent onomatopaeic call repeated endlessly by night; uttered with wing-tips below tail, head thrown back at soft preliminary *cluck*. Hunts insects on wing silently by night: many moths, beetles, gnats. Breeds May-June in N of range, laying 2 white or cream eggs, marbled pale brown, grey and lilac, on dead leaves. Incubation by ♀ *c.* 18 days; both parents feed young, who fly *c.* 2½ weeks. **461**

Carduelis carduelis *Fringillidae*
EURASIAN GOLDFINCH *c.* 4¾ ins
Palaearctic: combined breeding range with Grey-headed *C. caniceps*, (with which it hybridises freely) roughly rectangular between 30° and 60°N, 10°W and 90°E in Asia, with large gap between Caspian and Lake Balkash; also found Canary Is, Azores; introduced New Zealand, USA. Resident and migrant, northern birds winter in S of breeding range. Habitat: edges and clearings of coniferous and broadleaved forests; riverine strips; steppes with tree clumps; almost to tree limit in mountains; all types of cultivated and settled land with trees right into towns. Upperparts tawny brown; wings black with broad golden bar, white tips to flight feathers; black tail also white-tipped; black, white, crimson facial pattern; rump, underparts white. Legs pale flesh, bill pinkish white, eyes dark brown. Juvenile lacks head pattern, plumage streaked generally. Usually feeds low down on variety of seeds, especially thistles, fluttering round heads; on alders in winter; many insects taken in summer. Flocks in autumn. Dancing flight. ♂ displays gold wings to ♀. Call: constant, liquid *tswitt witt witt;*

aggressive *geeze*. Song developed from calls, pleasant, musical: from perch or air. Breeds April to September, solitary or in groups. ♀, attended ♂, builds compact nest of rootlets, grass, wool, plant down, bound cobwebs, softly lined; in end fork of rising or lateral branch, up to 45 ft, on variety of trees and bushes, usually broadleaved. 5 to 6 bluish-white eggs, marked dark chestnut-brown over grey, incubated ♀ 11-13 days; ♀ and ♂ feed young from throat; they fly 13-16 days. 2, occasionally 3 broods. **918**

Carduelis chloris *Fringillidae*
GREENFINCH   *c.* 5¾ ins
Palaearctic: almost all Europe, well into Scandinavia; NW Africa, Azores; Asia Minor, Palestine, N Iran; isolated population Turkestan but replaced E Asia by Oriental *C. sinica*; introduced New Zealand. Resident and migrant, northern birds moving SW in autumn. Habitat open mixed forest and edges, riverine strips with poplar, willows; orchards, plantations, olive and palm groves, cultivated land with hedges, roadsides, parks, gardens, well into European towns. ♂: generally olive green, darker above, yellower on rump, underparts, face, with bright patches on dark wings and forked, dark-tipped tail. ♀ duller, faintly streaked. Juvenile browner, clearly streaked. Legs pale flesh, bill whitish, eyes brown. Hops on ground, perches mainly trees. Flight less undulating than smaller relatives. Huge flocks autumn, winter, often with other seed-eaters. Calls: repeated *chup chup*; *cheu cheu*; querulous *jeee*; *tsooet* of alarm. Song, twittering blend of calls, from perch or in bat-like display flight. Takes variety of seeds, small fruit, buds; some insects, spiders, especially for young; regular at bird tables. Breeds early April to September, solitary or in small groups. ♀, attended ♂, builds substantial nest of moss, wool woven round twigs, rootlets; lined finer rootlets, hair, some feathers; in variety of sites 5 to 15 ft up or more, especially in wilder habitats; in thorny or evergreen bushes, ivy, creepers. 4 to 6 off-white to pale blue eggs, streaked and spotted red-brown over violet, indistinguishable from Crossbill, *Loxia curvirostra*, incubated ♀ 12-14 days; ♀ and ♂ feed young from throat; they fly 13-16 days. 2, occasionally 3 broods. **919**

Carduelis flammea see **Acanthis flammea**

Carduelis sinica see under **C. chloris**

Cariama cristata *Cariamidae*
RED-LEGGED SERIEMA   30 ins
Neotropical: E and Central Brazil to Uruguay, Paraguay, N Argentina, E Bolivia. Resident open semi-desert savannah. Upperparts from crown grey-brown; wings dark brown with white band; tail has black and terminal white bands; underparts from cheeks and throat to undertail pale grey, vermiculated dark grey on longer feathers; legs dark red. Hooked bill red with tuft or erect feathers at base, eyes light brown, facial skin bluish. Shy, running very fast, in preference to flying. Yelping contact call of parties intensified by ♂ in courtship when he displays his plumage to ♀. Diet varied: reptiles, including snakes, amphibians, insects; leaves and seeds. Beats large prey on ground to kill and soften it. Builds substantial nest in tree, 5 to 10 ft up; 2 buff eggs, marked red-brown, soon become dull during 25-26 day incubation; both parents tend young in nest until well grown. **241**

CARMINE BEE-EATER see **Merops nubicus**

Carpococcyx renauldi *Cuculidae*
RENAULD'S or
RED-BILLED GROUND CUCKOO   *c.* 24 ins
Oriental: Indochina to E Thailand; resident dense lowland and upland forests with undergrowth and boulders. Upperparts grey, washed green, flecked black; wingtips, tail purplish green; head, neck and breast black, glossed violet; underparts vermiculated greys; long legs, bill red, eyes light yellow, facial skin violet. Runs fast rather than fly. Noisy in dry season; ♂ perches in open, raising and lowering wings, raising head to utter rather harmonious call. Food mainly insects, some small reptiles and mammals. Builds

slight nest of leaves and sticks on ground or up to 12 ft in vegetation; ♀ and ♂ incubate 3 or 4 white eggs. **417**

Carpodacus mexicanus *Fringillidae*
HOUSE FINCH   5½ ins
Nearctic, Neotropical: breeds from N Wyoming, S British Columbia to S Mexico; E to W Kansas, Central Texas; mainly resident but some movement S in winter; introduced S New England, Long Island (NY). Habitat dry open country near water; suited by cultivation and increasing towns, villages. ♂: upperparts dull brown suffused red on crown, back; 'eyebrow', cheeks, rump red; wings, tail brown with pale feather edges; throat, breast red; underparts white, streaked dark brown. ♀, juvenile as ♂ without red; throat, breast as belly. Legs, bill yellowish horn, eyes dark brown. Call harsh chatter; song: 'clear, rolling warble of notes, varying greatly in pitch' (R. H. Pough). Food: seeds of wild plants, also wild and cultivated fruits. Breeds throughout summer; nest of locally available plant fibres, lined soft material, variously sited: holes in trees, buildings, nestboxes; old nests of swallows, orioles; shrubs, vines, cactus clumps, 4 or 5 pale blue eggs, lightly spotted black, incubated ♀. 2, sometimes 3 broods. **920**

CARRION CROW see **Corvus corone**

Casmerodius albus see **Egretta alba**

CASPIAN TERN see **Hydroprogne caspia**

CASSOWARY see **Casuarius casuarius**

Casuarius casuarius *Casuaridae*
AUSTRALIAN CASSOWARY   4½-5½ ft tall
Resident Australia (NE Queensland), New Guinea and adjacent islands in thick scrub and jungle. ♀ larger than ♂; flightless, with coarse black body feathers; bare blue neck and head surmounted by bony casque; red wattles; legs, bill and eyes light brown; innermost of 3 toes with sharp claw. Found singly, in pairs or sometimes small parties, with regular routes through undergrowth and across streams; swims well. Territorial and aggressive during breeding season. Calls deep boom or croak. Diet mainly vegetable: palm nuts, fruits and berries; some insects. Eggs laid July-August Queensland, 3 to 6, light to dark green with coarse granulated shells, in scrape on forest floor. Incubated *c.* 30 days by ♂, who also tends brood for *c.* 4 months. **3**

Catamblyrhynchus diadema *Emberizidae: Thraupinae*
PLUSH-CAPPED FINCH   5¼ ins
Neotropical: N Venezuela, Colombia S to N Bolivia and NW Argentina E of Andes; W of Andes S to Lambayeque, Peru. Resident open woodland and scrubby slopes 5,000 to 10,000 ft. Upperparts including wings, tail, dark grey; forecrown deep yellow, feathers plush-like; lores, hindcrown, nape black; cheeks, all underparts chestnut; legs, stubby bill greyish, eyes dark brown. Habits little studied; apparently insectivorous.

CATBIRD see **Dumetella carolinensis**

Catharacta skua see **Stercorarius skua**

Cathartes aura *Cathartidae*
TURKEY VULTURE   25 ins
Nearctic and Neotropical: Canada to Tierra del Fuego and Falkland Islands. Resident South America but migratory farther north. Inhabits open desert, plains, plateaux, forest and jungle. Blackish or blackish brown with silvery wing linings; head and neck bare, bristly; legs pale flesh, bill whitish, cere red, facial skin purplish, eyes grey-brown. Numbers gather at carrion but more social when roosting. Flies and glides buoyantly for long periods. Group 'dances' on ground as display. Makes quiet hisses and grunts. Feeds almost entirely on carrion, locally on eggs, nestlings, rotting fruit. Breeding season variable from March in Florida. No real nest built. Lays 2 creamy

white eggs, with heavy brown markings, in caves, stumps, dense ground cover. ♂ and ♀ incubate for 38-41 days, and feed chicks which fly *c.* 11 weeks. **130**

Catharus fuscater *Muscicapidae: Turdinae*
SLATY-BACKED NIGHTINGALE THRUSH   7 ins
Neotropical: Costa Rica, Panama, NW Venezuela, Colombia; Central Peru to N. Bolivia; resident thick forests, 4,500 to 7,500 ft. Upperparts, including wings, tail and cheeks, dark leaden grey, blacker on crown and nape (dark brownish grey in Peruvian race); throat, breast, flanks lighter grey than back; centre belly white; legs, bill orange, eyes light. Song musical, bell-like. Feeds on ground on invertebrates. **675**

Catharas minimus see under **C. ustulatus**

Catharus ustulatus or Hylocichla ustulata
Muscicapidae: Turdinae
OLIVE-BACKED OR SWAINSON'S THRUSH   7 ins
Nearctic: breeds from NW Alaska through most of N and W Canada to New England, mountains W Virginia, N. Michigan, Colorado, S California; winters S America to Argentina. Breeds spruce-fir forests, especially damp areas near water, and in young conifers mixed broad leaved trees; sometimes low scrub; woodland in winter. Upperparts generally olive brown; throat white with black streaks at side; cheeks, upper breast, flanks buffish, spotted black, thinning to white underparts; legs light brown, bill dark, eyes dark brown with buff orbits (helps distinguish from Grey-cheeked, *C. minimus*). Mellow whistles heard at night on migration. Usual calls abrupt *whit*, high-pitched *peep*. Musical, gurgling song, rising in pitch through dozen paired notes, some phrases repeated. Diet: mainly insects, from leaves, ground, e.g. grasshoppers, locusts in field, or in air. Breeds May to July, building neat nest of moss twigs, other plant material, sometimes hard lining, leaf-mould or mud; 3 to 15 ft in small, usually evergreen, tree or shrub. 3 or 4 pale greenish blue eggs, marked light brown; incubation by ♀; both parents feed young.

Catoptrophorus semipalmatus *Scolopacidae*
WILLET   14-17 ins
Nearctic and Neotropical: breeds E coast N America from Nova Scotia to Gulf of Florida, W Indies; inland from S Central Canada to Iowa and Nebraska as summer visitor; winters from Colombia, Venezuela to NE Brazil, Peru; eastern population breeds coastal marshes, beaches, islets, dunes; western by lakes; both winter salt marshes. Spring: upperparts pale grey-brown, darker streaks on head, neck, barred on back; rump white, tail mostly white; broad white bar on wings between black greater coverts and wingtips; underparts white, spotted and barred dark brown; legs blue-grey, bill, eyes dark. Pale grey above and white below in winter. Parties and flocks outside breeding season. Flies with shallow beats, holds wings upward after alighting. Swims easily with half-webbed feet. Spring call *pill will willet*; also loud *kay-ee*, repeated *kip kip*, *whee wee wee* in flight. Breeds May onwards, sometimes socially. Scrape or quite substantial nest of grass with finer lining, on raised ground if in marsh, holds 3 or 4 brownish or greenish buff eggs, blotched umber and lilac. Incubation by ♀ and ♂, who feign injury and are said to carry young. **283**

CATTLE EGRET see **Bubulcus ibis**

Cecropis daurica see **Hirundo daurica**

Cecropis senegalensis see **Hirundo senegalensis**

CEDAR WAXWING see **Bombycilla cedorum**

CELEBES STARLING see **Scissirostrum dubium**

Celeus elegans *Picidae*
YELLOW-CRESTED OR CHESTNUT WOODPECKER 11 ins
Neotropical: Venezuela and Colombia E of Andes S to N Bolivia and Amazonian Brazil; Trinidad; resident forests, mangrove swamps, savannah, sea level to

4,000 ft. Mainly chestnut; crown and crest (raised when excited) buffy white to buff or chestnut according to race; crimson moustachial stripe (not in ♀); rump light buffy yellow or dark buff; inner webs flight feathers barred black and buff; tail black; flanks buffy white; bill ivory white, eyes reddish, facial skin dark grey. Forms small parties; noisy, with loud drumming by ♂ in breeding season. Diet: insects extracted from decayed wood, ants and termites from nests. Breeds April and May Trinidad, excavating hole in dead tree, 3 glossy white eggs incubated by ♀ and ♂, who both tend young.

Centrocercus urophasianus *Tetraonidae*
SAGE GROUSE   ♀: 22: ♂: 28 ins
Nearctic: local W North America from S Saskatchewan, W Dakotas and N New Mexico W to Central Washington and E California; moving within area to foothills in summer and desert areas in winter. ♀: mottled yellow-brown, black and white all over from crown to long, pointed tail, except black belly. ♂: similar but has black face and throat split by white half collar and white breast with 2 yellow air sacs and wattles over dark brown eyes; legs greyish, bill dark. Lives in flocks of up to 100, feeding on leaves and shoots of sage in winter, leguminous plants in summer; also berries, seeds and (especially when young) insects; drinks twice a day. Clucking call in flight. In spring up to 400 ♂♂ gather on bare 'strutting ground' when they display, fanning tails, puffing white breasts and inflating sacs, each bout ending in loud *plop*. ♀♀ come to be mated, then lay 6 to 8 olive or greenish white eggs in lined scrape often under sage bush, incubating them for 22 days. Young fly in 1 to 2 weeks. ♂ does not assist at all.

Centropus senegalensis *Cuculidae*
SENEGAL COUCAL   16 ins
Ethiopian: SE Palaearctic (Egypt) and Ethiopian: Senegal and Gambia E to Somalia, S to Angola, Botswana, Transvaal, Rhodesia, Malawi; migratory in part of range. Habitat: bush and grassy open woodland, occasionally forest edge. Upperparts: back and wings chestnut, head and nape blue-black, washed iridescent green; upper tail coverts dark blue green, long tail iridescent green; underparts white; legs lead-grey, bill black, eyes red. Variety '*epomidis*' in W Africa: upper and underparts chestnut brown; head, neck, upper breast black with green iridescence. Remains in thick cover, hopping from bough to bough up bush, then flying heavily to next; largely crepuscular, giving 'water bubbling' call in evenings and night; also calls quiet *tok* at nest. Diet: locusts and other insects, small reptiles, rodents, nestlings. Breeding season variable; makes untidy nest of sticks and other plant material, thickly lined and loosely domed, with entrance at side, usually a few feet off ground. The 4 white eggs become stained during incubation. **418**

Centropus sinensis *Cuculidae*
COMMON COUCAL or CROW PHEASANT   18-21 ins
Oriental: widespread throughout region; resident in savannah grassland and dense secondary forest, cultivated land; up to 4,000 ft. Whole body from head to long tail black, glossed purple head, neck; dark blue on underparts; the whole finely streaked white; legs and deep, curved bill black, eyes crimson. Hunts mud banks of rivers, walking sedately with tail lifted, flying to cover with leisurely flap and glide action. Climbs trees by hops like relatives, often sunning at top after rain. Dull, booming call *boob boob boob boob* repeated and sometimes extended into melodious run up and down scale; also clicking *titektak*. Diet: insects, especially grasshoppers, ants; centipedes; snails; seeds and berries. Breeds February to September in India, ♀ and ♂ building ball or cup nest of grasses, sometimes in grass or in bush or tree. 2 to 5 white eggs incubated by ♀ and ♂, who both tend young. Probably 2 broods in parts of range. **419**

Centropus superciliosus *Cuculidae*
WHITE-BROWED COUCAL   17 ins
SE Palaearctic (S Arabia); Ethiopian: 3 races cover most of the region. Resident in reedbeds, dense riparian

cover and tall elephant grass; also gardens and parks in S Africa. Differs from *C. senegalensis* in having crown and mantle dull brown (but black in S race *burchellii*) and distinct white 'eyebrow'; upper tail coverts and bases of tail feathers barred. Behaviour much as *C. senegalensis* with same call 'like water pouring out of bottle', uttered with head thrown back and bill pointed downwards; ♀ often answers ♂; also hoarse *tschak* and hiss of alarm. Diet omnivorous, taking many mice. Breeding season variable; nesting much as *C. senegalensis* but said to interlace twigs round nest and parent carries young between thighs when nest threatened; 2 to 4 white eggs laid. **420**

Centurus carolinus *Picidae*
RED-BELLIED WOODPECKER   8½ ins
Nearctic: Eastern USA, Great Lakes to Florida; resident woodland and its edge; orange groves. ♂: upperparts, including wing coverts and tail, barred black and white; wingtips black with white patch in centre; rump white; 2 black streaks down double-pointed tail; crown, nape red; underparts, including collar, grey-buff, flanks flecked darker. ♀ has forehead grey, flanks unmarked. Legs, bill blackish, eyes dark brown, orbits red. Works up trees jerkily and spirally; sometimes feeds on ground, taking insects and their larvae, especially beetles and bugs; also fruit (bores into oranges), seeds, acorns, occasionally corn. Rattling call, also lower-pitched *churr* and series of flicker-like (*Colaptes*) notes. Breeds May, making hole in tree or telegraph pole with 12 ins shaft; clutch 3 to 6 white eggs incubated by ♀ and ♂, who both tend young. **540**

Centurus rubicapillus see **Melanerpes rubicapillus**

Centurus uropygialis *Picidae*
GILA WOODPECKER   8¼ ins
Nearctic to Neotropical: extreme SW USA and Mexico. Resident saguaro (giant cactus) country, but extending now into cities. Very similar to *C. carolinus* but ♂ has only small red cap and ♀'s head is uniform grey-buff; both have yellow patch on belly. Noisy and conspicuous in desert habitat, with loud, high-pitched *yip* repeated 2 to 6 times rapidly; also 'conversational' rasping *churr*. Drums frequently on tin. Diet: cactus fruits and desert berries; also variety of insects. Breeds April and May, making holes in cacti, cottonwoods, mesquites and sycamores, 15 ft up or more; excavates excess holes, which are used by other species. 3 to 6 white eggs incubated by ♀ and ♂, who also feed young. 2 broods. **541**

Cephalopterus ornatus *Cotingidae*
UMBRELLABIRD   16-19 ins
Neotropical: Guyanas, Venezuela S of Orinoco, Colombia E of Andes to E Peru, N Bolivia; Amazonian Brazil; forest from sea level to *c.* 4,000 ft, often on islands in larger rivers. (Long-wattled Umbrellabird, *C. penduliger*, sometimes regarded as race of *C. ornatus*, inhabits Pacific slopes Colombia from Cauca S to W Ecuador, ranging higher up mountains.) Uniformly glossy blue-black; erect crest of silky filoplumous feathers with white shafts; short, flat feathered wattle at base of neck. (*C. penduliger* has smaller, rounder crest, but cylindrical feathered lappet up to 18 ins long). ♀: duller, with smaller wattle. Legs slaty grey; bill: upper grey, lower yellowish horn; eyes white or light grey (brown in *C. penduliger*). Crow-like actions but little studied, as haunts treetops, where feeds on fruit. Spreads crest in display to cover crown and 'produces rumbling sound modified trachea and syrinx' (D. W. Snow). **590**

Cephalopterus penduliger see under **C. ornatus**

Cepphus columba *Alcidae*
PIGEON GUILLEMOT   14 ins
W Nearctic and E Palaearctic: rocky coasts and islands from Santa Barbara, California, round N Pacific to Kuriles; movement in winter N to Pribilof and Aleutian Islands. Very similar to Black Guillemot, *C. grylle*, except for black bar partly across white wing patch; underwing usually black. Swims near colonies in mornings, in intricate manoeuvres with calling and display of red gape; swims underwater with wings

partly folded. Call a sibilant *see-oo;* also *tsit* reiterated into trill. Food bottom-living fish, crustaceans, molluscs and worms. Breeds from May in small colonies up to 50 pairs, similar sites to Black Guillemot but tunnels in banks Puget Sound. 2 eggs, like Black Guillemot but more heavily marked, incubated by ♀ and ♂ 28 days; young fledge 34-40 days, fed by parents.

Cepphus grylle *Alcidae*
BLACK GUILLEMOT   *c.* 13½ ins
Holarctic, discontinuous but wide distribution along temperate, subarctic, arctic coasts, including Baltic; winters mainly offshore. Breeds rocky but not precipitous sea coasts, well up sheltered fjords, sea lochs and in harbours. Summer: uniform glossy blackish brown with broad white wing bar (underwing also mostly white), legs red, bill black (conspicuous red inside), eyes brown. Winter: upperparts barred black and white, giving grey effect; flight feathers, tail blackish-grey; underparts white. Often seen alone at sea or in small parties, diving in concert or displaying as Pigeon Guillemot, *C. columba*. Moves better on land than relatives and often hauls out on rocks; buoyant in water, taking off heavily but flying fast and low. Rather feeble whistle in breeding season, *cf* Pigeon Guillemot. Takes fish from near bottom and marine animals from wrack zone; plankton in winter near sea ice. Breeds socially from early May; 2 white to pale blue-green eggs marked dark brown and grey laid in crevice or under boulders, incubated by ♀ and ♂ 21-24 days; parents feed young *c.* 5 weeks. **344**

Cercomela familiaris *Muscicapidae: Turdinae*
FAMILIAR or RED-TAILED CHAT   6 ins
Ethiopian: distributed most of region from Ghana to Ethiopia and southern Africa, absent much of NE; resident rocky, wooded hillsides, scrub, cultivated lands and vicinity of man. Upperparts dark brown, underparts pale brown, lighter on belly; wings dusky, upper tail coverts russet, central tail feathers black, others russet, tipped black; ear coverts rust brown; legs, bill black, eyes brown. Juvenile duller, more spotted. Active, flicks wings sideways and forwards. Call repeated *tjree tjree tjree;* alarm squeaky *whee-chuc-chuc*. Arboreal, but takes insects off ground as well as on wing. Breeding season varies with range; builds large, bulky nest of plant materials and mud, thickly lined wool, hair, feathers; in shallow hole of tree, rock, bank, wall, very like European Robin, *Erithacus rubecula*. 3 or 4 bright greenish blue eggs, marked rufous or chestnut especially at big end. **676**

Cercotrichas galactotes *Muscicapidae: Turdinae*
RUFOUS BUSH CHAT   6 ins
Palaearctic, marginally Oriental, Ethiopian: S Iberia, NW Africa eastward between 30° and 40°N to Aral Sea, Lake Balkash: separate sedentary population across Africa between 10° and 20°N, extending to Somalia, Ethiopa. Northern population winters in area of southern birds, also NW Indian subcontinent. Habitat dry scrub and bare ground with scattered bushes; acacia savannah; vineyards, olive groves, roadsides, parks, gardens. Upperparts western race *C. g. galactotes* rufous, brightest on long, graduated tail with black and white tips outer feathers; eastern *syriacus* greyish olive brown except rump, tail; underparts pale buff; white stripe over, dark through eye; legs pale brown, bill mainly dark brown, eyes brown. Partly terrestrial and conspicuous, constantly spreading and moving tail up and down, also droops and flicks wings. Call: *tec tec;* song medley of 'clear, lark-like notes' (H. F. Witherby) delivered from high perch or in butterfly display flight. Food mainly larger insects, spiders, earthworms, usually from bare or shaded ground. Breeds second half May, early June in Mediterranean area; rather untidy nest of local plant debris, with lining finer stems, hair, often piece snake skin; usually in bush, stump, hedge of prickly pear, fairly low. 4 or 6 greyish or greenish grey eggs, densely marked umber and ashy brown. 2 broods in part of range. **677**

Cereopsis novaehollandiae *Anatidae*
CAPE BARREN GOOSE   *c.* 32-34 ins
Australasian: breeds islands off W Australia, S Australia and in Bass Strait; occasionally visits nearby mainland in summer. Habitat: beaches, rocky prominences and grassed areas. Ash grey, head paler with white crown; scapulars and wing coverts blotched with dark grey, terminal half of primaries and tips of secondaries black; tail black with grey under coverts. Long legs pink descending to black feet, bill black with greenish yellow cere, eyes dark brown. In small groups; grazes on plants, usually grass, on land at edge of lakes and seashore, only enters sea when pursued. Wary, flies strongly. Call: grunt; ♂ may also trumpet. Breeds May or June onwards in strongly defended territories, usually on W side of island amongst scrub. Nest is heap of plant debris lined with grey down, occasionally built in dense scrub. 3 to 5 white eggs, incubated by both parents; young leave territory *c.* 6 weeks, forming nomadic flocks. **109**

Certhia brachydactyla see under **C. familiaris**

Certhia familiaris *Certhiidae*
TREECREEPER OR BROWN CREEPER   *c.* 5 ins
Holarctic, Neotropical: main range lies across Eurasia between 50° and 60°N, across N America between 40° and 50°N, but with many extensions and outliers, e.g. S Europe, between Black Sea and Caspian, Himalayas and Chinese Mountains; W coast Pacific to Alaska; through Mexico into Central America. Resident dark spruce, fir forests, lowland to subalpine, also mixed forests and their edges e.g. taiga; to 7,000 ft (Himalayas), 8,500 ft (Guatemala); also in European broadleaved woods, parks, riversides where Short-toed Treecreeper, *C. brachydactyla*, does not occur. Upperparts from crown brown, streaked pale buff, rufous on rump; wings with buff bars; whitish 'eyebrow'; underparts from chin pure white; legs pale brown, bill mainly dark brown, eyes brown. Climbs spirally up trunks, along undersides of branches, feet well apart, stiff graduated tail acting as woodpecker's. Short undulating flight from top of one tree to foot of next. Often solitary but with tit flocks autumn, winter. Roosts clefts or characteristically excavates body hole in soft wood or *Sequoia* bark. ♂ chases ♀ in display and feeds her. Calls shrill *tsuu*, often rapidly repeated, softer *tsit*; song thin, high-pitched, recalling Goldcrest, *Regulus regulus*, but louder, with terminal flourish. Food chiefly insects and larvae, spiders and eggs, wood-lice. Breeds early April to early July Britain; ♀ and ♂ squeeze nest into narrow crack, especially behind bark, ivy, sometimes in walls, nestboxes; substantial foundation twigs, wood chips, then cup (often oval) of plant debris, lined bark, feathers, hair, wool; ground level to 30 ft. 5 to 7 white eggs, red-brown markings zoned at big end; incubated mainly ♀ 14-15 days; young, fed ♀ and ♂, fly 14-15 days. Sometimes 2 broods. **813**

Ceryle rudis *Alcedinidae*
PIED KINGFISHER   10 ins
S Palaearctic, Ethiopian: Cyprus (visitor), Asia minor, Iran, Egypt, all sub-Sahara Africa except Somalia; also mainland Oriental region. Common alongside rivers, lakes, sea shore; small groups fishing from perches on bare boughs, wires, boats' masts; often hovers rather clumsily over water, then plunges in. Entirely black and white; mainly black above, streaked and spotted white, especially wings, tail; white below apart from two black bands across chest in ♂, one incomplete in ♀; low crest, long stout bill. Noisy at nesting colony, sharp *keek keek* and repeated jingling call. 3 to 6 white eggs in large chamber end of long tunnel in bank, excavated by ♀ and ♂; both parents feed young and may share incubation. **485**

Cettia cetti *Muscicapidae: Sylviinae*
CETTI'S WARBLER   5½ ins
Palaearctic: patchy distribution E from England (recent colonist), Spain, N Africa across S Europe, Turkey, Central Asia to 80°E. Mainly resident, eastern population winters Iraq to Pakistan; marked population decline in severe winters. Habitat: dense bushes on stream banks, near marshes, reedbeds;

occasionally away from water. Uniform dark chestnut upperparts; dull white 'eyebrow'; underparts greyish white, barred brown under tail; broad graduated tail often cocked; legs brown, bill black, paler at base, eyes dark sepia. Very secretive, skulking in thick cover. Song: distinctive loud outburst *chee, chewee, chewee* . . . ; also tremulous *twic*, stuttering alarm note. Feeds on small insects, spiders, snails, earthworms. Breeds from end April onwards; ♀ builds neat cup nest of grass, lined fine grass, hair, in bush near ground. 3 to 5 brick red eggs. Young fed both parents. **732**

Cettia diphone *Muscicapidae: Sylviinae*
CHINESE BUSH WARBLER   ♀: 5, ♂: 5¾ ins
E Palaearctic: breeds China from 35°N to S Mongolia, Manchuria, N Korea; also Japan, Taiwan, N Philippines; winters (October to April) SE China. Variety of bushy grassy habitats, always near water. Upperparts grey-brown, redder on crown, tail: dark eyestripe, buffish 'eyebrow' more conspicuous in worn plumage; underparts dingy white; yellow brown on breast, flanks, under tail coverts; bill brown. ♀ smaller. Very skulking; call distinctive repeated *tyok*; short melodious song delivered from crown of tree or other concealed perch throughout day. Mainly insectivorous. Breeds May to July; building deep cup nest of broad leaves woven around twigs in bush, near ground. 4 or 5 dark pink-red eggs, occasionally speckled darker. Possibly 2 broods.

Cettia squameiceps or *Cisticola squameiceps*
Muscicapidae: Sylviinae
SHORT-TAILED BUSH WARBLER   4 ins
E Palaearctic: breeds E Siberia, Korea, E Manchuria, S Sakhalin, Japan; winters Taiwan, SE China to Indochina, Thailand, Burma, Philippines. Habitat: mixed and broadleaved forests, riverine alders with nettle ground layer in E Siberia; lowlands (Hokkaido) to *c.* 4,500 ft (Kyushu) in Japan, thick undergrowth usually near water. Upperparts dark brown; fine streaks on head, white 'eyebrow', black eyestripe; underparts buffish, paler on throat and belly; very short dark tail. Very active but keeps much to cover; in family parties, or singly on migration and in winter. Alarm call: rattling *chmok chmok*; song: high-pitched *si-si-si*, repeated ten times, gradually rising and accelerating in tempo. Food: insects from ground, e.g. small beetles in winter in Burma. Breeds from late May E Siberia; cup nest of dead leaves and broad stems, lined fine grass, in hollow in bank of stream, under roots or fallen tree, at base of bush. 5 to 7 pale pink eggs, densely marked reddish or purplish over lilac. **733**

CETTI'S WARBLER see **Cettia cetti**

CEYLON CRIMSON-BACKED WOODPECKER see **Chrysocolaptes lucidus stricklandi**

CHACHALACA see **Ortalis vetula**

CHACHALACA, RUFOUS-VENTED see **Ortalis ruficauda**

Chaetorhynchus papuensis *Dicruridae*
MOUNTAIN DRONGO   8 ins
Australasian: New Guinea; resident mountain forests, 2,000 to 4,800 ft. Black, head and body glossed blue, including short crest; hidden white at base scapulars; tail nearly square; legs, rather heavy, hooked bill black, eyes dark brown. Sits upright like flycatcher on branch in lower storeys of forest.

CHAFFINCH see **Fringilla coelebs**

CHAFFINCH, BLUE see under **Fringilla coelebs**

Chalcites lucidus *Cuculidae*
SHINING CUCKOO   6½ ins
New Zealand: widespread summer visitor, up to 4,000 ft and including Stewart I, Chatham Is, in habitat of its chief fosterers Grey Warbler, *Gerygone igata*, and endemic Chatham Island *G. albofrontata*; performs remarkable 2,000 mile migration mainly over ocean to Solomon Is, Bismarck Archipelago; sometimes winters North Island. ♂: upperparts from

crown metallic green, glinting gold or coppery; flight feathers dark brown; longish tail terminally barred dark brown, outer feathers barred white; cheeks, underparts white, finely barred glossy green, looking black at distance. ♀ similar but crown, nape more purplish bronze, bars on belly more bronze. Legs black, soles of feet yellow, rather broad bill black, eyes dark brown. Juvenile striped on breast; bars on throat, breast indistinct. Call: clear *tsee-ew* or *tsiu*, heard on night passage, also by day when several birds chase in and out of tree clump. Ventriloquial song rendered in Maori: *kui kui whiti-whiti ora tio-o*. Diet: mainly insects, especially hairy larvae. Courtship feeding when pairing. Egg, greenish or bluish white to dark olive brown, laid in nests of Grey Warbler, other small passerines, including introduced species.

Chalcites xanthorhynchus *Cuculidae*
VIOLET CUCKOO   6½ ins
Oriental: widespread resident, nomad, local migrant W to Assam, inhabiting evergreen forest, also gardens, e.g. in Sarawak, and edges of mangrove swamps. ♂: upperparts and breast glossy violet, underparts heavily barred; legs grey or olive-green, bill yellow, base red, eyes and orbits red. ♀: upperparts bronze green, bill dull yellow. Juvenile: upperparts barred rufous and brown, underparts white, barred brown. Often sits sluggishly in tree and creeps quietly up and down branches, taking off to hawk fly and return. Call: high-pitched *kievik kievik*, also monosyllabic whistles. Diet: flies, ants, beetles and other insects often taken on wing; also fruit. Lays pure white or pink eggs, with zone of reddish spots at big end, in nests of Little Spider-hunter, *Arachnothera longirostris*, and Sunbird, *Aethopyga*.

Chalcomitra senegalensis *Nectariniidae*
SCARLET-CHESTED SUNBIRD   6 ins
Ethiopian: Senegal E to Sudan, down E side Africa to Rhodesia; also Angola, Natal, E Cape (S Africa); resident, some races partly migratory, forest edge, open woodland, savannah, parkland, riverine acacias, cultivated areas, gardens. ♂: satiny dark brown or blackish with metallic green cap and bib, scarlet breast. ♀: upperparts dull dark brown; wings, tail washed bronze, primary wing coverts edged white; underparts heavily mottled. Legs, bill black, eyes dark brown. Juvenile like ♀, with dusky throat. Noisy, especially when in party; best known calls: repeated *tssp teee tee*, sharp *zit* in flight; song, loud trilling warble. Takes flying ants and larger insects than most sunbirds, hawked on wing. Breeding season variable throughout range. Nest-site, sometimes associated with hornets' nest, often used successive years; ♀ builds large oval of various plant materials, usually hanging from fairly low branch. Usually 2 white, cream or bluish white eggs, heavily marked brown or grey, incubated ♀. **820**

Chalcophaps indica *Columbidae*
EMERALD DOVE   *c.* 10 ins
Oriental, Australasian: N Indian subcontinent, Assam and Hainan S and E to Philippines, New Guinea and E Australia. Habitat: wooded country. ♂: brownish pink with brilliant bronzed emerald green upperparts, crown and neck grey, prominent white forehead and eyebrows, band of white-fringed feathers across lower back, white-bordered vinous grey patch on shoulder; rump grey, tail brown and grey with broad black cross-band broken in middle. ♀: less white on forehead, white patch on shoulder and white barring on rump less pronounced; central tail feathers redder brown. Legs pinkish grey, bill orange-red or brown with purplish base and ivory tip, eyes dark brown with purplish orbital skin. Race in SE New Guinea across to E Australia differs in ♂ having no white or grey on head and neck, and ♀ having chestnut in place of grey on tail feathers apart from outer two. Single or in pairs, often in clearings or on earth roads, ground feeder taking seeds, grain, fruits and small animals, chiefly termites; flight silent, low and swift. Call: deep soft moaning note repeated at intervals. Breeds all months; fairly compact twig platform usually 5 to 10 ft up in trees or shrubs. 2 creamy buff eggs, incubated *c.* 14 days; young fly *c.* 12 days. **351**

Chamaea fasciata *Muscicapidae: Timaliinae*

WRENTIT 6½ ins

Nearctic: resident most of California W of higher Sierra Nevada and SE deserts, N into Oregon and S to NW Lower California; dense chaparral, evergreen scrub in lower mountains, deciduous thickets along watercourses, damp slopes with mixed shrubs and trees; shrub understorey and clearings in redwood areas. Upperparts from crown to long, rounded tail dark brown; pale edges to flight feathers of short wings; cheeks greyish; underparts buff-brown with long dark streaks; legs, short bill blackish; eyes white. Pairs for life, occupying territory of ¾ to 2½ acres all year, though immatures wander into open woodland. Tends to stay in thick cover, rarely flying more than 20 yds, but hopping rapidly from twig to twig, searching for insects; berries important autumn, winter. Many calls include rasping purr; ♂'s song series of *yips*, speeding up into trill; ♀'s song lacks trill; often answer each other; also both sing slower series: *weeka weeka weeka*. Deep cup nest of plant fibres bound or decorated cobwebs, lichen, usually 1 to 5 ft up in dense canopy near 'edge', e.g. path. 3 to 5 pale greenish blue eggs incubated 16 days; young fly 16 days.

CHANTING GOSHAWK,
DARK see **Melierax metabates**
PALE see **Melierax canorus**

Charadrius alexandrinus *Charadriidae*

KENTISH or SNOWY PLOVER 6¼ ins

Cosmopolitan: Holarctic, N Temperate, S to Cape of Good Hope, Tasmania and parts of W coast S America; inland in Central Asia, E Africa, W USA; sedentary and migratory apparently throughout range. Habitat: sand and shingle shores and inland equivalents by rivers and lakes in steppes and deserts; also coral limestone coasts in tropics. Resembles Ringed Plover, *C. hiaticula*, but black marks reduced in ♂, not meeting across breast, while ♀ lacks dark mark on forehead. Legs lead grey, bill black, eyes dark brown. Habits much as Ringed Plover but runs even faster. Parties and small flocks in autumn. Usual call *wit wit wit*, run into trill as 'song' during wavering display flight, when body thrown from side to side with wings stretched. Food: insects, their larvae and pupae, also small water animals. Breeds May onwards in N temperate zone; usually bare but sometimes lined and adorned scrape in sand in which 3 stone buff eggs, spotted and scrawled black, are often partly or largely buried. Incubation by ♀ and ♂ *c*. 26½ days; parents tend young who fly in *c*. 6 weeks; possibly two broods at times. **256**

Charadrius cucullatus *Charadriidae*

HOODED DOTTEREL *c*. 8½ ins

Southern Australia and Tasmania; resident on sandy shores and by inland salt lakes. Upperparts dark brown; head and throat black with band round neck enclosing white nape; underparts white, sides of breast with black crescents; white stripe on wings, outer tail coverts white; legs flesh pink, bill orange, tip dark, eyes brown. Behaviour and habits much as Ringed Plover, *C. hiaticula*. Feeds on tidal zone insects and small water animals. Breeds September to January. Scrape in sand close to tideline holds 2 or 3 pale stone eggs, marked purplish black and lavender; incubation and fledging as Ringed Plover. **257**

Charadrius hiaticula *Charadriidae*

RINGED PLOVER *c*. 7½ ins

Palaearctic: temperate to arctic, from Iceland and Ireland to Bering Straits, also Nearctic Greenland and Baffin Island; northern populations migratory. Habitats: sand and shingle shores, low rocky islands, inland up rivers and beside lakes; tundra moorland; mainly sandy and muddy shores and estuaries outside breeding season. Upperparts, including hindcrown, dark brown; forehead white, front of crown black, joining stripe from bill to eye above broad white bar on brown wing; tail brown in centre, black subterminal band edged white; legs orange yellow, bill yellow, tip dark, eyes brown. Immature, resembles Kentish Plover, *C. alexandrinus*, but legs yellow. Characteristic plover actions, running and stopping short to dip quickly at prey; bobs head rapidly when agitated; flies low with syncopated wingbeat. Forms small flocks, often with other waders. Usual call *turrp* and liquid *tooi*, repeated to make 'song' in aerial displays; also elaborate actions on ground. Food as Kentish Plover. Breeds from March in S, much later in far N, making scrape, sometimes lined small pebbles, in sand, shingle, turf, even on rock. Usually 4 stone buff eggs with black speckles and scrawls, incubated by ♀ and ♂ 24-25 days; young tended by parents who often feign injury when endangered, fly *c*. 25 days; 2, perhaps sometimes 3 broods. **258**

Charadrius melanops *Charadriidae*

BLACK-FRONTED DOTTEREL 7 ins

Continental Australia and Tasmania, colonising New Zealand (Hawkes Bay) since *c*. 1960. Resident shingle and mud banks of rivers (as in NZ), lakes and pools. Upperparts brown; forehead, eyestripe, V band across breast black; white 'eyebrows' meet behind crown; wings with black tips and white area shown in flight, scapulars dark chestnut; upper tail coverts rust red, tail dark brown edged white; throat and underparts white; legs orange-pink, bill red, tip black, eyes dark brown with red orbits. Behaviour much as other ringed plovers but flight 'jerky and dipping'. Forms small flocks in winter. Typical calls: high-pitched whistle, soft *tink tink*, clicking *tik tik tik*. Food: water insects, small crustaceans, worms; seeds occasionally. Breeds August onwards S Australia, NZ; April onwards in N. Scrape, sometimes lined pebbles and usually near water, holds 3 stone or greyish-yellow eggs, marked brown and lavender. Incubation (*c*. 18 days) and fledging as other ringed plovers. **259**

Charadrius pecuarius *Charadriidae*

KITTLITZ'S SAND PLOVER *c*. 6½ ins

SE Palaearctic (NE Egypt) and throughout Ethiopian region, including Madagascar; distinct race St Helena. Resident and partial migrant: sand banks of lakes, e.g. Lake Victoria, rivers and coastal beaches; open grassland near water and dry sandy areas at some distance from it. Upperparts brownish black with blackish shoulders and wings; black band behind white forehead, black stripe from bill to eye, white collar joining up over eye with forehead; underparts mainly brown, with rich chestnut lower neck and breast; legs and bill black, eyes brown. Immature no black on head. Usually in small parties, but sometimes up to 100; flies low with feet showing beyond tail. Calls: *pi-peep* in flight, *chirrrt* of alarm. Food: small beetles, other insects and water animals. Breeds throughout year in parts of range. Scrape in sand, not always near water, holds 2 stone buff eggs, heavily marked black and grey-brown, usually buried in sand. Incubation 23-26 days; fledging much as other ringed plovers. **260**

Charadrius tricollaris *Charadriidae*

THREE-BANDED PLOVER *c*. 7 ins

Ethiopian: S from Nigeria and Sudan; distinct race Madagascar. Haunts inland waters, e.g. lakes, lagoons, reservoirs, even fast-flowing rivers with bare shores; also salt marshes. Upperparts rich dark brown; forehead, stripe over eye, cheeks and throat white; two black bars across chest with white between; wingbar and terminal bar on tail white as are underparts; legs dark flesh, bill black, base red, eyes brown with red wattled orbits. Feathers of juvenile's upperparts tipped buff, chest bands less distinct. Usually in pairs at water's edge, feeding like other ringed plovers. Flight call loud *tiuu-it tiuu-it*; high-pitched *tui tui* of alarm uttered with body leaning forward and bobbing up and down. Food as other ringed plovers. Breeding season variable throughout range. Shallow scrape in sand, sometimes on mound, adorned with pebbles and shells, holds usually 2 eggs resembling Kittlitz's Plover, *C. pecuarius*, but not buried. Incubation and fledging much as relatives. **261**

Charadrius vociferus *Charadriidae*

KILLDEER *c*. 9½ ins

Nearctic and Neotropical: N Canada S throughout N America with populations W Indies, Peru, W Chile; northern birds migrate S, wintering from S British Columbia in W and New York in E to N South America. Habitat: grasslands and cultivated fields, even lawns near houses; winters on grasslands and sea shores. Upperparts dark brown; white stripe from forehead through eye bordered black above and below; white band round chin extends to collar, above two black bands with white between; underparts white; wings blackish with white bar; upper tail coverts and tail chestnut with white-edged black terminal band; legs dull yellow, bill black, eyes brown. Behaves much as Ringed Plover, *C. hiaticula*, but more excitable and noisy, typical call *kill-dee* giving name; prolonged trill of excitement and many other notes recorded. Food almost all animal: insects, spiders, molluscs, crustaceans, worms. Spring displays by pair hovering in air and calling, also on ground. Breeds Texas from March, later farther N. Scrape, lined or with rim ornamented, holds usually 4 light buff eggs, well marked blackish brown. Incubation by ♀ and ♂ *c*. 27-28 days; young tended by both parents; probably two broods in N of range. **262**

CHAT,
CAPE ROBIN see **Cossypha caffra**
CLIFF see **Thamnolaea cinnamomeiventris**
CRIMSON see **Ephthianura tricolor**
FAMILIAR see **Cercomela familiaris**
KAROO see **Erythropygia coryphaeus**
MOCKING see **Thamnolaea cinnamomeiventris**
MOUNTAIN see **Oenanthe monticola**
ORANGE see **Ephthianura aurifrons**
PALM see **Dulus dominicus**
RED-TAILED see **Cercomela familiaris**
RUFOUS BUSH see **Cercotrichas galactotes**
SNOWY-CROWNED ROBIN see **Thamnolaea coronata**
SOOTY see **Myrmecocichla nigra**
WHITE-CROWNED CLIFF see **Thamnolaea coronata**
WHITE-FRONTED see **Ephthianura albifrons**
WHITE-HEADED BLACK see under **Myrmecocichla nigra**
WHITE-THROATED ROBIN see **Cossypha humeralis**
YELLOW-BREASTED see **Icteria virens**

Chauna chavaria *Anhimidae*

NORTHERN or BLACK-NECKED SCREAMER 34 ins

Neotropical: NW Venezuela and N Colombia; resident in grasslands and marshes. Dark grey with green gloss; crown and crest grey, rest of head white, neck black; under wing coverts white; legs, facial skin red, bill light horn, eyes brown; spur on forward edge of wing. Habits much as other screamers see *Anhima cornuta*: utters sonorous trumpeting call. Diet mainly stems and seeds of water plants, some damage to crops alleged. Builds shallow nest of local plants in marsh; lays 2 white eggs, incubated by ♀ and ♂ *c*. 6 weeks; young leave nest at once and follow parents.

Chelictinia riocourii *Accipitridae*

SWALLOW-TAILED KITE 14½ ins

Ethiopian: Senegal and Gambia E to Somalia, S to N Kenya; breeds deserts or semi-deserts, migrating S to savannah October to February; N and E April to June. Upperparts, including crown, deeply forked tail, most of wings, grey, washed sooty between scapulars (blackish outer margins); primaries pale grey, white inner webs to secondaries; entire underparts from forehead and cheeks white, except for long black patch on under wing coverts; small black patch behind eye; legs yellow, cere and bill grey, eyes red. ♀ slightly larger. Immature much browner. Generally in small parties of 5 to 10, roosting in trees. Spends much of day on wing, hovering *c*. 50 ft up, plunging on prey, chiefly insects, sometimes taken in flight; also small mammals and reptiles: young fed on skinks (W Africa). Silent on migration, noisy at colonies and roosts; rasping *tchee tchi tchi*, rapidly repeated *ti ti ti ti*, softer whistle and feeble mew. Breeds May-June in small colonies, building stick nests usually in acacias 15 to 25 ft up, sometimes close to other species, e.g. Brown Harrier, *Circaetus cinereus*, in Kenya; lays 4 pale sandy eggs, speckled brown. **141**

Chelidoptera tenebrosa *Bucconidae*
SWALLOW-WING   6½ ins
Neotropical; generally distributed S America E of
Andes S to N Bolivia and Brazil; forest edge, savannah,
clearings, riverside. Generally blackish with long
swallow-like wings, white underneath; rump and
under tail coverts also white; belly chestnut bordered
pale grey; curved, slender bill black. Perches in pairs
on stag-headed trees beside rivers, darting out to take
flying insects. Breeds, sometimes in groups of 3 or 4
pairs, March to May along Orinoco, August to
December Surinam, in long dry season. Excavates
slanting tunnel in bank or level ground, laying 2
white eggs in bare chamber. Sometimes sparsely
lined (F. Haverschmidt).

CHESTNUT
   CUCKOO see **Piaya cayana**
   QUAIL THRUSH see **Cinclosoma castanotum**
   WOODPECKER see **Celeus elegans**

CHESTNUT-BELLIED
   NUTHATCH see **Sitta canadensis**
   SAND GROUSE see **Pterocles exustus**

CHESTNUT-BREASTED
   FINCH see **Donacola castaneothorax**
   WREN see **Cyphorhinus thoracicus**

CHESTNUT-CAPPED PUFFBIRD see **Bucco
macrodactylus**

CHESTNUT-SIDED SHRIKE VIREO see **Cireolanius
meliophrys**

CHESTNUT-TAILED
   FOLIAGE GLEANER see under **Automolus
     leucophthalmus**
   THORNBILL see **Acanthiza uropygialis**

Chibia bracteata see under **Sphecotheres
flaviventris**

CHICKADEE BLACK-CAPPED see **Parus
atricapillus**

CHICKEN, GREATER PRAIRIE see **Tympanuchus
cupido**

CHIFFCHAFF see **Phylloscopus collybita**

CHILEAN
   PLANTCUTTER see **Phytotoma rara**
   TINAMOU see **Nothoprocta perdicaria**

CHINESE BUSH WARBLER see **Cettia diphone**

CHIN-SPOT PUFFBACK see **Batis molitor**

Chionis alba *Chionidae*
YELLOW-BILLED SHEATHBILL   16-17 ins
Antarctic and subantarctic: breeds mainly S Atlantic
Ocean, e.g. S Georgia, S Sandwich, S Orkneys, S
Shetlands into antarctic archipelago beyond 65°S;
partly sedentary even in far south, but wanders in
some numbers to Falkland Is and S Patagonia. Pure
white; bare pinkish-yellow facial patch with warty
caruncles round heavy bill, which has bluish green
sheath over base of upper mandible; rest bill yellow or
flesh pink, legs blue-grey, eyes dark brown. Small
spur at 'wrist' used in fighting. Described as walking
like rail, flying like pigeon, behaving like domestic
hen; but can run, hop, take off and land from one foot.
Reluctant to fly or swim but seen hundreds of miles
from land. Very tame and inquisitive. Bowing
display; pairs probably for life. Omnivorous: expert
scavenger, robbing penguins of food by jumping on
chick's back and taking regurgitated krill, also robs
nests by cooperative action; eats carrion, faeces, seaweed (presumably for its animal life), seal afterbirths.
Starts building end November; nest of stones, sticks,
feathers, debris, in crevice, forming scattered colony
often close to penguin rookery; sometimes in petrel
burrows. 2 or 3 greyish or off-white eggs, marked dark
brown, incubated ♀ and ♂ c. 29 days. Young (often

only one survives) flies 7-8 weeks, tended by both
parents. **315**

CHIPPING SPARROW see under **Helmitheros
vermivorus**

Chiroxiphia linearis *Pipridae*
LONG-TAILED MANAKIN   ♂: 8 (tail 4) ins
Neotropical: S Mexico to Costa Rica, resident mangroves, woodland edge and secondary growth, sea
level to 4,500 ft. ♂: mainly black, back bright light
blue, crown red, central tail feathers elongated; legs
orange, bill black, eyes dark brown. ♀ almost uniformly dull green, but underparts slightly paler;
central tail feathers somewhat elongated. Feeding
habits as other manakins. Many notes known,
especially call *to-le-do*. Courtship most intense April-
May at start of rains: 2 ♂ perform together, 'bounc-
ing' with mewing call and cart-wheeling in turns on
low perch; in second form they neatly change places;
♀ may join in (Paul Slud). Breeds May, suspending cup
nest of leaves, fronds and moss 7 to 10 ft up in bush.
Clutch 2 eggs, incubation and fledging much as other
manakins, e.g. *Manacus manacus*. **587**

Chlamydera maculata *Ptilinorhynchidae*
SPOTTED BOWER BIRD   c. 11 ins
Australia: Western race, *C. m. guttata*, Pilbara district,
W. Australia, S to c. 30°S, E to Central Australia and
N to S Australia; *maculata*, Cloncurry Range, Queensland, E almost to coast, inland S to N Victoria.
Habitat: scrubby, relatively low rainfall areas; *guttata*
often associated with native fig *Ficus platypoda*.
Brownish, mottled with rufous and golden buff, small
erectile mantle or neck frill pink (conspicuous when
raised, glistens in direct sunlight), tail tipped orange-
brown; *guttata* darker and more conspicuously spotted.
Legs olive-green, bill black, eyes brown. Juveniles
have more heavily marked throat and breast, lack
crest. Territorial; small flocks outside breeding
season; flight straight with rapid wingbeats. Feeds on
fruit, also insects, especially when young. Calls:
squeals, clicking and odd sounds; accurate mimic.
♂ builds (April to August) simple double-walled
bower never far from water and roughly similar to
Satin Bower Bird, *Ptilinorhynchus violaceus*, used for
display to ♀ although spectators may also attend;
outer part of each wall thin twigs, inner grass stems
and long thin leaves (sometimes painted with mixture
of saliva and plant material), concealed beneath trees,
one end decorated with bleached bones and
shells (wide range of bright objects also used), other
end large stick platform, whole structure c. 10 to 20
ins high and c. 15 to 30 ins long. Displays start September and breeding c. October, varying in areas of less
regular rainfall; shallow twig nest scantily lined
leaves and thin twigs, in tree or bush within few 100
yds of bower; 2 grey to greenish eggs, sometimes with
darker markings; ♀ incubates. **986**

Chlidonias hybrida *Laridae*
WHISKERED TERN   c. 10 ins
Palaearctic, Ethiopian, Oriental, Australasian: S
Europe, Tunisia, SW Asia, Central Middle East
across to Turkestan; eastern half of Southern Africa
S of L. Victoria, India, E China, Australia and subspecies *C. h. albostriatus* South I., New Zealand. Some
birds move S in winter. Habitat: marshy lagoons and
swamp pools with plenty of aquatic vegetation; larger,
more open waters in winter. Grey with black cap and
conspicuous white streak running back from bill to
nape of neck, white under tail coverts and edge to
slightly forked grey tail. In winter forehead and
underparts white; immature similar but crown
brownish and mantle mottled. African race, *sclateri*,
generally much darker. Legs dark red, bill dark red
but blackish in winter, eyes red-brown. Often seen
skimming over water like swallow taking insects, also
feeds on small fish and other aquatic animals; awk-
ward walker. Usually perched on stone or post sticking
out of water. Call: two syllabled rasping sound. Breeds
late May onwards in Europe; loosely built heap of
weeds floating in shallow water among rushes or other
aquatic vegetation to which it may be attached; in
colonies in marshes or similar wet places. *Albostriatus*

makes scrape in sand amongst large stones, October
onwards. Usually 3 bluish green eggs spotted with
blackish brown and ashy grey, chiefly incubated ♀
c. 21 days, both parents tend young. **319**

Chlidonias niger *Laridae*
BLACK TERN   c. 9½ ins
Holarctic: nominate race breeds from SW Europe
(local Iberia) into W Asia mainly between 40° and
60°N to about 95°E; winters lakes, rivers and coasts
of tropical Africa S to Angola and Tanzania; Nearctic race, *C. n. surinamensis*, breeds from E Alaska S
over most of Canada to Pennsylvania across to central
California, winters S America down to Chile. Habitat:
inland marshes, ponds and lakes when breeding,
visiting adjacent grasslands; winters also on coastal
and inshore waters. Head and body black, short
notched tail, broad wings slate grey above and paler
below. Legs dark red-brown, bill black, eyes dark
brown. Winter: forehead and forecrown white, rest of
crown and nape sooty brown, throat, sides of neck and
underparts white, rest of upperparts pale slate grey,
primaries and secondaries greyer. Immature: forehead white, crown and nape sooty brown, mantle and
back mottled blackish brown, scapulars greyer, wings
mostly dark grey; underparts white with dark brown
patch on sides of upper breast; legs dark yellowish, bill
blackish. Feeds inland mainly on insects on wing or
ground, sometimes aquatic animals from water by
shallow diving; otherwise picks up small fish and
invertebrates from surface of water while hovering
briefly. Call: monosyllabic *kik, kik*. Breeds May onwards in loose colonies on marshes or shallow lakes;
3 olive or buff eggs heavily marked with dark brown
and ash, in hollow in floating mass of vegetation, old
nests of other species or cup of stems lined with finer
matter. Both parents incubate c. 21 days and tend
young, who fly c. 4 weeks. **320**

Chloephaga hybrida *Anatidae*
KELP GOOSE   30 ins
Neotropical: Lesser Kelp Goose, *C. h. hybrida*, coast of
S Chile to Tierra del Fuego; Greater Kelp Goose,
malvinarum, Falkland Is. Habitat: rocky oceanic
shores; often seen hopping from rock to rock feeding
on sea-weeds, usually in pairs and fairly tame. ♂:
white plumage; bill black, legs lemon-yellow, eyes
dark brown. ♀: crown light brown with pale ring
round eyes, rest of head and neck blackish brown with
fine white lines, mantle and wings dark brown with
white coverts and secondaries; metallic green speculum; back, tail, belly white; breast and flanks black
barred with white (broader barring in *malvinarum*).
Bill yellowish flesh colour, legs deep yellow, eyes dark
brown. Nests November on ground among cover
lined down and feathers; lays usually 5 or 6 creamy
white eggs, incubated c. 30 days. Young tended
mainly by ♀. **110**

Chloephaga picta *Anatidae*
MAGELLAN or UPLAND GOOSE   28 ins
Neotropical: Lesser Magellan Goose, *C. p. picta*, Chile
and S Argentina including Tierra del Fuego, some
movement N in winter; Greater Magellan Goose,
leucoptera, Falkland Is. Habitat: low ground, on hills
and plateaux but seldom near sea, moving in relation
to food supplies. ♂: white with black, or black and
white, tail; black bars on mantle and flanks; wings
white and dark grey with metallic green speculum. ♀:
smaller, deep reddish cinnamon barred with black on
mantle and lower parts. Legs, ♀ yellow, ♂ black; bill
black. 2 phases in ♂: barred form predominating in
S, white breasted form elsewhere. *Leucoptera* larger and
♂ always white breasted. Tame unless persecuted;
gregarious, feeds on grass. Call: ♂ high soft whistle,
♀ deep harsh cackle. Nests August to November in
territories vigorously held by pair; 5 to 7 creamy,
glossy eggs in nest on ground down lined amongst
bushes and grass. ♀ incubates 30-32 days guarded by
♂, they quickly lead young to water and both tend
them. **111**

Chloris chloris see **Carduelis chloris**

Chloroceryle aenea *Alcedinidae*

AMERICAN PYGMY KINGFISHER $5\frac{1}{2}$ ins
Neotropical: Nicaragua and Panama southwards: E of Andes to S Brazil, E Peru, N Bolivia; W of Andes to W Ecuador; Trinidad; resident by shaded forest pools, small streams and ditches, mangrove swamps. Upperparts dark green, wings and tail spotted buffish white; throat buff, deepening to russet on white-centred belly; ♀ has green and white band on breast. Closely resembles larger (9 ins) Green and Rufous Kingfisher, *C. indica*, which lacks white on belly. Has loud rattling call. Feeds on small fish and flying insects taken from perch. Breeds June to September Trinidad. Excavates nest hole 12 to 15 ins in sandy bank, or artificial earth-face often distant from water; clutch usually 4 glossy white eggs.

Chloroceryle indica see under **C. aenea**

Chlorochrysa phoenicotis *Emberizidae: Thraupinae*
GLISTENING GREEN TANAGER $5\frac{1}{4}$ ins
Neotropical: headwaters of Rio San Juan, Pacific Colombia, S to NW Ecuador; creepers on forest trees, *c.* 2,500 to *c.* 5,000 ft. Glossy emerald green all over, except for glossy grey wing coverts, small patch grey 'enamel-like' feathers and orange tuft on side of head. Diet: fruit, insects. **875**

Chlorodrepanis virens see **Loxops virens**

Chloropsis aurifrons or Aegithina aurifrons
Irenidae
GOLDEN-FRONTED LEAFBIRD $7\frac{1}{2}$ ins
Oriental: Indian subcontinent (from Gulf of Cambay S and E round coastal ranges of peninsula; Himalayan foothills from Garhwal E to Nepal, Assam); Ceylon to Indochina, Sumatra. Resident with local movements in open broadleaved and deciduous forest and secondary scrub to *c.* 5,500 ft. Generally leaf-green, shoulder patches blue; forehead orange, throat dark blue, broadly bordered black from bill and eye; legs, bill grey, eyes brown. Pairs or small parties blend with foliage, which they hunt acrobatically for insects, spiders, even swinging round twig as on trapeze. Pollinate blossoms in search for nectar; also take berries. Aggressive to other species. Strong, rapid flight. Call (race *aurifrons*) drongo-like *swich-chich-chich-wee* ending in whistle; *frontalis* has 'voluble rattle' (Salim Ali); also repeated *tzik* and *chup-chaw*: accomplished mimic. Breeds January to August in parts of range, building shallow cup of pine twigs, grass, leaves, moss, reinforced cobweb, partially suspended near tip of thin lateral branch; also between upright twigs; 25 to 40 ft up. 2 or 3 pale or buffish cream eggs, lightly freckled pale red, incubated probably by ♀. **643**

Chlorostilbon maugaeus *Trochilidae*
PUERTO RICAN EMERALD HUMMINGBIRD $3\frac{1}{2}$-4 ins
Neotropical: confined to Puerto Rico; resident from coastal mangrove swamps to forest-covered hilltops, favouring open areas; also coffee plantations. ♂: iridescent green with blackish wingtips and forked tail; legs, bill, eyes dark except pinkish base to lower mandible. ♀: upperparts green; tail feathers violet towards ends, outer ones tipped greyish white; cheeks dusky; underparts whitish with some green on flanks. See *Aglaiocercus kingi* for general hummingbird habits and behaviour. **469**

Chordeiles minor *Caprimulgidae*
COMMON NIGHTHAWK 9 ins
Nearctic and Neotropical: breeds throughout N America from subarctic zone S to W Indies, possibly NW Colombia; winters S to Argentina (Cordoba, Buenos Aires) migrating often in parties by day. Habitat: open pine woods to rocky hillsides, right into city centres; savannah in winter. Rather grey-brown nightjar type plumage with faint white 'eyebrow', white throat, rectangular white patches in centre of blackish flight feathers on pointed wings; black sub-terminal white patches on dark, slightly forked tail; underparts strikingly barred grey-brown and white; no bristles at gape, eyes dark brown. Perches length-wise on branches, diagonally on wires. Active often

long before dusk, with erratic swooping flight above trees and house tops: takes insects on wing, small gnats to large moths. Call: *peent*. Musical hum from feathers, when ♂, after diving with closed wings, zooms upward again. Breeds from May, laying 2 greyish-white eggs, marbled, spotted darker grey, on open ground or on gravelled flat roofs of houses. Sitting ♀ may hiss at intruder with gape wide open or feign injury. Incubation 2 weeks; young, fed by both parents, fly 18 days. **462**

Choriotis kori or Ardeotis kori *Otididae*
KORI BUSTARD Up to 55 ins (♀ smaller)
Ethiopian: E and Southern Africa: resident in open thorn bush and short grass plains. Upperparts buff with close black vermiculations; flight feathers black, barred and mottled white but inner secondaries buff; upper wing coverts white with black spots near points, showing as line on closed wing; tail black and white, barred buff; forehead and crown mottled black and white, tapering to crest; white 'eyebrow'; chin, throat and loose neck feathers whitish with thin black bands; underparts white. Legs yellow, bill horn, eyes yellow. Usually single or in pairs; moves fast on ground and reluctant to fly, taking off with kick, then extends neck but folds legs. Sways head and neck in walk, with tail drooping; but in display ♂ puffs himself out to appear almost white all over, like Great Bustard, *Otis tarda*. Mating call, deep repeated *woum*; usual call nasal *kaa kaa ka*. Eats small vertebrates, insects, especially locusts; seeds and acacia gum, hence Afrikaans *Gom Paauw*. Breeding season varies throughout range according to rains; often nests sociably. Lays 2 pale greenish-brown eggs, streaked darker brown, on bare ground; incubated by ♀ *c.* 4 weeks. Young, fed at first by ♀, probably fledge *c.* 5 weeks. **242**

CHOUGH see under **Pyrrhocorax graculus**

CHOUGH,
ALPINE see **Pyrrhocorax graculus**
WHITE-WINGED see **Corcorax melanorhamphus**

Chrysococcyx basalis see under **Malurus leucopterus**

Chrysococcyx caprius *Cuculidae*
DIDRIC CUCKOO 20 ins
Ethiopian: whole region, resident open thorn bush, also plantations of introduced trees and built up areas in S Africa. ♂: upperparts iridescent bottle green, glossed bronze, gold and violet; white stripe behind eye and white on crown; white spots on wing coverts, secondaries and greenish black tail; underparts white, flanks barred bronze green, underwing barred black and white; legs blue-black, bill blackish, eyes and orbits red. ♀ duller above than ♂ and barring extends from flanks to breast and neck. Juvenile barred green all over, bill coral red. Frequently perches lengthwise on branch. ♂♂ noisy and aggressive in small territories (sometimes single tree with weaver colony); chase ♀♀ in display with spread tail and quivering wings. ♂'s plaintive whistling *dee dee deederik*, origin of name; ♀ replies *deea deea deea*; often calls in open and in flight. Diet mainly insects, clinging woodpecker-like to tree to search for caterpillars. Lays variable, elongated blue, greenish or pinkish white egg, plain or spotted brown and grey, in nests of variety of passerines, especially weavers, Cape Sparrow, *Passer melanurus*; Red Bishop, *Euplectes orix*, and Pied Wagtail, *Motacilla aguimp*. May feed juveniles after they leave foster nest, pursued by insistent *cheep cheep* calls. **421**

Chrysococcyx
klass see under **Cinnyris venustus**
osculans see under **Chthonicola sagittata**

Chrysocolaptes lucidus stricklandi *Picidae*
CEYLON CRIMSON-BACKED WOODPECKER $11\frac{1}{2}$ ins
Endemic subspecies of Golden-backed Woodpecker, widespread in Oriental region. Upperparts from crown and crest to rump bright crimson, wings duller; upper tail coverts, tail black; facial pattern black and white stripes; underparts buff-white, 'scaled' black, intense on neck and breast. ♀ has crown and crest

black, speckled white. Legs dull greenish brown, bill horn brown or grey to whitish tip, eyes yellowish, outer ring red. Pairs, family parties move from tree to tree in bounding flight; seldom feeds on ground, occasionally hawks winged insects; also takes larvae, nectar from flowers. Discordant trilling laugh, chiefly in flight. Drums on wood in breeding season, chiefly December-January. Bores vertically oval hole, 6 to 15 ft up in variety of trees, same chamber used several years with fresh entrance holes. 1 to 3 white eggs incubated ♀ 14-15 days; young fly 24-26 days.

Chrysolophus amherstiae *Phasianidae*
LADY AMHERST'S PHEASANT ♀: 26-27 (tail 12-15) ins
♂: 52-68 (tail 34-46) ins
E Palaearctic and Oriental: SE Tibet, SW China, NE Burma; introduced Britain; resident, unless driven down by snow, in thickets, especially bamboo, in rocky mountainous country; also in woods and scrub. ♂: mantle and scapulars glossy blue-green; lower back yellow, rump orange; long central tail feathers white barred black; wings metallic blue; neck ruff white with blue-black margins; head dark green with crimson crest; underparts white, to black under tail coverts; legs, bill bluish grey, eyes yellow, facial skin white. ♀: like Golden Pheasant *C. pictus* but more rufous and strongly marked glossy black; tail feathers rounded; legs, bill blue-grey, eyes brown to yellow. Flocks of 20-30 through winter, fly more readily than Golden Pheasant. Display, voice, food similar to Golden Pheasant, also nesting habits. 6 to 8 buff to cream eggs incubated by ♀, who hardly ever leaves nest, 23 days. **192**

Chrysolophus pictus *Phasianidae*
GOLDEN PHEASANT ♀: 25-27 (tail 14-15) ins
♂: 40-44 (tail 32) ins
E Palaearctic: Central China; introduced Britain. Resident on rocky hills covered with bamboo and other scrub. ♂: upper back dark green, feathers edged black; lower back and rump, 'silky', crown and crest golden yellow; short rounded wings with dark brown primaries, chestnut and black secondaries, deep blue tertiaries; long central curved tail feathers black, spotted cinnamon; tips of tail coverts scarlet; ruff light orange barred black, underparts scarlet; legs (with short spurs), bill horn yellow, eyes and facial skin light yellow. ♀: mixture of browns with glossy black streaks, spots and bars; legs, bill horn yellow, eyes brown, facial skin red, grey-green in Amherst Pheasant. Solitary or in pairs, reluctant to fly. Courtship: ♂ raises crest and spreads ruff, trails one wing towards ♀, tail vertically open; then jumps from side to side of ♀, whistling and clicking. Food: seeds, leaves, tender shoots, e.g. bamboos; insects. Breeds probably May-June in wild, nesting on ground, clutch *c.* 8 pale buff to cream eggs, incubated by ♀ 22 days; ♂ may help with brood as probably monogamous. **193**

Chthonicola sagittata *Muscicapidae: Malurinae*
SPECKLED WARBLER *c.* 5 ins
Australia: SE Queensland, E New South Wales to edge of plains, Victoria and perhaps E South Australia; sedentary. Habitat: open forest with some cover, favours stony hillsides with sparse timber and scrub. Upperparts dull olive brown broadly streaked dark brown; primaries brown with whitish edges; dark tail tipped with white; 'eyebrow' white; underparts white washed olive yellow and strongly streaked black. Legs dark greyish brown, bill dark brownish, eyes dark brown. Usually in pairs or small groups; feeds on insects, sometimes seeds on ground or in low shrubs, often in association with thornbills and other small ground birds; takes to low trees when disturbed or for display. Call: rapid, harsh, rattling sound; quiet song of few ascending notes in spring; also mimics. Breeds August onwards; on ground in small depression below shrub, in, or under, tussock; domed nest with side entrance, of grass and bark lined lightly softer plant material, fur and/or feathers; 3, sometimes 4, glossy reddish brown eggs; parasitised by Black-eared Cuckoo, *Chrysococcyx osculans*. **758**

CHUKOR see under **Alectoris rufa**

leave nest after 2 days and accompany ♂; mature in second year. **4**

Dromas ardeola *Dromadidae*
CRAB PLOVER *c.* 15 ins
Ethiopian, marginally Palaearctic, Oriental: coasts of Indian Ocean, breeding Port Sudan to Somalia, N coast Kenya, Persian Gulf; visitor S Africa, Madagascar; Pakistan, India, Ceylon, Andamans, Nicobars, open sandy shores and reefs. White except for black mantle and primaries of long, pointed wings; long legs blue grey, stout bill black, eyes dark brown. Immature greyish above. Noisy and gregarious, sometimes forming large blocks. Upright stance often with head sunk between wings; flies with legs, neck stretched. Call: *tchuk tchuk* by nest holes and at night. Diet: crustaceans, especially crabs, molluscs, worms. Breeds from late April Persian Gulf, July to September Kenya, in large colonies, excavating tunnels in sand up to ½ mile from sea; single proportionally very large white egg laid in chamber up to 5 ft from entrance. Incubation period at least 4 weeks; parents bring crabs to young one. **305**

DRONGO,
    BLACK see under **Dicrurus annectans**
    CROW-BILLED see **Dicrurus annectans**
    FORK-TAILED see **Dicrurus adsimilis**
    GREATER RACKET-TAILED see under **Dicrurus annectans**
    MOUNTAIN see **Chaetorhynchus papuensis**
    SPANGLED see under **Sphecotheres flaviventris**

Dryomodus brunneipygia *Muscicapidae*: *Muscicapinae*
SOUTHERN SCRUB ROBIN *c.* 8 ins
Australasian: interior S and SW continental Australia; resident lowland scrub; mallee, mulga, pine. Upperparts uniform brown with 2 narrow white bars on closed wing; tail long, graduated at end; underparts ashy, becoming buff on belly; pale 'eyebrow'; legs, bill, eyes dark, white orbits. Usually in pairs and rather tame, answering imitations of its call: *chip-pip-ee.* Feeds on insects from ground and leaf litter. Breeds September to January in different parts of range; very small nest loosely built of bark, twigs, lined grass, rootlets; in slight scrape on ground among scrub, single greenish-grey egg, marked brown often in zone at big end. Building and incubation probably by ♀, as Northern Scrub Robin, *D. superciliaris* (E Northern Territory, N Queensland), which is more rufous on upperparts, and has black and pale blue facial markings. **777**

Dryomodus superciliaris see under **D. brunneipygia**

Dryoscopus cubla *Laniidae*
BLACK PUFF-BACKED SHRIKE 6¼ ins
Ethiopian: Central Kenya, Tanzania, Malawi, SE Zaire, Angola, S Africa to Cape; resident open woodland and bush, riverine forest, sometimes near habitations. ♂: upperparts from crown to mantle, wings and short tail glossy blue-black, tail tipped white; soft downy rump greyish white; inner secondaries, edges wing coverts white; underparts white tinged grey. ♀: white streak from bill halfway over eye; lower back and rump grey. Legs grey, bill black, eyes yellowish orange. Immature has white areas washed buff. Sociable, often joining other species in trees, where hunts larvae; also takes insects on wing; eggs and young birds; occasionally buds. Many calls: hissing *swarr; chak* of alarm followed by *skurr;* whistling *twhew twhew twhew* during prolonged breeding season. Puffed out feathers of back and rump almost surround excited ♂; also buzzes and crackles wings in display, drops vertically with series of whistles and clacks. Nest cup of bark fibres, rootlets, bound cobwebs, well hidden in fork of tree, usually at a height. 2 or 3 white or creamy eggs, marked brown and lilac in zone at big end. **645**

DUCK,
    ANDEAN CRESTED see **Lophonetta specularoides alticola**
    BLUE-BILLED see **Oxyura australis**
    COMB see **Sarkidiornis melanotos**
    FLIGHTLESS STEAMER see **Tachyeres pteneres**
    FLYING STEAMER see under **Tachyeres pteneres**
    LONG-TAILED see **Clangula hyemalis**
    MUSCOVY see **Cairina moschata**
    MUSK see **Biziura lobata**
    TUFTED see **Aythya fuligula**
    WHITE-FACED TREE see **Dendrocygna viduata**

Dulus dominicus *Dulidae*
PALM CHAT *c.* 7 ins
Neotropical: confined to Hispaniola and Gonave I, W Indies; resident open country with trees, especially royal palms, from low altitudes up to 4,500 ft. Upperparts greyish white to olive brown; short wings greenish; rump dark green; head darker than back; underparts white, striped dark brown; legs blackish, heavy bill horn brown, eyes brown. Juvenile has throat dark brown, rump buffish. Greyer race on Gonave. Usually in flocks, tree-living, active and uttering variety of harsh and musical calls. Resting posture upright, tail pointed down; no 'individual distance' when perched. Diet: berries and blossoms. Breeds March to June, several birds working at once on large communal nest, used outside breeding season and made of dead twigs up to 30 ins long, carried crosswise in bill; usually high in leaf or fruiting fronds of palm; pine tree nests in highlands smaller, housing one or two pairs. Separate entrances lead to nest chambers at end of tunnels; also passages among loose twigs at top of nest. 2 to 4 slightly glossy white eggs, spotted dark grey, often in zone.

Dumetella carolinensis *Mimidae*
CATBIRD 9 ins
Nearctic: breeds Southern Canada S to Central Florida, SE Texas, NE New Mexico, N Utah, NE Oregon, W Washington; winters S to Cuba, Panama. Habitat dense scrub and vine tangles near streams, ponds, swamps, extending into man-modified shrubberies, hedgerows, gardens. Uniformly grey with black crown, blackish central tail feathers, chestnut-brown under tail coverts. Secretive, keeping to cover as a wandering voice with 'catlike, mewing scold' (R. H. Pough); other calls soft cluck, snapping note. Courtship includes song, chasing of ♀ by ♂ and display of under tail coverts. Song short phrase 5 or 6 notes interspersed with mewing and mimicry; sings in moonlight; autumn subsong. Diet: small fruits in season, otherwise mainly insects (some from water), on which young reared. Breeds May to June New England, building rather untidy nest of local plant materials, lined finer fibres. 4 to 6 glossy blue-green eggs incubated mainly by ♀ 12-13 days. Both parents feed young, who fly *c.* 2 weeks. 2 broods. **669**

DUNLIN see **Calidris alpina**

DUNNOCK see **Prunella modularis**

DUSKY
    FLYCATCHER see **Alseonax adustus**
    LORIKEET see **Pseudeos fuscata**
    MOORHEN see under **Gallinula chloropus**
    NIGHTJAR see **Caprimulgus pectoralis**
    WOOD SWALLOW see under **Artamus superciliosus**

EAGLE,
    AFRICAN FISH see **Haliaeetus vocifer**
    BOOTED see **Hieraetus pennatus**
    CROWNED see **Stephanoaetus coronatus**
    GOLDEN see **Aquila chrysaetos**
    HARPY see **Harpia harpyja**
    LONG-CRESTED HAWK see **Lophoaetus occipitalis**
    MARTIAL see **Polemaetus bellicosus**
    MEXICAN see **Polyborus plancus**
    MONKEY-EATING see **Pithecophaga jefferyi**
    SNAKE see **Circaetus cinereus**
    TAWNY see **Aquila rapax**
    VERREAUX'S see **Aquila verreauxi**
    WAHLBERG'S see **Aquila wahlbergi**
    WEDGE-TAILED see **Aquila audax**
    WHISTLING see **Haliastur sphenorus**

WHITE-BREASTED SEA see **Haliaeetus leucogaster**
WHITE-TAILED see **Haliaeetus albicilla**

EAGLE OWL see **Bubo bubo**

EAGLE OWL,
    SPOTTED see **Bubo africanus**
    VERREAUX'S GIANT see **Bubo lacteus**

EARED DOVE see **Zenaida auriculata**

EASTERN
    BLUEBIRD see **Sialia sialis**
    KINGBIRD see **Tyrannus tyrannus**
    MEADOWLARK see **Sturnella magna**
    ROCK NUTHATCH see under **Sitta neumayer**
    ROSELLA see under **Platycercus eximius** and **Psephotus haematodus**
    SPINEBILL see **Acanthorhynchus tenuirostris**
    WHIPBIRD see **Psophodes olivaceus**
    WOOD PEWEE see **Contopus virens**

ECLECTUS PARROT see **Lorius roratus**

EGRET,
    CATTLE see **Bubulcus ibis**
    COMMON see **Egretta alba**
    SNOWY see **Egretta thula**

Egretta alba or Casmerodius albus *Ardeidae*
GREAT WHITE HERON or
COMMON EGRET 35 (body 15) ins
S Palaearctic, Ethiopian, Oriental, Australasian, Nearctic, Neotropical, but very local in this huge area; widespread dispersal after breeding. Pure white, long neck plumes in spring; legs black and yellow, bill black to black and yellow, eyes yellow. Usually gregarious, up to 200 together after breeding, in swamps, shallow lakes, riversides, even bare sea shores; but sometimes solitary. Perches and roosts in trees or on ground. Diet varies seasonally: fish, amphibians, aquatic insects, molluscs, worms; small birds and mammals in dry season. Very silent; low croaking at nest, where young chatter. Breeding season variable; from April onwards in Palaearctic; usually rather diffuse colonies in dense reedbeds, nest a pile of reeds up to 3 ft high; eggs 3 to 5, pale blue, incubated 25-26 days by ♀ and ♂, who tend young during *c.* 6 weeks fledging period. **58**

Egretta sacra *Ardeidae*
REEF HERON 26 ins
Oriental and Australasian: coasts and islands of India, SE Asia, Japan, Polynesia, Australia, Tasmania, New Zealand. Slaty grey, darker above, paler below and tinged brown; narrow white streak on chin and throat; long plumes on lower neck and back during courtship. Legs yellowish-green with lemon-yellow soles, bill brown, eyes yellow, surrounding skin greenish yellow. White plumage phase (not New Zealand) and piebald intermediate occur. Crouching gait with heavy bill and rather short legs; flies usually low over water. Generally hunts alone for tidal fish, molluscs, crustaceans, other marine animals, but parties form at roosts. Guttural croak and bill-snapping during breeding season; alarm note *crraw.* Breeds almost throughout year over whole range, sometimes colonially, in scrub jungle, palms, mangroves, vegetation on cliff, caves, crevices, human artefacts; nest of sticks and leaves holds 2 to 3 pale greenish blue eggs, incubated 25-28 days by ♀ and ♂, who tend young for *c.* 5½ week fledging period. **59**

Egretta thula or Leucophoyx thula *Ardeidae*
SNOWY EGRET 22-26 ins
Nearctic and Neotropical: southern USA to Chile and Argentina, in fresh and salt marshes, ponds and ricefields; northern birds move S after breeding. Snow white, with plumes in breeding season; legs black but feet of adults bright yellow, thin bill black with yellow skin at base, eyes pale yellow. Slimmer and more active than other American white herons; flight more graceful than Cattle Egret's, *Bubulcus ibis*; courtship social. Shuffles in water when feeding, to stir up water ani-

mals. Breeding season varies with latitude; colonies usually in mangroves or other swamp trees; nests of sticks. Both sexes incubate 2 to 5 greenish-blue eggs and tend the brood. **60**

EGYPTIAN
GOOSE see **Alopochen aegyptiaca**
PLOVER see **Pluvianus aegyptius**
VULTURE see **Neophron percnopterus**

EIDER, STELLER'S see **Polysticta stelleri**

Elanus caeruleus *Accipitridae*
BLACK-SHOULDERED KITE 12 ins
Cosmopolitan: Palaearctic (SE Iberia, N Africa, Egypt); Oriental (Indian subcontinent, Ceylon, SE Asia); all Ethiopian (not Madagascar); Australasian (regarded by some as separate species *E. notatus:* Celebes, continental Australia, very local New Guinea); Nearctic and Neotropical (regarded by some as separate species *E. leucurus:* SW California, local Central and S America); resident and irregularly migratory or nomadic, on grass savannah, steppes, meadows and cultivated land with trees, often dry or arid, up to 9,000 ft. Upperparts grey, with black shoulders and primaries; underparts white; breast, flanks washed grey; tail short and square; legs, cere yellow, bill black, eyes crimson. Chooses exposed perches, sitting with drooping wingtips and tail moving up and down. Roosts communally up to 120 birds. Flies slowly, hovers like kestrel, often checking several times before dropping on prey, mainly small rodents, reptiles, large insects (sometimes taken in air); follows grass fires and locust swarms; takes offal off Arabian coast. No spectacular displays: pair soars and chases; also short gently fluttering flights. Breeding season varies with range: March to May Europe, September to October S Africa. Pairs build small twig nest, 5 to 60 ft often in isolated tree, which may be used several seasons; rocky ledges in Arabia. 3 to 5 cream or pale buff eggs, marked dark brown, purple and grey, incubated mainly by ♀, fed by ♂, 25-28 days. First ♂, then ♀ takes major share feeding young, who fly 30-40 days. Possibly 2 broods Malaysia, E Africa. **145**

ELEGANT
GRASS PARAKEET see **Neophema elegans**
TERN see **Thalasseus elegans**

ELF OWL see **Micrathene whitneyi**

ELWES'S EARED PHEASANT see **Crossoptilon crossoptilon**

Emberiza
bruniceps see under **E. melanocephalus**
buchanani see under **E. hortulana**

Emberiza calandra *Emberizidae: Emberizinae*
CORN BUNTING *c.* 7 ins
Palaearctic: more or less confined to Europe (including NW Africa) and Near East SW of line from Gulf of Riga to Caspian, with extension through Iran to S of Lake Balkash. Mainly sedentary in open, arid, flat or hilly areas, especially extensive open cornfields, dry steppes with bushes, stony steppes and slopes, even low maquis and coastal scrub. Almost uniformly dull brown streaked black, with dark 'necklace' and paler underparts, belly not streaked; much heavier looking than relatives and lacks white outer feathers on rather short tail. Hops on ground. Short flights often with legs dangling, undulating over longer distances. Perches dumpily isolated bushes, posts, poles, wires. Flocks in autumn, sometimes with other seed-eaters. In display succession of short upward flights by ♂ above ♀, then drops to ground where waves wings, spreads tail. Flight note in flock repeated abrupt *quit;* breeding season call hard *chip,* grating *zeep* when scolding. Song: rapid ticking notes ending in jangle 'like bunch of little keys'. Food mainly vegetable: variety of seeds, wild fruits, grain; also insects, spiders, other invertebrates. Breeds second half May to September; strongly territorial but several pairs close together and some males polygamous. ♀ builds nest of grass, deep cup lined rootlets, bents, hair; usually well hidden in ground cover, crops, rough grass, tangle, but sometimes in bushes up to 6 ft. 3 to 5 off-white to reddish-brown eggs, boldly marked and scrawled blackish-brown, incubated ♀ 12-13 days; ♀, often accompanied ♂, feeds young, who fly 11-14 days. Sometimes 2 broods. **853**

Emberiza cia *Emberizidae: Emberizinae*
ROCK BUNTING *c.* 6¼ ins
Palaearctic: from Iberia, NW Africa across Eurasia to Yellow Sea, roughly between 30° and 50°N; only N of 50° in Siberia or S of 30° in Iran, S China. Sedentary and migratory: vertical movements in mountains; northern birds winter in S of breeding range, e.g. in large flocks with Cirl Buntings, *E. cirlus,* N Africa. Breeds high, open coniferous zone, also subalpine scrub among rocky meadows and scree; villages, vineyards, gardens; up to 6,000 ft Europe; tropical lowlands to 17,500 ft W China. ♂: upperparts brown streaked black, forewing greyish with narrow white bar, rump chestnut, white outer tail feathers; head, breast grey with black stripes above, through, below eye; underparts reddish buff. ♀ duller, head markings less distinct. Legs straw brown, bill dark grey, eyes dark brown. Juvenile like Yellowhammer, *E. citrinella,* but underparts reddish buff. Behaves much as Yellowhammer; terrestrial, perching mainly rocks, bushes. Sharp *zit* call resembles *E. cirlus; bubbling tucc* becomes twitter in flight; song shrill *zi zi zi zirr.* Diet: seeds of grain and grasses; also insects, especially grasshoppers. Breeds from early April lowlands to May and June; nest of grass, bark strips, moss, lined fine rootlets, hair; among stones, on steep banks, up to 2 ft in heath or stone wall. 4 to 6 greenish white to violet brown eggs, with zone of scrawls round big end, dark brown over ashy spots. Incubation mainly ♀; period and fledging much as *E. citrinella.* **854**

Emberiza cirlus see under **E. cia**

Emberiza citrinella *Emberizidae: Emberizinae*
YELLOWHAMMER or YELLOW BUNTING *c.* 6½ ins
Palaearctic: combined range of western Yellowhammer and eastern Pine Bunting, *E. leucocephala,* crosses Eurasia between 50° and 60°N, from Britain and Ireland to Sea of Okhotsk, extending to N in Scandinavia, USSR, to S in S Europe, Caucasus with isolated group near headwaters Hoangho. Introduced New Zealand. Yellowhammer mainly sedentary, except northernmost populations; E Asian Pine Buntings winter temperate Asia: Iran to China. Habitat (both species) edges, clearings broadleaved and coniferous forests N to subarctic birch zone and up to subalpine meadows with stunted trees; Yellowhammer also in cultivated land, heaths, commons, but seldom gardens. ♂: upperparts, including wings, chestnut streaked black, rump rufous, outer tail feathers white; head, underparts yellow, varyingly streaked greenish brown, with broad band across breast. Yellow reduced in winter and in ♀, though some as bright as some ♂♂. Legs pale flesh brown, bill: upper dark bluish horn, lower paler; eyes dark brown. Juveniles darker. Spends much time on ground where hops, but perches trees, posts, wires, often flicking tail. Flight finch-like with wing closing, more or less undulating. Flocks autumn with other seed-eaters, roosts socially. Calls: *tink,* single *twick* in flight, *twit-up* in winter flocks; song rendered *little bit of bread and no cheese,* with varying emphasis. ♂ chases ♀ in courtship, also postures before her. Food chiefly vegetable: corn, seeds, fruits, leaves, grass; smaller insects, other invertebrates, including worms. Breeds end March to September; ♂ and ♀ build substantial nest of straw, grass, stalks, lined fine grass, hair, often with 'doorstep' in front; in bank or low in small bush, brambles, other tangle, from ground level to 6 ft in hedge or bush. 3 to 5 whitish, purple white or light red brown eggs, variously scrawled and spotted dark brown or black, incubated ♀ 12-14 days; ♀ and ♂ (from throat at first) feed young, who fly 12-13 days. 2, sometimes 3 brood. **855**

Emberiza flaviventris *Emberizidae: Emberizinae*
GOLDEN-BREASTED BUNTING 6 ins
Ethiopian: Nigeria to Ethiopia, S to S Africa; resident open savannah woodland, stony hillsides with scattered bushes, short grass, gardens. ♂: back rufous grey to blackish, wings with white tipped coverts forming 2 bars, rump grey; white outer feathers to blackish tail; crown, cheeks black with white stripe centre crown and either side eye; chin white, underparts shades of yellow; flanks, under tail coverts pale grey; legs pale brown, bill mainly horn, eyes brown. ♀ similar but duller, with dark streaked crown, greyish breast. Juvenile buffish on head, underparts pale yellow. Often perched on tree, but feeds mainly bare ground, crouching when not walking. Normal call single plaintive *droll-peer,* mate answering soft *sitee; chip* in flight; contact between pair quiet *tsip tsip tsip;* simple varied song: *chwee chi it twee.* Pairs or small parties; takes seeds, insects, mainly from ground. Breeding variable within range; nest frail cup of twigs, grass, fibres, often quite open, a few ft from ground in fork of shrub. 2 or 3 greyish white, greenish or bluish eggs, zoned black and sepia spots, scrawls, incubation and fledging much as *E. citrinella.* Probably 3 or 4 broods Kenya. **856**

Emberiza hortulana *Emberizidae: Emberizinae*
ORTOLAN *c.* 6¼ ins
Palaearctic: most of Europe except NW and N; Asia Minor to Iran and into W Asia roughly between 45° and 55°N as far as Lake Kos Gol; replaced in E by closely related Grey-necked Bunting, *E. buchanani.* Winters W Africa to Somalia, Arabia. Breeds arid country with scattered trees; corn and other arable fields; meadows, cultivated and natural steppes; riparian meadows Siberia; open maquis, mountain slopes up to 6,500 ft Alps, above tree line Greece; winters steppes, savannahs. ♂: upperparts brown streaked black, some white on tail; head, breast greyish olive, narrow yellowish 'spectacles', underparts pinkish buff. ♀ duller, breast streaked; legs, bill brownish red, eyes brown. Rather unobtrusive but habits like other *Emberiza* species; flocks in autumn, often joining Tree Pipits, *Anthus trivialis.* Calls include shrill *tsee-ip,* short *tsip,* piping *tseu* when breeding. Song more musical than Yellowhammer, delivered from elevated perch, sometimes at night. Food seeds and grain; insects (Orthoptera, beetles, moth larvae), snails, young locusts on migration. Breeds from early May Spain, early June Finland; nest of grass, roots, lined fine rootlets, hair; in crop fields, ground cover of *Artemisia,* other tall plants. 4 to 6 bluish white to pinkish or reddish grey eggs, spotted and streaked blackish brown, incubated mainly ♀ 11-14 days; fledging period *c.* 12 days. 2 broods Central Europe. **857**

Emberiza leucocephala *Emberizidae: Emberizinae*
PINE BUNTING *c.* 6½ ins
E Palaearctic: see Yellowhammer, *E. citrinella,* for range, habitats; often considered conspecific. ♂: upperparts much as Yellowhammer; crown white, bordered black; white cheek surrounded by chestnut mask, throat; underparts white, streaked brown breast, flanks; head pattern obscured in winter. ♀ much as Yellowhammer, white replacing yellow. Habits also as Yellowhammer; flocks in autumn; often seen roads, paths Mongolia. Call as Yellowhammer; song like Chaffinch, *Fringilla coelebs.* Food, seeds of grasses, mountain plants; young fed on insects. Breeds end May to July; nest like Yellowhammer, on ground among grass, small bushes, at edge of thicket. 4 to 6 eggs much as Yellowhammer's, incubation and fledging as Yellowhammer. 2 broods. **858**

Emberiza melanocephalus *Emberizidae: Emberizinae*
BLACK-HEADED BUNTING *c.* 6½ ins
Palaearctic: combined range with eastern Red-headed Bunting *E. bruniceps,* now regarded as conspecific: NE Mediterranean area, Georgia, Caucasus, Iran to mountains of Turkestan, all between 30° and 50°N. Both forms winter mainly in plains of NW Indian subcontinent. Breeds sunny lowlands or mountain slopes with dry scrub; bushy steppes, cultivated land with vineyards, orchards, olive groves; riverine strips; winters cultivated land, scrub jungle. ♂: upperparts chestnut, wings, tail (no white outer

feathers) dull brown with pale feather margins; head black, surrounded yellow nape, chin down to underparts; head pattern much obscured winter. ♀: streaked brown above, pale to bright yellow below. Legs dark flesh brown, bill mainly lead blue, eyes brown. Red-headed ♂ has head, throat to upper breast chestnut to golden, greenish mantle, greenish yellow rump; otherwise like Black-headed ♀ indistinguishable. ♂ flies dangling legs like Corn Bunting, *E. calandra*. Huge flocks winter India, flying into trees when disturbed. Call sharp *zitt;* low *zee* (anxiety); monotonous *chiririri;* musical warbling song. Food summer mainly insects from ground; winter: grain and other seeds. Breeds mid May to end June; nest of grass and dead stems, lined fine bents, hair, well hidden on ground under scrub, among thistles, also up to 3 ft or more in bushes. 4 or 5 light greenish blue eggs, evenly spotted brown over violet, incubated ♀ 14 days; ♀, helped ♂, feeds young. **859**

Emberiza schoeniclus *Emberizidae: Emberizinae*
REED BUNTING   *c.* 6 ins
Palaearctic: virtually all Europe (except Iceland) and large area Central Asia between 30° and 70°N, extending more narrowly to Pacific coast, Sakhalin, Hokkaido, Kuriles, Kamtchatka. Partly sedentary but northern population migrates to S of breeding range, also N Africa, N Indian subcontinent. Variety of wet habitats: marshes, swamps, bogs; lake and river fringes; reedbeds; damp meadows, wet areas in grass steppes, clearings in woodland, N to scrub tundra. In Britain and Ireland also in dry scrub, hedgerows away from water; often winters cultivated land. ♂: upperparts dark and chestnut brown streaked black with white outer tail feathers; head, throat black with white collar, underparts off-white, streaked on flanks; head pattern suffused brown in winter. ♀: brown head with buff 'eyebrow', dark moustachial stripe; underparts buff, streaked dark on flanks. Hops, runs, walks on ground; flight jerky rather than undulating. Flocks winter, often with other species. ♂ chases ♀ in courtship, displays by showing off head and collar, vibrating one or both wings. Calls: sharp *tseep,* metallic *ching, chit* of alarm. Simple but variable song: *tweek tweek tweek tititic,* from stem of plant. Eats seeds of marsh plants and grasses; small insects in summer picked off vegetation or taken in air. Breeds mid April to August; nest of dry grasses, sedge, lined fine bents, hair usually built ♀, well hidden in ground cover, on tussock, stump, sometimes up to 12 ft in bush. 4 to 5 olive brown or buff eggs, boldly marked and scrawled dark brown, incubated ♀ and ♂ 13-14 days; both parents feed young, who fly 10-13 days. Injury feigning common. 2, perhaps sometimes 3 broods. **860**

Emberiza striolata see under **Melophus lathami**

Empidonax alnorum see under **E. traillii**

Empidonax flavirostris *Tyrannidae*
YELLOW-BELLIED FLYCATCHER   5½ ins
Nearctic: breeds from Newfoundland, Central Quebec and Manitoba, S Mackenzie to S New Hampshire, N Pennsylvania, S Wisconsin and Central Alberta; winters from N Mexico to Panama. Habitat: northern forests of conifers and birch with sphagnum ground layer; on migration in alder swamps; upperparts olive-green with dark brown wings and tail, feather edges making white bars on wings; underparts, especially throat, yellower at all seasons than other *Empidonax* species; legs dark, bill dark with pale lower mandible, eyes dark brown with whitish orbits. Song an ascending *pse-ek,* delivered 'like a sneeze' with jerk of head; call leisurely or 'mournful' *che-bunk.* Diet principally insects taken on wing, especially mosquitos in breeding area, flying ants; takes berries when normal food short. Breeds June onwards, making bulky cup of moss and small roots, lined rootlets and grass, on side of mossy mound or in roots of fallen tree. 3 or 4 white eggs, sparsely marked brown, incubated by ♀ *c.* 12 days; both parents feed young who fledge in about same time. **578**

Empidonax minimus *Tyrannidae*
LEAST FLYCATCHER   5¼ ins
Nearctic: breeds Nova Scotia, Ontario, N Alberta, W Central Mackenzie, to N New Jersey, SW N Carolina, Indiana and SW Missouri W to SE Wyoming, E British Columbia; winters NE Mexico to Panama. Wide range of habitats: open country with trees, orchards, gardens, parks but not dense woodland. Upperparts greyer, underparts whiter and lower mandible darker than other *Empidonax* species. Song repeated and distinctive *chebec,* delivered with jerk of head and flirt of tail; call: short *whit.* Jumbled notes in song flight. Diet: small insects taken on wing from variety of perches; also off plants, leaves and the ground. Breeds May onwards, building rather frail-looking cup of plant materials, softly lined, woven into fork of tree usually 6 to 40 ft up. 3 to 6 creamy white eggs, occasionally spotted red-brown, incubated by ♀; young tended by both parents. **579**

Empidonax traillii *Tyrannidae*
TRAILL'S FLYCATCHER   6 ins
Nearctic, marginally Neotropical: breeds over most of Alaska and Canada within tree limit and throughout USA (except SE) into NW Mexico; winters from S Mexico to Venezuela and Ecuador. Northern and eastern populations breed scrub thickets and swamps of alder and willow; Mid-western birds favour dry upland pastures with scrub, as well as orchards, gardens and roadsides. Upperparts olive-brown with darker wings and tail and white wingbars; throat whitest of *Empidonax* species but not separable in field from slightly smaller Acadian Flycatcher, *E. virescens.* Song of N and E birds emphatic *fee-bee-o,* syllables short, accented, slurred; Midwestern song 'sneezy' *fitz-bew;* alarm call abrupt *wit.* Diet: insectivorous, as relatives. Breeds June onwards, building nest of plant materials, softly lined, usually 2 to 4 ft up in fork of shrub (not suspended) in swamp, occasionally in fern clump; Mid-western nests in dry habitats up to 20 ft in trees. 2 to 4 creamy white eggs, sparsely spotted brown, incubated by ♀ and young tended by both parents. (Two species recently defined: more northern, *E. alnorum,* Alder Flycatcher 'Fee-bee-o'; most southern, *E. traillii,* Willow Flycatcher 'Fitz-bew'.)

Empidonax virescens see under **E. traillii**

EMU see **Domaius novaehollandiae**

EMERALD
    DOVE see **Chalcophaps indica**
        HUMMINGBIRD, PUERTO RICAN see **Chlorostilbon maugaeus**
        SPOTTED WOOD DOVE see **Turtur chalcospilos**
        TOUCANET see **Aulacorhynchus prasinus**

EMPEROR
    BIRD OF PARADISE see **Paradisaea guilielmi**
    PENGUIN see **Aptenodytes forsteri**

Entomodestes coracinus *Muscicapidae: Turdinae*
BLACK SOLITAIRE   9 ins
Neotropical: Colombia (W Andes) to NW Ecuador; resident canopy of dense humid forest, 3,000 to 7,000 ft. Jet black, except for white areas: cheek patch, axillaries, patch on inner web inner flight feathers, lower part outer tail feathers. Legs and bill noticeably short. Lives in tree tops; has fine song; mainly insectivorous. **680**

Entomyzon cyanotus *Meliphagidae*
BLUE-FACED HONEYEATER   12 ins
Australasian: mainly continental coasts from N Kimberleys, Cape York, S to New South Wales, S Australia; resident open forest country, mainly eucalypts, usually near water. Upperparts to long white-tipped tail golden olive; head to lower neck black with white patches side of head, throat, breast; chin, throat, breast grey, belly white; legs dark grey, bill black, eyes white in blue facial skin. In pairs or small parties, very aggressive to other birds and humans, but can easily be tamed. Acrobatic on blossom when taking nectar; also insects, frequently

from under bark, berries, fruits, doing some damage to orchards. Calls: shrill, whistle, *tweet.* Breeds June to January, even to April; nest of bark strips, lined finer pieces, grass, hair, usually on outer lateral branch, 10 to 30 ft; often takes old nests of babblers, magpie larks, other species. 2 or 3 salmon pink to buff eggs, sparingly marked purplish red, chestnut over pale grey. Sometimes 3 broods. **838**

Eopsaltria australis *Muscicapidae: Muscicapinae*
YELLOW ROBIN   6¾ ins
Australasian: E continental Australia; resident, with some local movements, in forests with thick undergrowth. Upperparts dark grey, upper tail coverts and rump bright yellow-green (yellow in northern race), tail tinged olive; chin greyish white shading into bright yellow underparts; flanks tinged olive. ♀ duller. Legs olive green, bill black, eyes very light brown. Perches on bark of trunk as well as on twigs. Call: loud prolonged piping on one note, beginning very early and continuing to dusk. Food: insects from ground, foliage, occasionally air. Breeds July to January, building nest of bark strips, grasses, bound cobwebs, decorated lichen and trailing bark; in tree fork, 3 to 30 ft. 2 to 4 pale or bluish green eggs, marked reddish brown. **779**

Eopsaltria georgiana or Quoyornis georgianus
Muscicapidae: Muscicapinae
WHITE-BREASTED ROBIN   *c.* 6 ins
Australasian: SW continental Australia; resident dense forests of 'big scrubs'. Upperparts dark grey, becoming dark brown on wings, with white tip to graduated tail; underparts from chin whitish; legs brown, bill dark grey, eyes brown. Usually in pairs, hard to see: clings to bark of tree trunks like nuthatch. Call: loud *kawhow kawhow whowah whow.* Insectivorous. Breeds October, building nest of small twigs, bark strips, leaves, lined small rootlets, grass. 2 olive or bronze-green eggs, darker at big end.

Eos squamata *Psittacidae*
VIOLET-HEADED LORIKEET or
MOLUCCAS RED LORY   11 ins
Australasian: Moluccas to islands of W New Guinea. Predominantly red, with purple collar, underparts; outer flight feathers black with red bases; black tips to inner quills and greater coverts; scapulars partly purple; tail red-purple above, red and golden below. Very little known about habits in wild; species of this genus lay 1 or 2 white eggs in tree holes. **392**

Ephippiorhynchus senegalensis *Ciconiidae*
SADDLEBILL   5½ ft
Ethiopian, except extreme S Africa, in swamps, marshes and on lake shores. Head, neck, upper wing and tail black, iridescent green, violet and blue; otherwise white, including flight feathers; legs red and black, long bill red with black band round middle and yellow frontal 'saddle', eyes bright yellow. Usually solitary, in pairs or family parties; feeds like heron with slow stalk and lightning stab, on water animals of many kinds, including fish, frogs and water beetles; also small mammals and birds. Flies with head and feet held lower than body. Silent except for bill-clattering during display. Breeding season varies with altitude; from June in Uganda; substantial nest of sticks, usually in trees, sometimes cliff ledge, holds 1 to 4 dull white and pitted eggs. **71**

Ephthianura albifrons *Muscicapidae: Malurinae*
WHITE-FRONTED CHAT   *c.* 4½ ins
Australia: S Queensland, New South Wales, Victoria, southern S Australia and S Western Australia as far N as Shark's Bay. Habitat: damp and rough places with low cover e.g. swamps and margins of estuaries and lakes. ♂: head down to upper breast white; broad black band round mid-breast and up nape and hind-crown; back grey, wings brown; tail blackish, outer feathers tipped white; belly white. Legs and bill black, eyes light brown. ♀: no black on head, chest band dark brown and thinner. Usually in pairs or gregarious when not breeding; rapid twisting flight, always on move; feeds on insects. Call: low, metallic *tang.* Breeds July to March, mainly September and Octo-

ber; nest of grass or fine twigs, lined rootlets, hair and fine grasses, in tall grass or low down in shrub, near water; 3, sometimes 4 white eggs, slightly tinged pinkish and marked with reddish or purplish browns; both parents incubate eggs and tend young.

Ephthianura aurifrons *Muscicapidae: Malurinae*
ORANGE CHAT *c.* 4 ins
Australia: W Queensland, W New South Wales, N South Australia, Central Australia, Western Australia S of Pibara district to Morawa and Eucla. Habitat: open country, with some bush cover, or samphire flats. ♂: crown and rump orange-yellow, sides of head yellower, rest of upperparts and wings brown with yellowish green margins to feathers, flight feathers dark grey, tail black; chin and throat black, rest of underparts orange-yellow. ♀: brownish upperparts, rump yellow, 'eyebrow' pale; underparts pale yellowish white. Legs and bill black, eyes dark brownish red. Behaviour and feeding: see Crimson Chat, *E. tricolor*. Call: mellow *cheek-cheek* in flight. Breeds usually September to February; cup-shaped nest of fine twigs, lined rootlets, in small bush *c.* 3 ft up; 3 white eggs, purplish red spots concentrated at larger end; both parents incubate. **760**

Ephthianura tricolor *Muscicapidae: Malurinae*
CRIMSON CHAT *c.* 4 ins
Australia: W of Great Dividing Range, Gulf of Carpentaria S to NW Victoria, N South Australia and Central Australia; Western Australia from Pilbara district S to Moore River; seasonal movements produced by weather. Habitat: open country with some bush cover. ♂: crown and rump scarlet, sides of head brown, back brown with dark streaks, wings brown with brownish white edges to primaries and secondaries; tail dark brown tipped white; throat white, breast scarlet, belly white. ♀: head brown, chest buff, scarlet only on rump. Legs and down-curved bill black, eyes pale buff. Strongly territorial when breeding, otherwise often in small flocks; timid; feeds on insects on ground; swift, twisting flight. Call: metallic *ting*, also various whistles; low chatter used in territorial display. Breeds usually after heavy rainfall, sometimes loose colonies; cup-shaped nest in top of low bush, of fine twigs and grass lined hairs, finer grass and bark fibres; 3, sometimes 4, white eggs with reddish purple spots; both parents build nest, incubate, and tend young.

Epimachus fastosus see under **E. meyeri**

Epimachus meyeri *Paradisaeidae*
SICKLE-BILLED BIRD OF PARADISE ♂: 39 (bill 3½) ins
Australasian: S and E New Guinea; resident tall montane forests 5,400 ft up to 10,000 ft, usually above range of *E. fastosus*. ♂: upperparts black glossed violet; part of back and rump oily green tinged blue; wings and very long graduated tail black; crown velvety with short glossy plumes; chin to upper neck blackish, suffused iridescent bronze-purple; cheeks blue-green; underparts dull olive brown, tinged purple on flanks; large erectile 'fans' on sides upper breast burnished dark brown to black, broadly tipped violet blue; behind these longer set sooty black tufts; similar double set sides lower breast. ♀: upperparts dull rusty to olive brown; crown to hindneck chestnut; base of upper bill, lores, cheeks brownish black, throat blackish brown; underparts buff densely barred black. Legs, bill black (gape yellow), eyes pale blue. Immature ♂ progresses from ♀-like to ♂ plumage. Searches mossy trunks and branches for grasshoppers, other insects; also takes fruits, berries. ♂ displays by expanding breast feathers, then flank plumes, with loud rattling call; turns breast upward, face framed in short feathers of upper breast, wings folded, tail slightly spread, bill closed. Second type makes more use of fans, bill opens to show gape, bird sometimes rotating in jerks (L. S. Crandall). Breeds April (incubated egg found) to mid July (nearly fledged nestling); nest of moss and vine stems attached fork of small tree in understorey, lined rootlets, skeleton leaves. Single egg cinnamon, marked longitudinally brown-grey, reddish brown, small brown and lavender spots, incubated ♀. **991**

Eremialector decoratus *Pteroclididae*
BLACK-FACED SANDGROUSE 10 ins
Ethiopian: 3 races in restricted range, Somalia to Kenya and Central Tanzania. Nomadic in dry bush country, occupying even small open spaces. ♂: upperparts brown, barred black; forehead, base of bill, throat black, white band between forehead and crown, extending over eye as stripe; sides of face, neck, breast dull brown, terminated by black band above white lower breast; belly, flanks black; under tail coverts white; tail pointed not elongated; legs feathered, feet horn, bill dark horn, eyes dark brown. ♀: upperparts with crescents rather than bars, no black on head; neck, upper breast barred and spotted black. Usually in pairs or parties, said to drink regularly in mornings. Calls: whistle of two long and one short note, also repeated *quit quit*. Diet: grass seeds and roots. Breeding season variable; 2 or 3 glossy buff eggs, marked reddish brown and grey, laid on bare ground, incubated by ♀ and ♂ (by night) 23-24 days. **347**

Eremialector quadricinctus *Pteroclididae*
FOUR-BANDED SANDGROUSE *c.* 11½ ins
Ethiopian: broad band from Senegal and Gambia to Lake Chad, Sudan, Ethiopia, NW Kenya and Uganda; W African population moves S in dry season. Habitat: bush or cultivated land in Sudan, Uganda, stony country in Kenya. ♂: upperparts generally brown, chestnut or white and black bars on mantle, rump, tail and wing coverts; crown streaked black, forehead black and white; chestnut, buffish white and black bands across breast; underparts closely barred black and white; underwing grey; tail pointed not elongated. ♀ lacks bands on breast. Legs feathered, feet horn, short bill dark horn, eyes dark brown. Small parties come to drink at dusk with twittering calls. Diet: seeds and roots. Breeds mainly January to March. 2 or 3 clay pink eggs, dotted pale brown and mauve, resemble fallen *Bauhinia* leaves among which often laid. **348**

Eremiornis carteri *Muscicapidae: Malurinae*
SPINIFEX BIRD *c.* 5¾ ins
Australasian: N Australia from Cloncurry, Queensland, to Halls Creek and Fitzroy River, Western Australia, S to Minilya River; also Monte Bello and Barrow Is, Western Australia. Habitat: arid country in spinifex and other low scrub. Upperparts bright brown, crown rufous, long tail darker towards tip; underparts dull white, washed buff towards flanks. Legs light brown, bill and eyes brown. Shy, usually in pairs and on ground; insectivorous. ♂'s call from top of bush likened to French words *je suis, à vous;* ♀ utters grating notes. Nest of finely shredded grass lined fine roots, built by ♀ in bunch of spinifex; 2 pinkish white eggs, well covered with minute pale lilac and purplish to reddish brown markings; both parents tend young.

Eremomela icteropygialis *Muscicapidae: Sylviinae*
YELLOW-BELLIED WARBLER 3½ ins
Ethiopian: from Eritrea westwards S of Sahara, but not reaching S Nigeria or Sierra Leone; southwards through eastern Africa to S Africa, but not in southernmost or eastern coastal areas. Resident dry open bush and true desert. Upperparts, including wings, very short tail, ashy grey; dusky eyestripe but faint pale ring round eye and pale 'eyebrow'; underparts from chin white, shading to pale yellow lower belly; under tail coverts, flanks greyish; legs black, bill blackish, eyes brown. Usually found in pairs or family parties; often with African Penduline Tits, *Anthoscopus caroli*, searching low in trees or bushes, especially *Calotropis* (sodom apple), for insects and their larvae. Calls: 4-syllabled jingle; plaintive *see see;* scolding *chee chiri chee chiri chit.* Breeding season variable within range; nest small, deep, semi-transparent cup of grass, wool, cobwebs, suspended by rim from two twigs or fork of low branch. 2 or 3 white eggs, spotted dark red and sepia over grey. **738**

EREMOMELA, YELLOW-BELLIED see **Eremomela icteropygialis**

Eremophila alpestris *Alaudidae*
SHORE LARK or HORNED LARK *c.* 6½ ins
Holarctic, Neotropical: 40 races; breeds in strip along N Palaearctic coasts from Scandinavia to 160°E in Siberia; also from N African coast, Middle East into mountain ranges of S Asia mainly between 30° and 50°N; almost all N America to 20°N (except NW Alaska, SE USA) with isolated group round Bogota, Colombia; most populations winter lowlands, but northern ones move to southern breeding range. Habitat: rocky alpine meadows up to 17,300 ft in Himalayas; stony steppes; stony areas of lichen tundra; stony deserts; in America, where no competing larks, in variety of open country from arable land to deserts and coastal dunes; grass savannah at *c.* 9,000 ft Colombia; winters coastal shingle and nearby fields. ♂: upperparts brownish; distinctive black and yellow head pattern with short black horns; underparts whitish. ♀ and juvenile have less black. Legs black, bill greyish horn, eyes dark brown. Flocks in winter, sometimes with buntings, usually walking or running over ground. Flight rather undulating. Call: *see-it* like Meadow Pipit, *Anthus pratensis*; song: sweet low warble, song flight not as prominent as most larks. Food: seeds, buds, insects and larvae in summer; also small molluscs, crustaceans in winter. Breeds mid May to July, building simple nest of plant stems, softly lined; pebbles, sheep droppings, plant debris arranged round site on ground. Usually 4 greenish-white eggs, thickly freckled fine yellowish-brown, incubated 10-14 days (N America). Young, fed by ♀ and ♂, leave nest 9-12 days, fly *c.* 7 days later. Usually 2 broods. **601**

Eremophila bilopha *Alaudidae*
TEMMINCK'S HORNED LARK 5¼ ins
Palaearctic: resident but wanders in winter from breeding grounds in S Morocco, E to Algeria, Egypt along coast; N Arabia to Iraq and Syrian Desert. Habitat: deserts and stony wastes but not in mountains so no overlap with *E. alpestris*. Plumage similar to *E. alpestris* but has white not yellow on face. Upperparts uniform sandy, underparts paler; primaries and tail darker; also smaller and less bulky than *E. alpestris*. Call: repeated *see-oo;* song less vigorous than *E. alpestris* but similar and song-flight is performed more often. Feeds on seeds and shoots of small desert plants. Breeding season begins March but mainly April and May; nests of plant stems on ground usually hidden under a clump of vegetation. 2 to 4 brownish speckled eggs. **602**

Eriocnemis mirabilis *Trochilidae*
COLOURFUL PUFFLEG 3¼ (bill ½) ins
Neotropical: only known from subtropical (4,500 to 7,500 ft) zone in W slope of S Western Andes in Cauca, Colombia, where caught and photographed by J. S. Dunning. Resident in forests. ♂: upperparts dark iridescent green; forehead emerald; white patch behind eyes; tail dark bronzy olive above, iridescent brassy olive below; throat and sides of neck iridescent blue green, merging into dark green breast; belly deep iridescent indigo speckled red; under tail coverts mixed iridescent ruby and gold; downy leg 'puffs' white, tipped cinnamon in front, all cinnamon behind. ♀: upperparts and flanks dark green; centre of throat and breast white with green spots; underparts white spotted reddish bronze, most pronounced on under tail coverts; tail mostly bronze green, tipped and edged blue black. Little known of habits as yet; relatives have simple warbling song and lay 1 or 2 white eggs, incubated 14-15 days. Both parents feed young. **472**

Erithacus rubecula *Muscicapidae: Turdinae*
(EUROPEAN) ROBIN 5½ ins
Palaearctic: W Europe, extending into Siberia between 50° and 60°N, and through Asia Minor, Caucasus to S Caspian; very local NW Africa, also Canaries, Azores; northern birds winter temperate W Europe, and Mediterranean E to Iran. Habitat broadleaved and coniferous woodland with thick undergrowth and ground cover; spruce forests with swampy areas in N, montane forests in S of range; parks, gardens, roadsides W Europe, especially

Britain. Upperparts olive brown, separated from orange forehead, throat, breast by grey-blue border; underparts white; legs brown, bill dark olive brown. eyes very dark brown. Juvenile has upperparts mottled buff, underparts mainly buff, 'scaled' brown. Solitary in winter, pairs in summer, strongly territorial. Confident in gardens, comes close in woodland, regarding human as large animal likely to stir prey in litter. Hops on ground, stopping to flick wings and tail, exaggerating this when excited. Usual call repeated, scolding *tic tic;* also soft *tsip:* song shrill but melodious and warbling, phrases lasting up to 3 secs; ♀ also sings. Opposing birds present breasts to each other, swaying body side to side on perch. ♂ feeds ♀ during breeding season, March to July in Britain. Feeds mainly on ground: smaller insects and larvae, spiders, worms, snails; berries and small fruit in autumn; bird tables in gardens. ♀ builds foundation of dead leaves, then mossy cup lined rootlets, hairs; in bank, often ivied, under tussock, in tree holes, stumps, roots; many human artefacts, up to 10 ft high. 5 to 7 white or bluish white eggs, freckled light red usually at big end, incubated by ♀ 12 to 14 days; both parents feed young, who fly 12-15 days. 2, sometimes 3 broods. **681**

Erolia fuscicollis see **Calidris fuscicollis**

Erythropygia coryphaeus *Muscicapidae: Turdinae*
KAROO CHAT   6¼ ins
Ethiopian: SW parts of Southern Africa; resident and numerous in dry, sandy areas. Upperparts sooty brown, tail black with white tips to outer feathers; 'eyebrow' white; centre of chin and throat white with thin black moustachial stripes; underparts uniform brown. Mainly terrestrial, flicking tail when disturbed before flying to cover. Scolds snakes, small carnivores. Mainly insectivorous. Nest of dead sticks, rootlets, lined down, hair, wool, well hidden under dead twigs, low bushes. 2 or 3 greenish-blue eggs, heavily marked reddish-brown. **682**

Erythropygia leucophrys see **E. zambesiana**

Erythropygia zambesiana or E. leucophrys
Muscicapidae: Turdinae
WHITE-BROWED or RED-BACKED SCRUB ROBIN 6 ins
Ethiopian: mainly S of Equator, from Congo to Sudan, then locally down E side to SE coast; resident and local migrant in scrub and secondary forest. Upperparts, including crown, rufous, faintly streaked blackish; flight feathers and wing coverts dusky, white covert tips forming bar on closed wing; rump and tail russet, with narrow blackish subterminal band, white tips; 'eyebrow' white, earcoverts brownish; underparts buffish white, heavily streaked black, throat to chest; legs stone-brown, bill dark brown, eyes brown. Juvenile mottled. Usually solitary or in pairs: can be summoned by imitating bird alarm calls. Flies low for cover if disturbed. Flicks and fans tail when excited. ♂ displays by running along branch, head down, tail cocked, wings drooping. Call *hee-er-wi-er-wi* (R. E. Moreau), scolding alarm; song from tree perch loud, rather monotonous descending notes, repeated. Mainly insectivorous. Breeds chiefly September to February E Africa. Nest deep grass cup, lined rootlets, in tuft or thick herbage on or near ground. 2 or 3 white eggs, marked rusty red over purple. Probably 2 broods. **683**

Esacus magnirostris or Orthorhamphus
magnirostris *Burhinidae*
BEACH CURLEW   21 ins
Oriental, Australasian; race *E. m. recurvirostris* 'Great Stone Curlew': Indian subcontinent, Burma; race *magnirostris*: Andamans, Indonesia, Philippines, New Guinea, northern Australia to coastal New South Wales, Solomon Is. Habitat: reefs, beaches, coastal and riverine mud banks. Resembles *Burhinus* stone curlews (*note:* Australian species is *B. magnirostris* also!) but upperparts unstreaked brown; 'shoulder' dark brown, white and grey wingbars, tip black and white; black band through eye, white above and below; throat, breast grey, belly white; legs greenish-yellow, powerful bill with pronounced gonys yellow, tipped black; eyes yellow. Usually solitary or in pairs, but

parties form in rains in Burma and visit grasslands; usual food small crustaceans and molluscs. Stands still when approached, whereas *Burhinus* crouches, but may bob body like lapwing *Vanellus*. Call: repeated *wer-loo*, often at night; *recurvirostris* utters whistling alarm and chatters when taking wing. Breeds October Australia, laying 1 or 2 creamy white eggs, streaked and blotched olive brown, on bare sand or mud, often close to water.

Estrilda astrild *Estrildidae*
COMMON WAXBILL   4½ ins
Ethiopian: resident in most of region; introduced Portugal, near Obidos. Habitat: wetlands, watersides with trees, tall grass; cultivated land especially when neglected; gardens, villages. ♂: upperparts pale brown, closely barred dusky; lores, eyestripe crimson; cheeks, neck, throat, greyish; centre breast crimson pink; under tail coverts black, rest underparts pale brown, faintly barred buff, tinged pink. ♀ as ♂ but less crimson. Legs, eyes brown, bill red. Immature much as ♀ but bill blackish. (Crimson-rumped Waxbill, *E. rhodopyga*, has similar habitat over much of range.) Very lively, constantly flicking tail side to side. Small parties become large after breeding season, take off calling *chairp chairp chairp,* then reedy twittering flock call; also excited *chee chee churrr chit;* ♂'s song subdued, melodious. Feeds on or near ground, mainly grass seeds. Breeding season variable throughout range; nest pear-shaped, of grass, with entrance at 'stalk'; lined down, feathers; often canopy on top for roosting; in low cover on banks or level grassland. 4 to 8 pink eggs incubated ♀ and ♂. Both feed young from throat. Usual host of Pintailed Whydah, *Vidua macroura.* **937**

Estrilda rhodopyga see under **E. astrild**

Estrilda temporalis *Estrildidae*
SYDNEY WAXBILL or RED-BROWED FINCH 4¾ ins
Australia: eastern coast and ranges from Cape York to SE South Australia; resident scrub or forest edge with dense undergrowth; bushy grassland; watercourses in mountains; gardens, roadsides, into towns. Upperparts, including wings, tail dull yellowish olive; rump crimson; crown, nape grey; face light grey with broad crimson stripe from red bill over eye to back of head; underparts from chin to undertail grey; legs pink, eyes red-brown. Juvenile browner on head, crimson areas duller, bill black. Usually in small groups, larger flocks in winter. Strong flight but prefers to hop on ground. Insistent contact call: piercing *sseee sseee;* twittering song derives from it. Food usually seeds from ground, grassheads, bushes; insects from foliage. Breeding peak October November New South Wales; builds tubular nest of dry and green grass, lined feathers, in dense thorn, sometimes in bunch of foliage, tangle of vines, fork of branch, generally below 6 ft. 4 to 6 white eggs.

Eubucco bourcierii *Capitonidae*
RED-HEADED BARBET   6½ ins
Neotropical: Costa Rica and Panama to Colombia and Ecuador, NE Peru; resident forest undergrowth, clearings, up to c. 7,500 ft in Andes. ♂: upperparts to tail rather dull green; whole head and throat scarlet, shading to orange on breast; narrow blue half collar on hind neck; underparts whitish streaked green; legs dark, stout bill yellow-green, eyes brown. ♀: upperparts green, cheeks blue, throat grey, upper breast orange yellow. Unlike flocking species of barbet, usually solitary and silent. Insectivorous: searches curled up dead leaves; also works vegetation 10 to 30 ft up, sometimes with parties of tanagers. Nests as relatives, in hole; both sexes incubate and tend young. **525**

Eudocimus albus *Threskiornithidae*
WHITE IBIS (AMERICAN)   21-27 ins
Nearctic and Neotropical: from southern USA to NE South America; some post-breeding dispersal. Habitat usually coastal salt, brackish and freshwater lakes. Almost entirely white, sometimes mottled on crown and nape; ends of 4 longest primaries greenish black; legs, slender curved bill and facial skin pinkish, eyes pale blue. Gregarious: concerted flights alternate

flapping and gliding, especially impressive on mass returns to tree roosts. Also feed together, picking up crabs in shallow water, probing mud; and take fish, frogs, snakes. Courtship and threat displays at colonies. Usually silent; harsh triple call in flight or alarm. Lays from March in Florida; colonial, often in large numbers and with other species, in mangroves and other trees. Nest of local material holds usually 3 pale blue or green eggs with brown blotches, incubated *c.* 21 days by ♀ and ♂. They tend young which fly at *c.* 5 weeks. **80**

Eudocimus ruber *Threskiornithidae*
SCARLET IBIS   21-27 ins
Neotropical: very local on NE coast South America, perhaps also SE Brazil; seasonal dispersal movements. Habitat tropical coasts: mangrove swamps, estuaries, mudflats. Generally scarlet, except blue-black ends of 4 longest primaries; legs, facial skin scarlet; bill black to brown, eyes dark. Behaviour much as *E. albus.* Usually silent; 'gurgling' alarm call; bill clattering when bickering. Breeds during heavy tropical rains in large colonies like E. albus. Nest of local materials holds usually 2 pale blue or green eggs, blotched brown, incubated *c.* 21 days by ♀ and ♂, who tend young until they fly at *c.* 5 weeks. **81**

Eudromias morinellus *Charadriidae*
DOTTEREL   c. 8½ ins
Palaearctic: distribution sporadic from Britain and Central Europe to Siberia; summer visitor to breeding areas; winters S coast Mediterranean, Red Sea and Persian Gulf. Habitat: flattish mountain tops in temperate (but recently colonised lowlying reclaimed land in Netherlands) and subarctic, tundra in arctic; coastal in winter. Upperparts blackish brown; 'eyebrow', throat whitish; brown breast separated by white band from chestnut lower breast and flanks; belly black, undertail white; legs dull yellow, bill black, eyes brown. In winter and juvenile underparts brown with pale band on breast; ♀ brighter than ♂ in summer. Often allows close approach both in passage 'trips' and on breeding area. Stop-go action when feeding like other plovers. Often raises one or both wings, sometimes before flying. Many notes recorded when breeding, but usual call *wit-e-wee wit-e-wee.* Displays complicated, ♀ taking lead. Diet: fly larvae in breeding season; otherwise small animals of tidal zone. Breeds from mid May Scotland. Lined scrape in moss or soil holds usually 3 light buff eggs, heavily marked brownish-black and grey. Incubation usually by ♂, 21½-25½ days; he also tends young, regularly feigning injury when threatened; they fly *c.* 30 days. **263**

Eudyptes chrysolophus *Spheniscidae*
MACARONI PENGUIN   26-30 ins
Subantarctic seas, with regular northward migrations from breeding colonies on bare islands. Penguin pattern of black and white with orange yellow head plumes extending backwards. Legs and bill orange pink; eyes dark; strong goat-like smell. Gregarious at all times, sometimes forming mixed colonies with Rockhopper Penguin E. crestatus. Diet squids and shrimps. Has braying call like its relatives. Nest of small stones, grasses and mud on bare headland or island; eggs 1 to 3, pale blue or chalky white, incubated by ♂ and ♀. ♂ guards while ♀ feeds chicks, but seldom more than one reared. **9**

Eudyptes crestatus see under **E. chrysolophus**

Eudyptes minor *Spheniscidae*
LITTLE BLUE PENGUIN   16 ins
Australasian: three subspecies inhabit southern coasts of continental Australia, Tasmania, New Zealand, Chatham and other islands; offshore outside breeding season. Smallest penguin: slaty blue not black upperparts; chin as well as underparts white; no crest; legs pale flesh pink, soles black; bill black, eyes silver grey. Not gregarious like most penguins and more vocal, with range from catlike mewing to screams, trumpetings and growls when on shore; ducklike quacks at sea. Diet small fishes, swallowed underwater. Breeds from highwater mark to several hundred yards inland,

sometimes climbing several hundred feet to nest usually in cavity, either taken over from petrels or excavated. 2 white eggs incubated mainly by ♂ for *c.* 40 days; both chicks usually reared by ♂ and ♀, fledging in *c.* 8 weeks. **10**

Eugenes fulgens see under **Lampornis clemenciae**

Eupetes macrocercus *Muscicapidae : Cinclosomatinae*
MALAY RAIL BABBLER 10-11½ ins
Oriental: Malaysia to Borneo; resident primary forest 2,000 to 4,000 ft. Generally rufous brown, varying in intensity from crown to end of long, graduated tail; broad black mask tapers down neck with white stripe above; small patch bare skin below on neck; belly earthy grey; long legs blue-black, straight bill blackish, eyes dark brown. Juvenile greyer, with white throat. Runs at speed with head raised, tail slightly depressed, over fallen tree trunks and forest debris in hillside ravines. Calls: ticking *tek;* repeated, rattling *chekchekchek.* Food includes cicadas, black beetles, spiders (T. H. Harrisson). Breeding habits apparently unknown.

Euphagus carolinus *Icteridae*
RUSTY BLACKBIRD 9½ ins
Nearctic: breeds from Alaska and northern Canada S to Central Canada and N New England; winters from New Jersey and Ohio River S to Gulf Coast, W to Central Texas. Habitat: wet woodland and thickly wooded swamps, especially with alder and open pools. ♂: uniformly black with green gloss; ♀: slaty grey, little gloss; legs grey, rather slender bill light grey, eyes whitish. Both become 'rusty' in autumn due to brown feather edges, especially on head, breast, upper back. Juvenile is even browner. Large flocks most of year, often with other blackbirds, grackles, keeping up 'constant babble of squeaks, clucks, and whistles' (R. H. Pough), continuing chorus from trees if disturbed. Walks and wades after insects on land and water; also takes seeds, grain, wild fruits. Usual calls: *cack* or lower *cuk;* rather gurgling song of mixed squeaks, musical notes. Breeds May and June, generally solitary; bulky nest of sticks and plant debris with mud cup, lined green grass, up to 20 ft in dense young conifers or shrubs near or over water. 3 to 5 pale blue-green eggs, heavily marked brown over grey.

Euphonia laniirostris see **Tanagra laniirostris**

EUPHONIA, THICK-BILLED see **Tanagra laniirostris**

Euplectes
hordacea see under **E. orix**
macrocercus see under **E. macrourus**

Euplectes macrourus or *Coliuspasser macrourus*
Ploceidae ♂ breeding: *c.* 9; non-breeding: *c.* 6½ ins
YELLOW-BACKED WIDOW BIRD
Ethiopian: Senegal across to Sudan, S to Angola, Malawi, Mozambique; local resident open grassy plains and swamps. ♂: generally black; mantle, 'shoulders' yellow; flight feathers pale-edged; long graduated tail; under wing coverts buff or buff and black; legs, bill black, eyes dark brown. ♀: brownish, upperparts streaked buff and black (but duller than ♀ Yellow-shouldered, *E. macrocercus*), rump brown; 'eyebrow', cheeks, throat yellowish-buff; feathers of 'shoulder' and 'elbow' edged yellow; underparts buff, faintly streaked yellow; bill horn. Non-breeding ♂ much as ♀, more broadly streaked dull black above; yellow on wings remains. Non-breeding ♀ has underparts suffused yellow. Rare all-black ♂♂ occur. Flits over grass, settling on tallest heads. Large flocks outside breeding season roost in reedbeds. Call: thin *z-e-e-e;* ♂ has short melodious song. Food: grass and other seeds. Breeding variable within range; December to March S Africa; rather unsubstantial ball nest of grasses, with living stems woven in, in short grass areas of swamp. Usually 2 blue or greenish blue eggs, densely marked speckles and scrawls of brown and grey. **949**

Euplectes nigroventris see under **E. orix**

Euplectes orix *Ploceidae*
RED BISHOP 5 ins
Ethiopian: Senegal E to Ethiopia, then S down E side continent to S Africa; breeds tall grass and herbage near water; sugar cane and maize cultivations; wanders to open plains and short grass country after breeding. ♂: generally red (orange-red when old); mantle brownish, crown, cheeks, earcoverts, underparts to belly, black; wings, tail dusky, feathers pale-edged; upper and under tail coverts often as long as tail; legs reddish brown, bill black, eyes brown. ♀: upperparts broadly streaked brownish, buff, black; 'eyebrow' buff; underparts buff to white; breast, flanks streaked dark brown, bill horn. Non-breeding ♂ as ♀ but larger. ♂ hovers over defined territory, puffing out feathers, wings purring; each has 3 or 4 mates whom he may chase in courtship. Courting call: 'sizzling' *zik zik zik;* variety of wheezing and mewing notes. Large roosts in reedbeds. Diet: mainly grass seeds but may attack crops; insects for young. Breeding variable and sporadic; colonies often widely separated and suddenly deserted. ♂ weaves flimsy oval grass nests in bullrushes, reeds *Phragmites* over water; also in corn; ♀ adds lining of grass seed heads; projecting porch. Usually 3 pale turquoise blue eggs incubated ♀ 11-14 days; she feeds young who fly 13-16 days. Very similar and local Zanzibar Red Bishop, *E. nigroventris,* (4 ins) has scarlet crown; Black-winged Red Bishop, *E. hordacea,* (5½ ins) has wings and tail black. **950**

Euplectes progne or *Coliuspasser progne Ploceidae*
LONG-TAILED WIDOW BIRD or ♀: 6, ♂ breeding:
SAKABULA 19-30, non-breeding 8-9 ins
Ethiopian: Angola, SE Zaire, W and Central Kenya, Zambia, S Africa; local resident open high-level grassland and moorland up to 6,000 ft or more; neighbourhood of swamps, dams, cultivations. ♂: 'one of most striking African birds' (J. G. Williams), jet black including neck ruff; 'shoulders' orange-red, median wing coverts white or buff; central tail feathers up to 2 ft long; legs, black, bill bluish-white, eyes dark brown. ♀: upperparts streaked buff, brown, black; shoulders orange-red, feathers black-centred; underparts pale buff, streaked dusky; under wing coverts black; tail feathers narrow, pointed; bill horn. Non-breeding ♂ much as ♀, more broadly streaked, retains shoulder and wing patches; bill horn. Immature ♂ as ♀. Rather silent; sharp chirping alarm call: *zik;* 'chuckling, swizzling song' (Roberts). Food mainly seeds; also termites. Polygamous ♂ may have 6 to 10 ♀♀, forming flock, sometimes with another ♂; but ♂♂ roost together even in breeding season. Slow, jerky flights of ♂, with tail drooping and spread; may become grounded in wet weather. Visits nests, churring to sitting ♀♀. Breeding depends on rains: October to January or March; ♀ builds rounded, thick-walled grass nest with entrance at side, well hidden in tussock under living stems. 2 to 4 pale greenish white or cream eggs, heavily spotted pale olive-brown and grey, with larger blotches, incubated ♀ 14 days; she also rears young. **951**

Eupodotis australis *Otididae*
AUSTRALIAN BUSTARD ♀: 35; ♂: 46 ins
Continental Australia, especially N; resident on plains, open scrub and forest. Upperparts generally dark brown with lighter markings; primaries brown, black area of white-tipped feathers on coverts; forehead, crown, elongated neck feathers black; underparts white with blackish band across breast; legs yellow, bill whitish to brown, eyes white. Singly or small groups, stand to watch humans but sometimes squat; walk or run rather than fly, needing long take off. ♂ inflates neck in display, draws head back, spreads ruff, droops wings to ground with tail fanned. Normally silent; deep *hoo* in display. Feeds on grasses and other plants, seeds, leaves and fruits, lizards, insects, especially locusts, small vertebrates. Breeding season July to November depending on rainfall. Lays 1 or 2 glossy, olive-streaked olive-brown eggs in scrape or bare ground on grassy knoll; ♀ incubates *c.* 4 weeks and feeds chick, which flies in 5-6 weeks. **243**

Eupodotis melanogaster see **Lissotis melanogaster**

Eupodotis senegalensis *Otididae*
WHITE-BELLIED BUSTARD 24 ins
Ethiopian: Sudan W across continent to N Nigeria and Senegal; resident on red sandstone desert, feeding on edge of scrub early and late, then resting in cover. ♂: mantle, breast, wing coverts, scapulars and inner secondaries rich light brown, vermiculated black, with buff white patch on inner primaries; forehead, crown, lower throat black; nape blue ringed black, chin white, neck and breast bluish, underparts buff white, axillaries white. ♀: crown sooty black, nape speckled tawny brown and black, throat white, neck light brown and blue. Legs, bill yellowish white, eyes pale wine red. Shy but reacts to noise with loud *wuk-caire* calls; also snort in breeding season. Stretches neck when running or in short flights. Eats insects, especially locusts, and acacia gum. Breeding season varies throughout range. Lays 2 eggs, olive-brown, spotted red or greenish-buff blotched stone colour, on bare ground. Incubation presumably by ♀, with ♂ in attendance, probably *c.* 3 weeks. **244**

EURASIAN
BROWN FLYCATCHER see **Muscicapa latirostris**
CUCKOO see **Cuculus canorus**
JAY see **Garrulus glandarius**
PYGMY OWL see **Glaucidium passerinum**

Eurocephalus anguitimens *Laniidae*
WHITE-CROWNED SHRIKE 9 ins
Ethiopian: S Sudan, Ethiopia to Tanzania; Rhodesia, Botswana, S Africa; Angola. Resident dry thornbush. Dusky brown mantle contrasts with white crown, rump; wings, tail, wide patch behind eye black; underparts white with brown patch side of breast. Immature has brown crown and barred upperparts. Usually perches on upper or outer branches of trees, but hunts insects, other small animals on ground. Noisy parties of 6 to 12 remain within range of each other, fly off calling, with short rapid wingbeats and glides. Call: harsh *kaa kaa kaa.* Breeding season varies with range. Nest small, compact, of plant materials bound cobwebs 'like little flat yellow cheeses stuck on boughs' (R. E. Moreau), also against tree trunks. Clutch probably 2 or 3 white or pale lilac eggs, blotched amber, ochre or violet; but 2 ♀♀ often use same nest. **646**

EUROPEAN
BEE-EATER see **Merops apiaster**
GOLDFINCH see **Carduelis carduelis**
ROBIN see **Erithacus rubecula**
ROLLER see **Coracias garrulus**
SPOONBILL see **Platalea leucorodia**

Eurostopodus guttatus *Caprimulgidae*
SPOTTED NIGHTJAR *c.* 12 ins
Australasia: continental Australia, Aru Is, New Ireland; resident open woodlands. Upperparts mottled and flecked buff, black and grey, with dark brown wings and barred tail; from bill through eye to back of neck grey; crown brown; throat mottled dark, 2 white patches on upper breast; underparts buff narrowly barred darker. Usually solitary by day on ground, but hawks at dusk in numbers over trees and grassland. Call rendered *caw caw caw gobble gobble gobble,* diminishing in volume. Diet: insects taken on wing. Breeds September to November, laying single yellowish-olive egg, sparsely marked reddish-purple and lavender, on bare ground. Incubation by ♂. **463**

Eurypyga helias *Eurypygidae*
SUN BITTERN *c.* 18 ins
Neotropical; 3 races from Central America to S Peru, S Brazil, N Bolivia; W of Andes to W Ecuador. Resident in dense tropical forests along streams and rivers up to at least 3,000 ft. Upperparts narrowly barred grey, brown and olive; underparts paler; wing at rest barred black and white, as is tail, with 2 wide black bands; head blackish with pale bars over and under eye; legs orange, upper bill dark, lower orange, eyes deep red. In display tail raised, wings spread with tips brought forward to frame head and neck, revealing red-orange area with paler penumbra on coverts. This takes place in sunlit glades, with circling,

Food: aerial insects. Breeds in southern summer. Mud nest large and building takes a long time, but same nest often used in successive years; retort-shaped with tubular entrance passage; in buildings and caves, rocks, culverts, drainpipes. 3 or 4 white eggs. **612**

Hirundo daurica or Cecropis daurica *Hirundinidae*
RED-RUMPED SWALLOW   7 ins
Palaearctic, Oriental, (Ethiopian): 12 races breed S Europe, N Africa, Asia Minor, S Iran to Himalayas, Indian subcontinent, Ceylon; also S Siberia, Korea, parts of Japan. Five races resident and breeding across S Sahara to Ethiopia, then S to Malawi, often considered separate *H. rufula;* and scattered populations SE Asia (e.g. Indo-China, Philippines, Lesser Sunda Is) as *H. striolata*. Habits of all three much the same. Southern races *daurica* resident, northern ones winter in southern breeding areas. Habitat from tropical savannah to temperate mountains, up to 15,500 ft Himalayas, also rocky limestone country, sea coasts, towns (e.g. Morocco, Israel). Upperparts blue-black, except for chestnut forehead, nape, rump; underparts buff, streaked darker; wings and deeply forked tail metallic blue; legs brown-black, bill black, eyes dark brown. Deliberate flight, also soars like House Martin, *Delichon urbica,* but not as gregarious. Distinctive 'wailing' flight-call rendered *quitsch;* nasal song similar to but not as pleasing as *H. rustica*. Food: aerial insects. Breeds early May to July in Europe, suspending distinctive spouted mud nest, softly lined, from roof of cave, cleft, inside various buildings. 3 to 5 pure white eggs; 2 broods. **613**

Hirundo dimidiata *Hirundinidae*
PEARL-BREASTED SWALLOW   5½ ins
Ethiopian: 2 races; resident, *dimidiata* in Rhodesia and Damaraland to Cape; *marwitzi*, Angola and Zambia to SW Tanzania. Habitat: open woodland and cultivated country. Upperparts including sides of face, breast, wings and tail, glossy steel blue; underparts white, greyer on chest; no white in tail. ♀ has shorter outer tail feathers. Young have greenish wash above. Legs and bill black, eyes brown. Song characteristic *chip-cheree-chip-chip* usually from perch. Food: aerial insects. Breeds mainly September to January, bowl-shaped mud nest built largely by ♂ plastered to wall and usually supported on ledge; also deep in wells. 3 pure white eggs. **614**

Hirundo fuligula or Ptyonoprogne fuligula *Hirundinidae*
AFRICAN ROCK MARTIN   4¾ ins
Ethiopian: 7 races; resident (some local migration) in all Africa S of Sahara. Habitat: precipitous cliffs and, increasingly, in towns, never far from water. Dark sooty brown except chin to chest and under wing coverts, which are pale russet; tail slightly forked with conspicuous white spots in flight; legs dusky brown, bill black, eyes brown. Flies weakly and does not stray far from habitat except when congregating round grass fire. Call: low twitter or high-pitched *twee;* song: high-pitched *cheep-cheep-cheep-churr* repeated several times, in flight. Food: aerial insects. Breeding season variable within range; builds mud and grass cup on ledge or half-cup against wall, if possible in overhung angle. Usually 3 white eggs, freely spotted with brown. **615**

Hirundo rufula see under **H. daurica**

Hirundo rupestris or Ptyonoprogne rupestris *Hirundinidae*
CRAG MARTIN   5¾ ins
Palaearctic: 2 races; *H.r. rupestris* breeds S Europe N to Pyrenees, Alps, Greece, Mediterranean islands, Morocco, Algeria, Asia Minor and across to all but easternmost China; winters in southern breeding range S to Sudan, Ethiopia, and S India. Race *theresae* apparently resident high in Atlas Mts. Habitat: mountain gorges, inland and coastal cliffs. Rather bulky, with broad triangular wings; upperparts brown, underparts buffish with streaked throat, no breast band; white circles on tail. Feeds on aerial insects off cliff faces and repeats same path along face several times. Call and song a weak twittering. Long

breeding season; builds half-cup mud nest softly lined in cleft rocks, caves, ruined or sometimes occupied buildings, in small colonies, often with other swallows and swifts. 3 or 4 white eggs, finely spotted brown; incubated 14 days. Young fledge 25-26 days. **616**

Hirundo rustica *Hirundinidae*
(BARN) SWALLOW   7½ ins
Holarctic, marginally Oriental: 7 (or 8) races; breeds in whole Palaearctic between 30°N and 70°N, extending to SE China and Taiwan; all N America (except some SE States and nothern half of Canada). Old World races winter Africa S of 12°N, Indian subcontinent and to N Australia; New World races from Panama to Central Chile and N Argentina. Habitat: open cultivated country with farms and buildings, usually near water. Upperparts metallic blue; forehead chestnut; chin and throat dark chestnut; lower throat has dark blue band, rest of underparts creamy to rufous-buff; tail deeply forked, with white spots. ♀ has shorter tail and less metallic throat band. Juvenile duller, short-tailed. Legs and bill black, eyes dark brown. Not very gregarious in summer but collects in autumn flocks and huge roosts in reed-beds, other vegetation. Call: characteristic *tswit-tswit;* song: warbling twitter with short trill. Food: insects from air and water surface. Breeds mid May to September, ♀ and ♂ building open mud and straw nest, lined feathers, on ledge usually in building of some kind; natural sites in caves or on cliffs now very rare. Usually 4 or 5 white eggs, marked reddish spots over ashy grey. Incubation mainly by ♀ 14-15 days. Young, fed by both parents, fledge *c.* 21 days. 2 (sometimes 3) broods. **617**

Hirundo senegalensis or Cecropis senegalensis *Hirundinidae*
MOSQUE SWALLOW   9 ins
Ethiopian: 3 races; resident from Senegal to Kordofan (Sudan) to 8°N, coastal Ghana and Congo E to Ethiopia then S to Zambia, Malawi and Mozambique; considerable local movements in small parties. Habitat: commonest in large timber woodland, also by houses. Plumage like *H. daurica* but no chestnut on nape; upperparts blue-black with chestnut rump; underparts, including tail coverts, pale rufous; legs and bill black, eyes brown. Rather lethargic and has the 'flutter and sail' flight as *H. abyssinica*. Calls: single note like tin trumpet and guttural croak; song a low twitter. Food: aerial insects. Breeding season variable within range; occupies hole in tree, filling it to correct size with mud, or builds large retort-shaped mud nest under cliff or bridge, or (if in house) rim of mud on board. 3 or 4 pure white eggs. **618**

Hirundo smithii *Hirundinidae*
WIRE-TAILED SWALLOW   6 ins
Ethiopian, Oriental: 2 races; resident, *H. s. smithii* in W Ghana to Benguela, and E Ethiopia to Zambia and Natal outside rain-forest areas; *filifera* in Afghanistan, most of Indian subcontinent, N Thailand, Laos, S Annam. Habitat: towns and villages, open country. Head chestnut, rest of upperparts glossy violet-blue, lores black; underparts white; tail with white patches and very narrow, elongated outer feathers. ♀ has much shorter tail. Young much duller. Legs and bill black, eyes brown. Rather solitary. Call: low twitter seldom heard. Food: aerial insects. Breeding season variable within range; builds open or half-cup nest of mud, lined feathers, placed very close to overhang and not supported below. Usually 3 eggs, white with rather heavy reddish or brown spots. Incubation by ♀ 14 days. Young, fed by both parents, fly 18 to 21 days. **619**

Hirundo striolata see under **H. daurica**

HISPANIOLA PARROT see **Amazonia ventralis**

Histrionicus histrionicus *Anatidae*
HARLEQUIN DUCK   16 ins
Holarctic: Atlantic race, *H. h. histrionicus*, breeds Iceland, Greenland, N Labrador, wintering S to Long Island, NY; Pacific, *pacificus*, breeds E Siberia and N America from S Alaska to mountains of California and Colorado; winters S to California and Japan. Habitat:

swift rivers and streams; winter: coastal, off rough, rocky shores. ♂: striking white markings bordered by black on blue-grey head and body; stripe on crown and flanks chestnut red; speculum metallic purple; longish tail dark brown. ♀: grey-brown with white patches on head, larger one on cheek, two smaller ones in front of and behind eyes. Legs pale bluish, short bill lead-blue, nail whitish, eyes reddish-brown; all duller on ♀. Usually in small parties, swimming buoyantly, sometimes in formation and not associating with other species. Walks easily, flies swiftly in small compact flocks, often swinging from side to side. ♂ has soft whistle, ♀ croaks. Day feeder, using short dive, sometimes from wing, taking small water animals. Breeds May to July, often socially, on small islands in shelter of rocks or vegetation. 5 to 8 creamy or light buff eggs laid in nest of down and plant debris; incubated by ♀ *c.* 28 days; she tends young, who fly *c.* 40 days. **116**

HOATZIN see **Opisthocomus hoatzin**

HONEY BUZZARD see **Pernis apivorus**

HONEY BUZZARD, CRESTED see under **Pernis apivorus**

HONEYCREEPER,
PURPLE see **Cyanerpes caeruleus**
YELLOW-LEGGED see **Cyanerpes caeruleus**

HONEYEATER,
BLACK see **Myzomela nigra**
BLUE-FACED see **Entomyzon cyanotus**
HELMETED see **Meliphaga cassidix**
SPINY-CHEEKED see **Acanthagenys rufogularis**
STRIPED see **Plectorhyncha lanceolata**
TAWNY-CROWNED see **Gliciphila melanops**
WHITE-BEARDED see **Meliornis novaehollandiae**
WHITE-CHEEKED see **Meliornis niger**
WHITE-EARED see **Meliphaga leucotis**
WHITE-FRONTED see **Gliciphila albifrons**
YELLOW-FACED see **Meliphaga chrysops**
YELLOW-TUFTED see **Meliphaga melanops**
YELLOW-WINGED see **Meliornis novaehollandiae**

HONEYGUIDE, LESSER see **Indicator minor**

HOODED
CROW see **Corvus corone**
DOTTEREL see **Charadrius cucullatus**
MERGANSER see **Mergus cucullatus**
ROBIN see **Petroica cucullata**
WHEATEAR see **Oenanthe monacha**

HOOPOE see **Upupa epops**

HOOPOE,
FOREST WOOD see under **Phoeniculus purpureus**
GREEN WOOD see **Phoeniculus purpureus**
WHITE-HEADED WOOD see under **Phoeniculus purpureus**

Hoplopterus
armatus see **Vanellus armatus**
spinosus see **Vanellus spinosus**

HORNBILL,
ABYSSINIAN GROUND see **Bucorvus abyssinicus**
ASIAN WHITE-CRESTED see **Berenicornis comatus**
CROWNED see **Tockus alboterminatus**
GREY see **Tockus nasutus**
GROUND see **Bucorvus leadbeateri**
INDIAN PIED see **Anthracocerus malabaricus**
PAPUAN see **Aceros plicatus**
RED-BILLED see **Tockus erythrorhynchus**
VAN DER DECKEN'S see **Tockus deckeni**
YELLOW-BILLED see **Tockus flavirostris**

HORNED
GREBE see **Podiceps auritus**
LARK see **Eremophila alpestris**

Hydranassa tricolor *Ardeidae*
LOUISIANA or TRICOLOURED HERON   24–28 ins
Nearctic and Neotropical: breeds from New Jersey and California S to central Argentina and NW Peru; wanders northward late summer. Habitat coastal mangrove swamps, mudflats and marshes. Upperparts slate grey with white to rufous line down neck to white belly and rump; purplish crest with white nuptial plumes, buff on back; immature more rufous; legs variable, yellow to orange, bill blackish, eyes orange. Slender-looking active heron, often wading deeply after fish, sometimes leaping out of water; also takes amphibians, reptiles and water animals, e.g. prawns. Utters variety of harsh croaks and deep groans, 'rasping *raah*' when bickering. Breeding season variable, May to August W Indies. Colonies, often with other species, in trees, especially mangroves a few ft above water, or on ground. Nest, slight platform of sticks, holds 3 to 7 pale blue green eggs, incubated by ♀ and ♂ for at least 3 weeks; they also tend the young. **62**

Hydrobates pelagicus *Hydrobatidae*
STORM PETREL   6 ins
N Atlantic (E side W to Iceland) and Mediterranean, dispersing after breeding; sometimes driven inland by storms. Sooty grey with squared tail and white rump; narrow pale wingbar in fresh plumage and white underwing; legs and bill black; eyes very dark brown. Fluttering zigzag flight and short glides behind ships, occasionally pattering over water or settling to swim buoyantly. Displays at colonies by night when visiting birds call and those on nests reply with long series of purring notes ending in sharp *chikka*. Food mainly plankton but will take scraps from ships' kitchens. Breeds May to September in excavated burrow, pile of stones or stone walls, on bare islands and headlands. One white, brown zoned, egg laid in vestigial nest and incubated 5½ weeks by ♀ and ♂, who tend chick for 8–9 weeks.

Hydroprogne caspia *Laridae*
CASPIAN TERN   *c.* 21 ins
Holarctic, Ethiopian, Oriental and Australasian: locally, N America, Europe, Africa and Asia through to New Zealand and Australia; tends to move to S of range in winter. Habitat: shallow, coastal waters, also inland lakes and larger rivers. Underparts white, crown black (streaked white outside breeding season), back and wings grey, rump and tail paler, often white; legs black, large bill red, eyes dark brown. Immature: underparts mottled, bill duller and more orange. Single or small groups, can soar to great heights; fishes by flying close to surface with bill down and plunging into water, also feeds on surface like gulls and may take small birds, eggs, and rob other birds. Call: deep, harsh *kaah* or *kaak-kaa*. Breeds sandy or rocky islands in colonies, groups or isolated, mid May onwards; 2 or 3 pinkish buff eggs spotted with dark brown in scrape on ground usually with light lining of plant debris, occasionally nests on mat of floating vegetation near shores of shallow lakes. Incubates *c.* 21 days, young fly *c.* 4½ weeks. **323**

Hylocichla mustelina *Muscicapidae: Turdinae*
WOOD THRUSH   8 ins
Nearctic: breeds from Central New Hampshire, SE Ontario, Central Wisconsin, SE Dakota, S to N Florida, Louisiana, E Texas; winters from S Mexico to W Panama. Habitat deciduous woodland with thick undergrowth, especially by streams, lakes, swamps; also parks and gardens with shady trees. Upperparts chestnut brown, head brightest; cheeks whitish, mottled chestnut; underparts white, spotted black from gorget to lower belly; legs pale flesh, bill brown, eyes dark brown, orbits white. Lives mainly on forest floor, scratching dead leaves and debris for insects and other small invertebrates; also takes small fruits. Call low *tuc tuc;* alarm rapid, repeated *pit.* Fluty rippling song like Hermit Thrush, *Catharus guttatus*, divided into short phrases and pauses, with final high-pitched trill audible close up. Breeds May to June New England, making compact nest local plant materials with cup of mud or hardened leaf-mould, lined rootlets. 3 or 4 greenish blue eggs incubated by ♀ *c.* 2 weeks; both parents feed young, who fledge rapidly *c.* 10 days. Sometimes 2 broods. **684**

Hylocichla ustulata see **Catharus ustulatus**

Hylomanes momotula *Momotidae*
TODY MOTMOT   6½–7 (bill 1) ins
Neotropical: S Mexico to NW Colombia but not continuous distribution; resident in undergrowth of humid forests sea level to *c.* 4,500 ft. Smallest motmot: upperparts, including short tail, dull green; crown dull chestnut, 'eyebrow' blue, ear coverts black, bordered white; throat and centre of belly dull white; rest of underparts pale olive brown. 'Elusive and little known' (A. F. Skutch). Flies out from perch to take insects in air or fruit from twigs; also takes eggs of other birds. Nesting habits much as relatives, see *Momotus momota*.

Hylophilus ochraceiceps *Vireonidae*
TAWNY-CROWNED GREENLET   4½ ins
Neotropical: Central America, Guyanas, adjacent Venezuela S into E Brazil; western race Venezuela (Amazonas), Colombia, E and NW Ecuador S to N Bolivia, W Amazonian Brazil; forest and woodland, sea level to 4,500 ft. Upperparts dark olive green to olive (tail dull rufous eastern race); crown bright orange, tinged olive towards nape (forehead, lores orange, crown olive, eastern race); throat grey, breast olivaceous to yellowish olive, belly grey (throat, breast buffish, underparts whitish eastern race). Legs brown, bill horn brown, eyes dark brown. **905**

Hypocolius ampelinus *Bombycillidae*
GREY HYPOCOLIUS   9 ins
S Palaearctic: restricted to parts of SW Asia, especially Iraq, migrating irregularly to NW Indian subcontinent. Habitat: scrub in semi-desert and cultivated land, palm groves, gardens. Generally pale grey, tinged blue on back, buffish on forehead, underparts; primaries black, tipped white; long tail broadly tipped black; black mask extending to thin erectile band round back of neck. ♀: duller, grey instead of black on head. Juvenile buff brown, without black except on tail. Legs light brown, rather strong bill black, eyes dark brown. Behaviour like waxwings *Bombycilla*, gregarious after breeding, not very active, but flight swift and direct into cover where parties remain silent. Call: squeaking note. Diet: fruits and berries, some insects. Breeds June, building large, rather untidy nest of twigs, softly lined, usually well hidden in leaves of palm tree. 4 or 5 pale grey eggs, marked blackish, sometimes very heavily.

Hypositta coralirostris *Sittidae*
MADAGASCAR or
CORAL-BILLED NUTHATCH   *c.* 5 ins
Madagascar: forests of humid east, nearly sea level to *c.* 5,500 ft. Upperparts dull greenish blue, flight feathers dark brown, edged blue green; tail dark brown, washed bluish; forehead and crown greenish brown; underparts tawny yellow, washed greenish; legs blackish, bill coral-red tipped black, eyes deep red. Behaves like treecreepers *Certhia*, hunting upper trunks and larger branches of forest trees, then flying down to next one. Often 2 or 3 in mixed flocks of other birds. Presumably mainly insectivorous. Breeds probably August and September.

Hypsipetes flavala or Microscelis flavalus *Pycnonotidae*
BROWN-EARED or ASHY BULBUL   8 ins
E Palaearctic-Oriental: Himalayas E to Yunnan, S through Burma, Thailand, Malaysia; resident primary and secondary forest. Upperparts, including crest, dark brown, shading to yellowish green on wings and dark-tipped tail; throat white, breast grey; under tail coverts bright yellow; legs blackish to flesh, bill black, eyes dark red, pale brown or greyish olive. Noisy parties work lower canopy, undergrowth, bamboo thickets. Puffs out white feathers of throat in display. Variety of calls, variously described, for different races. Breeds May in Burma, building flimsy cup of bamboo leaves suspended between stems, e.g. dead bracken, up to 15 ft. 3 to 5 eggs, pinkish grey, marked red, black and purple, incubated mainly by ♀, fed by ♂, who also helps with brood, fed at first on insects, then berries. **639**

Ibidorhyncha struthersii *Recurvirostridae*
IBISBILL   *c.* 16 ins
E Palaearctic, Oriental: W Turkestan through Himalayas and N Assam to Szechuan and Inner Mongolia; high plateaux usually between 6,000 and 10,000 ft; some movement to lower foothills in winter. Breeds along rocky and clear mountain streams, often where gradient has decreased in fairly wide valley. Front of head, throat, breast band, black; rest of upperparts mostly grey-brown; basal markings on rump black; tail ash grey with thin wavy blackish barring; white wing patch partly concealed; cheeks, neck, upper breast blue-grey, rest of underparts white; long legs blood red, long down-curved bill bright red, eyes dark red. Smooth flight; usually in pairs. Good swimmer; often feeds by wading breast-high and ducking head and neck under water, using bill to seek out small crustacea, insects, other water animals from under stones. Calls: in flight ringing whistle, quickly repeated; shrill mournful cry when disturbed. Wary when breeding, March onwards; scrape in ground, sometimes pebbled-lined, usually on crest of small ridge in or on edge of shingle bed, boulders on small island in stream or on bank. 3 or 4 stone grey eggs, sometimes tinged greenish or brownish, with sepia, pale bluish-grey or reddish markings. Incubating ♀ or ♂ blends perfectly with surrounding water-smoothed boulders.

IBIS,
BALD see **Geronticus calvus**
BLACK see **Pseudibis papillosa**
GLOSSY see **Plegadis falcinellus**
HADADA see **Hagedashia hagedash**
SACRED see **Threskiornis aethiopicus**
SCARLET see **Eudocimus ruber**
STRAW-NECKED see **Threskiornis spinicollis**
WATTLED see **Bostrychia carunculata**
WHITE (AMERICAN) see **Eudocimus albus**
WHITE (AUSTRALIAN) see under **Threskiornis spinicollis**

Ibis
ibis see **Mycteria ibis**
leucocephalus see **Mycteria leucocephalus**

Icterus galbula *Icteridae*
BALTIMORE ORIOLE   7½ ins
Nearctic: breeds southern Canada, including Nova Scotia, S to N Georgia, Central Louisiana, S Texas; W to Central Montana, E Colorado; winters S Mexico to Colombia. Habitat edge mature broad-leaved woodland especially by streams; also roadsides, parks, gardens. ♂: head, gorget, mantle, most of wings, base and centre tail glossy black; shoulder patch, lower back, rump, underparts from breast orange; wings white bar and edges; tips outer tail feathers orange yellow. ♀: variable, sometimes like 'faded' ♂, black flecked orange brown; or olive yellow above with yellow underparts, rump, tail. Immature much as ♀ but upperparts uniform olive yellow. Legs light grey, bill grey, eyes brown. (Usually enough orange to distinguish from Orchard Oriole, *I. spurius,* with black and maroon ♂, predominantly green ♀). ♂ displays to ♀ on branch, exposing plumage features and singing: mixture of whistled 2-note phrases and softer single notes, individual to each ♂; some song from ♀, and ♂ sings after moult. Call mellow single or double whistle; rattle of alarm. Food mainly insects, some fruit. Breeds May-June; ♀, ♂ nearby, builds bag-nest *c.* 6 ins deep, narrow at tip, usually of light-coloured plant fibres, bark, hair, twine, suspended from end twigs of drooping branch; returns annually to same site. 4 to 6 pale grey eggs, marked and scrawled black and brown at big end, incubated mainly ♀: 12-14 days; ♀ and ♂ feed young, who fly *c.* 2 weeks. **910**

Icteria virens *Parulidae*
YELLOW-BREASTED CHAT   7½ ins
Nearctic, marginally Neotropical: breeds Connecticut, S Ontario, Iowa, Montana, S British Columbia S to N Florida, Gulf Coast, E Mexico; winters N Mexico S to Costa Rica. Habitat dense bush and vine tangles with scattered trees, probably originally by streams, pools, now in young growth on burnt or cut-over land, abandoned fields. Upperparts from crown dark olive green, tinged brown flight feathers, tail; broad white 'eyebrow' and short white stripe from gape enclose blue-black mask round white-ringed eye; underparts from chin to belly yellow, under tail coverts white; legs, powerful bill black, eyes dark brown. Hard to see as keeps to canopy or dense thicket, occasionally flying up to 'sing' in air, flapping slowly or hovering with legs dangling. Calls, emphatic *chuck* or *chuck-uck;* song: disjointed phrases, often widely spaced; whistles, mews, squeaks, scolding and trumpeting sounds, singly or repeated. Insectivorous but takes much fruit. Breeds May to July, building bulky nest of dead leaves, grass, bark, lined fine grass, 3 to 5 ft up in bushes, vine tangles. 4 white eggs, evenly spotted brown; incubation (♀) and fledging periods *c.* 2 weeks. If parasitised by Cowbird, *Molothrus ater,* often destroys own clutch with intruders egg. **895**

Icterus spurius see under **I. galbula**

INCA TERN see **Larosterna inca**

INDIAN
CRESTED SWIFT see **Hemiprocne longipennis**
HILL MYNAH see **Gracula religiosa**
PEAFOWL see **Pavo cristatus**
PIED HORNBILL see **Anthracocerus malabaricus**

RING-NECKED PARAKEET see **Psittacula krameri**
ROLLER see **Coracias benghalensis**
WHITE-BACKED VULTURE see **Gyps bengalensis**
WHITE-EYE see **Zosterops palpebrosa**

Indicator indicator *Indicatoridae*
GREATER or
BLACK-THROATED HONEYGUIDE   8 ins
Ethiopian: whole region except W African rainforests and Kalahari, in wide variety of habitats. Greyish brown above, off-white below, bright pink bill; ♂ has black throat patch; white outer tail feathers conspicuous in flight. Feeds on wax, grubs, honey from bees' nests to which it attracts humans, honeybadgers (ratels) by excited chattering. Parasitises hole-nesting barbets, woodpeckers, bee-eaters, laying similar white eggs in their nests.

Indicator minor *Indicatoridae*
LESSER HONEYGUIDE   5½ ins
Ethiopian: same range, habitats as preceeding species, but not in fact a guide to honey though does eat bees' wax, grubs as well as other insects, caterpillars. Dull olive above, pale grey to white below, white outer tail feathers. Perches inconspicuously on branch, calling monotonously *pew pew pew.* Also parasitises small hole-nesting barbets, kingfishers etc. **533**

Irediparra gallinacea *Jacanidae*
LOTUS BIRD or AUSTRALIAN JACANA   *c.* 12 ins
Oriental, Australasian: Borneo, Moluccas, Celebes, New Guinea, Continental Australia; resident in swamps and ponds. Upperparts brown glossed green; nape, back of neck, breast and flanks black; throat and upper breast white framed golden yellow, which extends to head; downward dark stripe from eye; underparts white but under wing coverts black; legs green, bill, dark tipped, with light base merging into red frontal comb, eyes light brown. Behaviour much as relatives but flight weaker. Call of alarm sharp and 'trumpet-like'. Food: water animals and plants. Breeds September to February in Australia; April in Borneo. Nest a pile of green water plants, half submerged or on platform out from shore. Usually 4 glossy, yellowish olive eggs marked with blotches and interlacing dark brown lines. Incubation and fledging much as African Jacana, *Actophilornis africana.* **249**

Irena puella *Irenidae*
FAIRY BLUEBIRD   11 ins
Oriental: widespread in region; resident evergreen forest. Rather thrush-like in shape but more slender; ♂: upperparts from crown to upper tail coverts purplish blue; flight feathers, tail, underparts and face black; legs, bill blackish, eyes red. ♀: dull blue-green; primaries and tail dark brown, black patch round eye. Juvenile ♂ as ♀, but feathers of upperparts fringed blue. Usually in flocks, occasionally solitary or pairs, constantly on move from tree to tree. Drinks and bathes midday. Call: repeated *be quick;* also sharp, loud whistle, sometimes followed by bubbling call. Diet: exclusively fruit, especially figs, gathering with other species at ripe tree. Breeds March to May (Burma), building rather flimsy cup of twigs, rootlets, moss, lined moss roots, in bush or sapling. 2 pale to reddish grey or buff eggs, marked brown, purple and grey. **644**

Iridoprocne bicolor see **Tachycineta bicolor**

Iridosornis rufivertex *Emberizidae: Thraupinae*
GOLDEN-CROWNED TANAGER   7 ins
Neotropical: very local Venezuela, most of Colombia, E and W Ecuador; forests of temperate zone (7,500 ft upwards). Upperparts glossy purplish blue, underparts similar but darker, under tail coverts chestnut (blue in one race); head black, centre crown golden yellow. **876**

Ispidina picta *Alcedinidae*
AFRICAN PYGMY KINGFISHER   4 ins
Ethiopian: whole of sub-Saharan Africa except Somalia, SW Africa. Habitat: forest, bush, savannah, not necessarily near water as mainly land feeder, on grass crickets etc, but small fish also taken. Perches on

low bush, pounces down into grass. Flies off with very rapid flight, calling squeakily. Mainly ultramarine above, tawny below, throat white; distinguished from very similar Malachite Kingfisher, *Corythornis cristata,* by lack of crest. 3 to 5 white eggs in short tunnel in bank. **492**

JABIRU see **Jabiru mycteria**

Jabiru mycteria *Ciconiidae*
JABIRU   4½ ft
Neotropical, from Central America to E Peru, Paraguay, Uruguay and N Argentina. Sedentary; habitat in Brazil open wet grasslands with ponds by rivers. White, with bare head and neck black, to red at base. Legs and very heavy bill black, eyes brown. Several hops to take off, then flight light and graceful, often soars to great height. Feeds singly, catching snakes in grassland, also fish, molluscs, especially *Ampullaria,* and crustaceans. Breeds usually on limbs of tall trees or rock, building large flat nest of sticks with thick lining of grass; 2 to 4 grey or yellowish white eggs incubated by ♀ and ♂; *c.* 4 months from incubation to fledging. **72**

JACAMAR,
RUFOUS-TAILED see **Galbula ruficauda**
THREE-TOED see **Jacamaralcyon tridactyla**
YELLOW-BILLED see **Galbula albirostris**

Jacamaralcyon tridactyla *Galbulidae*
THREE-TOED JACAMAR   6¼ (bill 1½) ins
Neotropical: SE Brazil from Minas Gerais to Parana; resident in forest. Upperparts blackish glossed green; head chestnut brown streaked buff; underparts white, flanks greyish; hind toe absent; long bill black. Insectivorous, taking flying insects in aerial sallies. Excavates nest hole like relatives (see *Galbula ruficauda*).

JACANA,
AFRICAN see **Actophilornis africanus**
AUSTRALIAN see **Irediparra gallinacea**
LESSER see **Microparra capensis**
WATTLED see **Jacana spinosa**

Jacana jacana see **J. spinosa**

Jacana spinosa or J. jacana *Jacanidae*
WATTLED or SOUTH AMERICAN JACANA   10 ins
Neotropical: resident from Mexico southward; widespread E of Andes to Bolivia and N Argentina; W of Andes to Colombia, W Ecuador, NW Peru; W Indies; marshes, swampy riversides and lakes. Head, neck, mantle black, rest of plumage dark chestnut except for yellow-green, dark-tipped flight feathers; legs dusky green, bill yellow, frontal shield and wattles red or yellow, eyes brown. Juvenile greyish-brown above, whitish below, with white 'eye-brow'. Habits much as other jacanas; cackling call. Food: water plants and invertebrate animals taken from their leaves. Breeds June to February, sex roles reversed, larger ♀ often polyandrous. Shallow untidy nest among water plants, holds 3 to 5 buff-brown eggs, heavily scrawled black, incubated by ♂ 22-24 days. Probably at least 2 broods. **250**

JACKASS, LAUGHING see **Dacelo nouaeguineae**

JACKASS PENGUIN see **Spheniscus demersus**

JACKDAW see **Corvus monedula**

JACK SNIPE see **Lymnocryptes minimus**

JACKSON'S FRANCOLIN see **Francolinus jacksoni**

JACKY WINTER see **Microeca fascinans**

JAMESON'S FIREFINCH see under **Lagonisticta rubricata**

JAPANESE CRANE see **Grus japonensis**

JAVAN BROWN WOOD OWL see **Strix leptogrammica**

Jynx torquilla *Picidae*
WRYNECK   c. 6½ ins
Palaearctic: main range across Eurasia from S Scandinavia, Britain (now very rare) and N Iberia between 50° and 60°N in W Asia to Pacific between 40° and 60°; also NW Africa, Crimea, Caucasus, mountains of Central Asia; northern populations winter S Asia and Africa N of Equator. Habitat: broadleaved forests, especially oak, larch woods, tree groups on steppes, riverine woodland, cultivated areas, roadsides, parks, gardens. Grey-brown: upperparts mottled, streaked and vermiculated various patterns; underparts pale brown or buff, barred on breast, flecked on belly, greyish tail with several darker bars; legs and bill pale brownish-horn, eyes hazel brown. Perches like passerine as well as clinging to trunks like woodpecker, sometimes with help of tail. Often on ground, hopping with tail raised, and perches on bushes. Flight rather laboured. Small parties form on migration. Spring call shrill, ringing *quee quee quee* . . . resembling calls of small falcons and Lesser Spotted Woodpecker, *Dendrocopos minor*; also repeated *tuk* of alarm; hisses and contorts neck if disturbed on nest. Mutual display; ♂ and ♀ face each other, shake heads and expose pink gape. Feeds largely on ants picked off from grass or tree crevices with rapid action of long vermiform tongue; also takes eggs and nestlings from nestboxes. Breeds mid April onwards, using, but not excavating, holes in trees, banks, ground, sometimes in walls, posts, nestboxes. 7 to 10 white eggs incubated by ♀ and ♂ 12-14 days; both feed young, who fly 19-21 days. Sometimes 2 broods. **549**

Lagonisticta rubricata *Estrildidae*
AFRICAN FIREFINCH   4½ ins
Ethiopian: Angola, W Africa E to Eritrea, Ethiopia, S through E Africa, Malawi, Zambia, E Rhodesia to S Africa; resident forest edge or riverine bush; thorn scrub with tall grass; neglected cultivation. ♂: generally claret red; crown, nape underlying grey; back, wings earth brown; belly, tail, under tail coverts black; white spots side breast. ♀ has brown crown; underparts pale claret, washed pale brown. Legs, eyes brown, bill blue-black. Very similar Jameson's Firefinch, *L. jamesoni*, is paler, favours more arid habitat. Pairs or small parties, keeping to thick undergrowth, fly low from bush to bush. Attracted by imitating alarm notes

of other species. Call: clear metallic trill, usually followed by *wink wink wink*; repeated *chit* of alarm; low chirping song. Diet: small seeds. Breeding season varies within range; builds flimsy grass nest with large side entrance, thinly lined feathers. 3 to 6 white eggs, incubated ♀; ♀ and ♂ feed young. **938**

Lagopus lagopus *Tetraonidae*
WILLOW and RED GROUSE   15-16 ins
Willow Grouse, *L.l. lagopus*, Holarctic temperate and subarctic from Scandinavia through N Eurasia to Alaska and parts N Canada; Red Grouse, *L.l. scoticus*, in Britain and Ireland, introduced Belgium. Resident on moorland and heaths with willow, birch and juniper scrub. Willow Grouse: dark rufous brown in spring with darker outer tail feathers, white wings and under tail coverts; becomes white in winter except for tail (thus very like ♀ Rock Ptarmigan, *L. mutus*); legs feathered white, bill black, eyes hazel with red wattles above. Red Grouse ♂: dark rufous brown all year with darker tail and wings, ♀ yellower on body in spring. Packs in autumn, flying up to 1 mile when disturbed; later pairs form and ♂ prominent in territory, calling *go-bak go-bak*. Burrows in snow for food and cover in winter. Diet heather, other shoots, berries and seeds; also insects, especially when young. Breeds from March in Britain, later in N; ♀ lines scrape in heath-type vegetation or tussocks, laying from 6 to 11 yellowish eggs, blotched smeary red-brown, incubates them for 23-26 days with ♂ near; he helps guard precocious brood, which fly 12-13 days. **183**

Lagopus leucurus *Tetraonidae*
WHITE-TAILED PTARMIGAN   12½ ins
Nearctic: Alpine zone from Cascade Mountains, and Rockies of New Mexico N to Central Alaska and NW Mackenzie. All white in winter; upperparts, including centre of tail and breast mottled yellow-brown, black and white in summer; belly, most of wings and outer tail feathers white; legs feathered white, bill black, red wattles over dark brown eyes. Found on high windswept ridges, in flocks of up to 100, feeding on dwarf willow and sheltering in snowbanks, but may come down to conifer forest to take needles, buds, flowers and fruits of low-growing plants in summer, also some insects. Cackling alarm call when flushed; also hoots and clucking notes, especially from ♂, who stays near ♀ when she lays (from mid June in S) usually 6 to 8 buff eggs marked in shades of brown in lined scrape, incubating them for c. 3 weeks. ♂ assists her look after precocious brood. **184**

Lagopus mutus *Tetraonidae*
ROCK PTARMIGAN   14 ins
Holarctic: temperate alpine and arctic zones; very local Europe, widespread Asia, Alaska, also arctic Canada and Greenland. Sedentary on shrub, moss and lichen tundra, also among rocks close to snow line in summer. ♂: body, head and centre of tail mottled grey brown in spring, outer tail feathers black, wings white; ♀ browner. Both greyer in autumn and white in winter when ♂ has black stripe through eye. Legs feathered white, bill black, eyes brown with red wattles above. Families form packs late autumn, which often crouch rather than fly and burrow in snow for cover and food. Curious snoring call when alerted; ♂ in spring has 'coughing' song during display by jumping, descending with spread wings. Diet of leaves, seeds, berries of many alpine-arctic plants. Breeds from May in Britain, ♀ lining scrape made by ♂, usually in open or among stones, laying 5 to 9 buff eggs, marked yellow-brown and incubating for 21½-26 days, with ♂ near. Both attend brood, which flies c. 10 days. Injury-feigning characteristic with eggs or young. **185**

Lalage sueurii *Campephagidae*
WHITE-WINGED TRILLER   7 ins
Oriental, Australasian; Java and adjacent islands E to Celebes; continental Australia; summer visitor to open woodland and scrub in Australia. ♂: crown, mantle, flight and tail feathers glossy black; lower back, rump grey; large shoulder patches, webs secondaries, all underparts white. ♀: brown above, with pale 'eyebrow'; underparts whitish, washed brown on breast. Two moults annually: in April ♂ becomes brown on

head and mantle. Legs, gill, eyes dark. Melodious song, with *joey joey* call as it flies between trees. Takes insects, especially cicadas, and larvae from foliage. Breeds September to January Australia; ♀ and ♂ building small open nest of plant material, bound cobwebs, decorated bark, spider's egg bags, typically in fork of lateral branch. One to 3 eggs, light or bright bluish-green, heavily marked red-brown. Incubation by ♀ and ♂ c. 14 days; both parents feed young, who fly c. 12 days.

LAMMERGEIER see **Gypaetus barbatus**

Lampornis clemenciae *Trochilidae*
BLUE-THROATED SYLPH or HUMMINGBIRD   5 ins
Nearctic to Neotropical: mountains of W Texas, S New Mexico and S Arizona to S Mexico; northern birds move S in autumn. Confined to dense riverine vegetation in mountainous canyons, 5,000 to 7,600 ft. ♂: generally dark green; white stripe behind eye, iridescent light blue gorget; flight feathers dark brown washed green; under tail coverts white, heavily flecked green; slightly forked tail blue-black with conspicuous white area on each extremity. ♀ similar but with white throat. Legs, bill, eyes dark. Closely resembles Rivoli's Hummingbird, *Eugenes fulgens*, but both sexes constantly fan tail, to show its more extensive white. Call, excited piercing *seep* uttered in flight and when perched, bird hunching restlessly from side to side. (J. T. Marshall). Feeds principally at flowers, chasing other species away; takes insects off sycamore leaves. Nest relatively large cup of plant materials bound with spider's web, attached to flower stalk or other slender support on stream bank. Incubation of 2 eggs and feeding as other hummingbirds (see *Aglaiocercus kingi*).

Lamprocolius chalybeus *Sturnidae*
BLUE-EARED GLOSSY STARLING   8½-9 ins
Ethiopian: Ethiopia across continent to W Africa, southward to NE South Africa. Some local movements from acacia bush and open woodlands, even entering towns. Very similar to Cape Glossy Starling, *L. nitens*; generally iridescent blue-green; earcoverts, belly violet blue, lores black; 'shoulders' magenta and bronze or violet blue according to race; black terminal spots on wing coverts; legs, bill black, eyes orange. Juvenile sooty black below, washed greenish all over; eyes dark grey. Large flocks form after breeding, flying up noisily from ground, where hops. Roosts trees, reedbeds with 'deafening chatter'. Call: loud nasal *squeare squeare*, followed by rattling whistle, becoming 'hysterical whistle' of alarm; also chirps and warblings. Food: fruit, berries, insects. Breeds September to January Rhodesia, in holes in trees, posts, other artefacts; sometimes takes over old nest at top of thorn tree; holes lined grass, feathers, sometimes snakeskin, 3 to 20 ft up or more. 3 or 4 pale blue eggs, sparingly speckled or marked umber over lilac. **969**

Lamprotornis australis *Sturnidae*
BURCHELL'S GLOSSY STARLING   12-14 ins
Ethiopian: much of Southern Africa, including Botswana, to S Angola, Ngamiland; resident dry open bush with tall trees. Upperparts metallic green with purple sheen, black subterminal spots on feathers; 'shoulder' bronze; long, graduated, wedge-shaped tail purple over dark barring; earcoverts, cheeks dark purple; hindneck, rump, belly purple; head, nape, chin to upper breast green, glossed purple; legs, bill black, eyes brown. Immature duller, browner below. Singly, pairs, large flocks, usually near water. Rather laboured flapping flight, but aerial manoeuvres before roosting in reedbeds. Walks on ground. Loud, harsh calls but not unmusical song. Diet: insects, fruit. Breeds November, December and March SW Africa, 6 ft upwards in tree holes, lined green grass. 3 or 4 sky blue eggs, speckled reddish-purple, often concentrated big end. Presumably 2 broods some areas. **970**

Laniarius aethiopicus *Laniidae*
BOUBOU   9 ins
Ethiopian: almost throughout region, from highland forest to scrub in dry watercourses, also bush, coastal scrub, gardens. Upperparts and cheeks glossy blue-black; middle and some secondary wing coverts white;

underparts white tinged pinkish; legs bluish slate, bill black, eye reddish brown. Immature duller. Pairs skulk in thick cover, betraying presence by clear bell-like calls. In duet ♂ gives three calls, answered so quickly by ♀'s 'groaning *huee*' that only one bird seems to be involved; at least seven combinations identified; also harsh alarm calls: *churr* and *tchak*. Varied shrike diet includes many young birds. Breeding season varies with range. Nest of tendrils, dry stems, rootlets, softly lined, in bush or fork of branch often quite open. 2 rather glossy blue-green or greenish buff eggs, spotted and speckled brown over lilac and grey. **647**

Lanioturdus torquatus *Laniidae*
WHITE-TAILED SHRIKE   5½ ins
Ethiopian: NW Southern Africa; resident open thorn bush, edges of mixed woodland. Upperparts grey; rather pointed wings black with prominent white bar when closed and flight feathers tipped white; short tail with 2 black subterminal spots; head black and white; underparts, chin to undertail white with broad black breast band and grey flanks. Pairs or small parties forage restlessly for insects, mainly on ground, sometimes up to 70 ft, creeping about foliage. Short, slow flights. Call: loud, clear *huo huo huo*, recorded duetting; alarm: *squee squee*; various other churring, croaking notes. Breeds January-February, building cup nest of grass, bark strips, bound cobwebs, lined fine grass, fairly high in tree fork. 2 dull white to blue-grey eggs, zoned dark and light brown markings.

Lanius cabanisi *Laniidae*
LONG-TAILED FISCAL SHRIKE   12 ins
Ethiopian: resident southern Somalia S to E Tanzania as far as Dar es Salaam; inland to Kenya: Kilosa and Nairobi. Habitat grasslands with scattered bushes, low open coastal scrub. Upperparts black, shading to grey on rump; very long tail black; white wingbar; underparts white; legs, bill dark grey, eyes reddish. Often in small parties perched together in same bush, raising, lowering and swinging tails like pendulum (J. G. Williams); also bickers noisily, but has clear whistle as well as harsh calls, commonest *chit-er-row*. Food as relatives. Breeding season protracted in Kenya. Large nest of grass, rootlets, finer lining, low in thick bush, often thorny. 3 or 4 buff or cream eggs, spotted and speckled brown over lavender. **648**

Lanius collaris *Laniidae*
FISCAL SHRIKE   9 ins
Ethiopian: widely distributed in region from Eritrea, Sudan S to S Africa (Transvaal); westwards S of Sahara to Sierra Leone, SW to Angola; some local migration. Variety of habitats, including lightly wooded country, cultivated areas, near houses. ♂: upperparts, including most of head, glossy back, white scapulars forming broad V on back; rump, upper tail coverts grey; wings black, white bases to primaries; tail black with white outermost and white tipped central feathers; underparts white, axillaries black and white; legs, bill black, eyes brown. ♀ has chestnut flanks. Immature ash-brown above, greyish brown below, finely barred. Usually perches telegraph poles, other vantage points, whence attacks large insects, especially Orthoptera, mice, small birds, impaling them on thorny larder, often sisal bush. Call: *cheee cheee cheee*; other harsh notes and a pleasing song. Breeds all through year Kenya, seasonally elsewhere. Neat nest of grass, rootlets, cotton, lined fine fibres, grass, hair, in fork of bush or tree. Usually 3 creamy or pinkish eggs, spotted sepia, brown, chestnut over lilac. Sometimes 2 broods. **649**

Lanius collurio *Laniidae*
RED-BACKED SHRIKE   6¾ ins
Palaearctic: from N Iberia, Mediterranean area to beyond 60°N in Scandinavia and Russia: E through Asia Minor, Crimea, Iran, Palestine to W Siberia, Turkestan, Outer Mongolia, NW Manchuria, W China. European birds migrate to Southern Africa; Black Sea, and Caspian birds to E Africa; Asian birds to India, SW Arabia, NE Africa. Habitat open scrub, e.g. heathland, commons in England, thickets, cultivated land with bushes; similarly in winter up to 6,000 ft Tanzania. ♂: back and most of wings chestnut,

flight feathers darker, crown, nape, rump blue-grey; tail black, edged white; mask black; underparts pinkish buff. Legs grey-black, bill black, eyes dark brown. ♀, juvenile duller, russet brown above, buffish below, with crescentic 'scaly' markings. Legs brownish-grey, bill brownish horn. Sometimes perches openly, sometimes skulks; frequent movements and spreading of tail; undulating flight with glide to new perch. Hawks flying insects, catches small birds, mammals, frogs, lizards, worms, impaling some on thorny larder. Usual call: *chack chack*, but many others recorded; also infrequent warbling, mimicking song. Breeds mid-May to July; ♂ mainly builds substantial nest of moss, grass, stalks, wool, feathers, softly lined, usually in thorny bush or creeper, e.g. brambles, sometimes small trees, from 6 ins to 7½ ft up. 3 to 6 very variable eggs, white, pink, buffish or green, markings of red, brown over grey usually in zone, incubated ♀ 13-16 days; both parents feed young, who fly c. 14 days. Parasitised by Cuckoo, *Cuculus canorus*, in Europe. **650**

Lanius cristatus *Laniidae*
BROWN SHRIKE   7½ ins
E Palaearctic: from Central Siberia, NE up Olenek River to Kamtchatka; also N Mongolia, China, Korea, Manchuria, Japan. The several races winter China, Thailand, Indian subcontinent, Ceylon, Malaysia, Philippines, Borneo. Habitat open country with bushes, riverine woods, orchards, parks. ♂: upperparts greyish-brown; head russet brown; forehead, 'eyebrow' white; wings grey-brown; tail yellowish-brown; underparts ochre; legs blackish, bill mainly black, eyes dark brown, orbit pale blue. ♀, juvenile much as *Lanius collurio*, with which sometimes considered conspecific, linked by red-tailed races. Habits much as *L. collurio*. Call: scolding *chr-r-r-r*; subsong in winter quarters. Food mainly insects, birds, small mammals. Large nest of grass, twigs, lined seed down, wool, scraps, usually low in thorny bush. 4 to 6 eggs cream to pink, marked chestnut over grey; incubation and fledging as *L. collurio*.

Lanius excubitor *Laniidae*
GREAT GREY SHRIKE   9½ ins
Holarctic, Oriental, marginally Ethiopian: Iberia through Europe E to Central Russia, Siberia and Kamtchatka; S to Iran, Arabia, Indian subcontinent; N Africa to c. 10°N; Alaska SE through Yukon to Hudson Bay, Quebec, Newfoundland; Eurasian birds winter Mediterranean area, Asia Minor; Siberian birds in Mongolia, N Manchuria; American birds to Kansas, California, New Mexico, Texas. Habitat: woodland edge, open country with bushes, marsh and scrub tundra to savannah and desert. ♂: upperparts grey; wings, tail black with white markings; white border above black mask (distinguishes from Lesser Grey Shrike, *L. minor*, but absent in juvenile); underparts white, sometimes tinged pink; rump white. ♀ slightly duller, with crescentic marks on underparts; juvenile brownish-grey above, underparts more marked. Legs black, bill mainly black-brown, eyes dark brown. Prominent perch from which to hunt or defend territory against other birds, even large hawks. Constant tail movements. Short low flights between perches with final glide upwards; longer flights undulating; hovers when hunting. Prey: largely insects, small birds, mammals, reptiles and frogs; sometimes stored in larder. Call: *truu*; harsh *sheck sheck* of alarm; song, sometimes in winter, medley of warblings, call notes, mimicry. Breeds from April to June; ♀ and ♂ build bulky nest of twigs, grass, moss, lined finer materials, up to 40 ft in fork of tree of bush. 5 to 7 eggs in N, fewer in S, greyish white to buff, marked olive brown over grey, incubated ♀ 14-16 days. Both parents feed young, who fly 18-20 days. Sometimes 2 broods in S. **651**

Lanius minor *Laniidae*
LESSER GREY SHRIKE   8 ins
Palaearctic: from France E across Europe to Asia Minor, NW Iran; separate race from S Urals to Turkestan, Altai, Afghanistan; both races winter E and S Africa. Habitat: grassland and edges of cultivation with bushes, trees; roadsides, groves, gardens; passage and winter in scrub and thorn bush. Very similar to

L. excubitor: upperparts including rump grey; wings, tail black and white; black mask meets over forehead but no white stripe above; underparts buff tinged pink. Juvenile buffish grey and scaly above. Legs brown-black, bill black, eyes dark brown. Habits much as other *Lanius* shrikes; aggressive against other species. Glides more than *Lanius collurio*; uses larder less for prey, chiefly insects; sometimes fruit. Call, probably alarm, harsh *sheck sheck*; jumbly, sometimes mimicking song. Breeds mid May onwards; ♀ and ♂ build nest of twigs, various plant stems, lined soft materials, usually 10 to 30 ft in broadleaved tree with good visibility. 5 to 7 bluish-green eggs, marked olive- and pale greenish-brown in zone, incubated mainly ♀ 15-16 days; both parents feed young, who fly 14-15 days. **652**

Lanius schach *Laniidae*

BLACK-HEADED or LONG-TAILED SHRIKE   9-10 ins
Oriental, Australasian: widespread in S and SE Asia to New Guinea; Indian subcontinent N to Himalayas; northern birds move S in winter. Habitat: cultivated and open country with bushes and scrub, from lowlands to 5,500 ft (Burma). Head, neck, mantle cinereous grey; wings black but major coverts rufous; rump, upper tail coverts red, tail brown; black mask across forehead, 'eyebrow' white; underparts whitish; legs, bill black, eyes dark brown. Habits much as other *Lanius* shrikes. Usual call harsh *garlik garlik*, followed by yapping *yaon yaon*; alarm like distant Corncrake, *Crex crex*; prolonged musical song in breeding season. Prey: insects, eggs, nestlings, small reptiles. Breeds March to July in different parts of range; nest of twigs, stems, wool, cotton, woven into fork 10 to 15 ft up in tree. 4 to 6 greenish-white eggs, marked olive-green, brown and black. Incubation and fledging much as relatives. **653**

Lanius senator *Laniidae*

WOODCHAT SHRIKE   6¾ ins
Palaearctic: Iberia, S France, Italy, Adriatic coast, Greece, Turkey, N Arabia, Iran; winters S Arabia and Africa S of Sahara but N of Equator. Habitat: open ground with scattered trees, shrubs: olive groves, orchards, gardens, woodland clearings and edge; sometimes thick woodland. ♂: mantle and wings black with large white patch; rump white; tail black, edged white; crown, nape chestnut; black mask meets over forehead; underparts from chin white. ♀ duller; juvenile like *L. collurio* but greyer, scapulars paler. Legs slate-black, bill mainly blackish-black, eyes dark brown. Habits much as *L. collurio* but perches higher and sits more within canopy of trees than other shrikes. Calls include harsh, chattering *kiwick kiwick*; song superior to other European shrikes, sustained warbling but with harsh and mimicking notes. Prey: insects and their larvae, worms, small birds and nestlings. Breeds late April onwards, substantial nest of weed stems, especially *Gnaphalium*, lined softly; usually over 10 ft up on lateral branch, sometimes in bush. 5 or 6 pale green eggs, marked grey-brown over ashy, usually in zone, incubated ♀ c. 16 days; both parents feed young, who fly 19-20 days. Occasionally 2 broods. **654**

Lanius tephronotus *Laniidae*

TIBETAN or GREY-BACKED SHRIKE   10 ins
E Palaearctic: Kashmir, Tibet, Yunnan (Likiang Range); winters to SE Asia. Habitat: open scrub at high altitudes; plains and cultivated land in winter. Upperparts from crown dark lead-grey; rump, upper tail coverts rufous; tail chestnut brown; wings blackish, feathers pale edged; black mask extends through ear coverts; underparts pale, becoming rufous lower belly. Legs, bill blackish, eyes dark brown. Habits as other *Lanius* shrikes. Harsh grating call. Food mainly insects: crickets, grasshoppers; also lizards, nestlings; uses larder. Breeds June-July, building untidy cup of wool, twigs, grass, rags, feathers, lined fine grass; usually 6 to 10 ft in thorn bush or small tree. 4 to 6 pale green eggs, blotched and spotted grey-brown; incubation and fledging much as other *Lanius* species.

LANNER see **Falco biarmicus**

LAPLAND BUNTING see **Calcarius lapponicus**

LAPWING see **Vanellus vanellus**

LARGER STRIPED SWALLOW see **Hirundo cucullata**

LARK,
    BIFASCIATED see **Alaemon alaudipes**
    BUSH see **Mirafra africana**
    CRESTED see **Galerida cristata**
    HORNED see **Eremophila alpestris**
    MAGPIE see **Grallina cyanoleuca**
    NIGERIAN CRESTED see **Galerida modesta**
    RUFOUS-NAPED see **Mirafra africana**
    SHORE see **Eremophila alpestris**
    SHORT-TOED see **Calandrella cinerea**
    TEMMINCK'S HORNED see **Eremophila bilopha**
    THEKLA see **Galerida theklae**
    THICK-BILLED see **Galerida magnirostris**
    WOOD see **Lullula arborea**

LARK QUAIL see **Ortyxeles meiffrenii**

Larosterna inca *Laridae*

INCA TERN   c. 16 ins
Neotropical: fairly sedentary, breeds coasts of Peru and Chile. Habitat: Humboldt current region, especially guano islands and rocky sections of shore line. Dark bluish grey, lighter on throat and under tail coverts, white moustachial streak from bill below eyes ending in long curling white feathers on cheeks; primaries and outer tail coverts brownish black, four outer primaries edged white, secondaries mostly broadly tipped white. Legs crimson, bill strong, somewhat curved, blood-red. Immature: browner and head paler, moustachial streak greyish, legs and bill reddish brown. In flight rapid wing-beats giving fluttering effect. Catches small fish by plunging into water at angle, also scavenges off other predators; plaintive call. Breeds throughout year on islands, in burrows, crevices amongst rocks or under tangled vegetation; 2 brown eggs, spotted and blotched with darker brown and grey. **324**

Larus argentatus *Laridae*

HERRING GULL   c. 22 ins
Holarctic: breeds SE Alaska, Canada, Atlantic coast USA down to Long I, Britain and Ireland; NW France, Netherlands, Scandinavia; fairly sedentary, some movement S in winter with younger birds reaching subtropics. (Closely related Lesser Black-backed Gull, *L. fuscus*, breeds SE Iceland, Britain and Ireland, Portugal, Brittany (France), Netherlands, Scandinavia, N USSR, W Asia S to Caspian Sea across to L. Baikal; also Mediterranean; migratory, wintering Mediterranean, Persian Gulf, Arabian Sea, Red Sea and coast and inland lakes tropical Africa.) Variation with race; head, hindneck, throat and breast white (streaked brown in winter), mantle, back and scapulars pale blue-grey, rest of body and tail white; wings grey with narrow white border on hind edge, black and white tips. Legs pinkish or yellow, bill deep yellow, vermilion spot on gonys and white tip; eyes pale yellow, orbital ring orange. Immature: light brown mottled with dark brown, wings darker and belly paler, generally paler with age; bill brownish. (*Fuscus*: mantle from blackish to slate-grey, head and neck dusky streaking in winter, legs yellow.) Gregarious, follows ships within continental shelf. Call: often dry *kak-kak-kak* or loud trumpeting *kyow-kyow-kyow*. Scavenger, takes fish and other small aquatic animals, robs nests, breaks open molluscs by dropping on hard surface. Breeds late April onwards, usually in colonies; nest rough pile of seaweed, grass and litter, sometimes only lined scrape, sited among littoral vegetation or rocks, also dunes, cliff ledges and roof tops; 2 or 3 eggs varying from pale blue and shades of green to dark brown, spotted and streaked very dark brown. Both parents incubate 28-33 days and tend young, who fly c. 6 weeks. **325**

Larus californicus *Laridae*

CALIFORNIA GULL   c. 21 ins
Nearctic: breeds eastern N Dakota and S Mackenzie S to Wyoming, N Utah and E California; winters coast Texas, and S British Columbia inland to N Utah and S to SW Mexico. Habitat: inland lakes and marshes and adjacent uplands, favours Pacific coast in winter. Looks similar to Herring Gull, *L. argentatus*, but larger white patches at wing tips, mantle greyer, black along with red tip to yellow bill; legs greenish grey-yellow. In large flocks at good feeding places, takes fish and other aquatic animals, insects from freshly cultivated land, sometimes other terrestrial animals, also scavenges amongst garbage. Call: dry *kak-kak-kak*. Breeds in colonies often with Ring-billed Gull, *L. delawarensis*, on islands in lakes or marshes usually near water's edge; 3 olive or buff to buff-brown eggs, spotted with brown, in variably lined scrape on ground or more substantial nest of weeds and other plant debris. Incubation and care of young by both sexes. **326**

Larus canus *Laridae*

COMMON GULL   c. 17 ins
Holarctic; breeds N America: N Mackenzie and NW Alaska S to N Saskatchewan and central British Columbia; Europe and Asia; Iceland (rare), Faeroes, N Scandinavia and N USSR S to Baltic and Caspian Sea, Mongolia and Kamtchatka; winters S as far as S California, Mediterranean and S China coasts. Habitat: coastal and inland waters, bogs and marshes. Head, neck, body and tail white, lower mantle, back, scapulars and most of wings pale blue-grey; white tips to secondaries, wing tips black with terminal white fringe. Legs greenish, bill yellow-green, eyes brown to whitish with red orbital ring. Winter: head and neck streaked dark grey. Immature: mottled brown on crown, hindneck, back and wings; black band on tail. Habits similar to other gulls e.g. Herring Gull, *L. argentatus*. Call: like Herring Gull but shriller and shorter. Feeds inland on insects, worms, seeds; on coast as other gulls. Breeds late April to mid June in colonies or solitary pairs on rocky knolls and ledges, or among vegetation, also water's edge among boulders or rushes, bogs and moorland; nest varies from lined scrape to platform of plant debris; 2 or 3 pale blue or green to dark olive eggs, blotched and streaked brown often mainly at big end. Both parents incubate 22-25 days and tend young, who leave nest 3-5 days and fly c. 5 weeks. **327**

Larus cirrocephalus *Laridae*

GREY-HEADED GULL   c. 16 ins
Neotropical (*L.c. cirrocephalus*): breeds inland eastern S America; winters coasts Peru, Argentina and S Brazil. Ethiopian (*poiocephalus*): breeds Gambia and Ethiopia S to S Africa; winters coasts W Africa from Gambia to Walvisch Bay and eastern Africa (including Madagascar) to Port Elizabeth. Habitat: lakes and coast. Head and throat pale grey, mantle grey; neck, tail and underparts white. Legs and bill red, eyes pale yellow. Winter: head and throat white with pale grey half-hood. Immature: upperparts and tip of tail ash-brown, head white with dark patches; legs yellowish brown, bill yellowish. Usually solitary or small parties, flocks at good feeding and roosting places; feeds on small fish, molluscs and insects; cackling cry. Usually breeds June onwards making nest among rushes of roots and mud covered with grass and rushes, or floating nest of old weeds, also nests on rocky islets using scarcely any material; 2 or 3 olive brown eggs, blotched darker brown with grey undermarkings. Incubation (Africa) c. 21 days. **328**

Larus delawarensis see under **L. californicus**

Larus fuscus see under **L. argentatus**

Larus heermanni *Laridae*

HEERMANN'S GULL   c. 18 ins
Neotropical: Pacific coast N America; breeds NW Mexico and Baja California then spreads N as far as Vancouver Is and S to Guatemala; keeps to coastline. Head and upper neck white, greyish brown in winter, mantle slate coloured; lower neck, underparts and upper tail coverts pale grey, tail dull black tipped white, wing quills mostly white tipped, underwing greyish brown; legs black, bill red. Immature: deep brown, wings and tail darker, buff edges to tail, legs and bill blackish. Usually feeds over kelp beds just

offshore, taking chiefly small fish and shrimps, sometimes robs fish from Brown Pelicans, *Pelecanus occidentalis*, as they surface, and eggs of other birds. Call: high-pitched *whee-ee*, often series of muffled cackling notes in winter. Nests April to June on coastal islands in large colonies; 2 or 3 light grey, cream or bluish eggs with lavender, brown or dark olive markings, in depression in sand or among small rocks, sometimes lightly lined with sticks or grass; occasionally more of a nest among grass or seaweeds.

Larus hyperboreus *Laridae*
GLAUCOUS GULL   *c.* 28 ins
Holarctic: islands and coast of Arctic Ocean; S to Newfoundland, James Bay, N Mackenzie and Pribilof Is. in N America, wintering edge of open water S to Long I. (NY), Great Lakes and California; in Palae-arctic ranges from Franz Josef Land S to Iceland and N coast USSR, wintering S to Mediterranean, Caspian Sea and Japan. Outside breeding season frequents sea-coast, sometimes harbours, inland lakes and rivers. Mantle, back, and scapulars pale grey, primaries and secondaries pale grey tipped white; winter, white head, neck and throat streaked pale brown, more so in ♀. Immature: creamish buff mottled pale brown, primaries brown. Legs flesh colour, thick bill yellow with pale tip and vermilion gonys (angle), eyes and orbital ring yellow. Heavy, powerful flight, usually solitary; feeds on carrion, fish, crabs, sometimes seaweed, robs and kills other birds, their young and eggs. Call: hoarse long croaks. Breeds colonies, sometimes small, late May onwards on high cliff ledges, also coastal dunes and small islets in lakes. 3 greyish brown eggs marked with dark brown, incubated *c.* 28 days by both parents; both also tend young.

Larus maculipennis see under **L. ridibundus**

Larus minutus *Laridae*
LITTLE GULL   *c.* 11 ins.
Palaearctic: breeds locally N Netherlands, Baltic countries, USSR from White Sea, L. Onega and L. Ladoga across to Okhotsk Sea, S to N Transcaucasia and L. Zaisan; winters coasts Europe and E Asia S to Mediterranean, Black and Caspian Seas, and Yang-tse-Kiang. Habitat: swampy grasslands, marshes and marshy lakes in breeding season, otherwise moves to coast, inshore waters, estuaries and large lakes inland. Hood black, upperwing grey, underwing blackish (paler when immature), tail and body white, scapulars and back pale grey; in winter pale grey on mantle, hindneck and sides of upper breast, hood reduced to dark grey cap. Legs red, browner winter and immatures, bill red-brown, blackish winter and immatures, eyes dark brown. Solitary or small flocks, flight similar to terns', snatches food (fish and other small aquatic animals) from surface water and takes insects on wing. Call: *kek-kek-kek*. Breeds late May to mid June usually in colonies; loosely built nest of aquatic plant debris in tussock or amongst reeds. Usually 3 eggs, yellowish buff to olive brown marked dark brown and ash-grey; both sexes incubate. **329**

Larus novaehollandiae *Laridae*
SILVER GULL   *c.* 16 ins
Australasian, Ethiopian: coasts Australia, Tasmania, New Caledonia; replaced New Zealand, Chatham and Auckland Is by Red-billed Gull *L. scopulinus*; also coast S Africa from Namaqualand to Natal, where named Hartlaub's Gull. Habitat: coastlines, estuaries and sometimes inland waters. White with pale grey back; outer primaries mainly black with large white spot near tip, most of other primaries white with black band near tip. Legs and bill red, eyes white, narrow orbital ring orange-red. Immature: similar, but mantle mottled brown, brown markings on wing and narrow subterminal brown band on tail; legs greyish, bill brownish, eyes and orbital ring dark. Feeds chiefly on fish; also takes other aquatic animals, flying ants and other insects on the wing; visits freshly cultivated land and scavenges near towns and ports. Call: strident, repeated *ki-och*. Breeds April to December in colonies or isolated pairs, on offshore islands, also islands in estuaries and salt lakes; 2 or 3 usually brownish olive eggs, blotched and marked with brown and black, in

nest or nearby plant debris, lined finer grass stems. Both parents incubate *c.* 24 days; young leave nest *c.* 4 weeks and disperse *c.* 2 weeks later. Generally 2 broods.

Larus pacificus *Laridae*
PACIFIC GULL   *c.* 25 ins
Australasian: Australian waters from Sharks Bay, Western Australia, to Tasmania and S New South Wales; breeds throughout range, sedentary when adult. Habitat: coastal waters, estuaries and shores, often harbours and offshore islands. Head, neck and underparts white; wings black above, white below; tail has black subterminal band. Legs yellow, heavy bill orange-yellow with plum-red tip, eyes white with yellow ring. Immature brownish, becoming mottled with age, legs and bill greyish. Call: deep, harsh *kiaw*. Feeds on carrion, fish, crabs and other aquatic inverte-brates, seabird eggs and young. Breeds August to January in colonies or isolated pairs, on rocky head-lands, along coastline or on lower sandy sites and edges of lagoons; 2 or 3 deep grey-brown eggs, blotched darker brown, in substantial nest of long grass stems and other plant debris. **330**

Larus philadelphia *Laridae*
BONAPARTE'S GULL   *c.* 14 ins
Nearctic: breeds interior Alaska and W Canada, winters coasts Mexico, USA, and occasionally Peru, Hawaiian Is, Bermuda, Britain. Habitat: coastal bays, harbours, estuaries and sometimes fresh waters; lakes and rivers of spruce forest belt for breeding. Head bluish black, narrow white ring round eye with gap at front, mantle pearl grey, outer primaries largely white with black tips; underparts, rump and tail white. Legs orange-red, small bill black, sometimes reddish at base, eyes brown with black orbital ring. Winter: head white with dusky cheek patch. Immature: similar cheek patches; crown, nape, scapulars and back greyish brown; forehead, neck and underparts white; tail white with subterminal dusky band, bill dusky, legs pale brownish. Flight tern-like; gregarious, less noisy that other gulls; feeds on small fish, crustaceans and marine worms, picked from surface while flutter-ing over water, also swims on surface to feed, can catch prey on wing and relies on insects when breeding in-land. Call: rough *cherr*. Nests June and July, building loose twig and stick platform, lined dried moss, grass and lichens, on horizontal branches of low coniferous trees; 2 to 4 brownish yellow to dark olive-buff eggs with brown markings, incubated mainly by ♀; young leave nest within 5-6 days.

Larus pipixcan *Laridae*
FRANKLIN'S GULL   *c.* 13½ ins
Nearctic: breeds S Manitoba and S Alberta S to SW Minnesota, S Dakota and Utah; winters Gulf coast Texas S to W coast S America as far as Chile. Habitat: marshes or along shallow lake shores, visiting culti-vated land during day. Head black, back and wings grey, wing tips black bordered white; in winter black on head reduced to dusky area across back, immature similar but browner with no black on wing tips. Legs and bill red, eyes dark. Graceful and agile flyer; feeds on aquatic and terrestrial insects, especially latter when breeding, sometimes taken on wing. Call: shrill, clear *po-lee*, also cluckings and mews. Breeds early summer onwards in colonies among reeds in shallow water; 3 pale buffish eggs with darker brown markings in well finished cup in large floating mass of old stalks attached to surrounding plants. Adults may tend each others' young. **331**

Larus ridibundus *Laridae*
BLACK-HEADED GULL   *c.* 15 ins
Palaearctic: breeds Britain, Ireland and W Europe to Turkestan and E Asia; winters coasts Europe, N Africa and Asia S to Gambia, Red Sea, Persian Gulf, India, Philippines, China and Japan. Other similar species, e.g. Patagonian Black-headed Gull *L. maculipennis* southern S America N to Brazil and Chile. Habitat: coastal and inland, favouring sandy and muddy shores, estuaries, harbours, semi-tidal rivers, lakes and reservoirs, feeding over farmland and, in winter, in cities, especially in Britain. Hood coffee brown,

reduced to few dusky markings in winter, neck and body white, lower mantle, back and wings blue-grey; white band on front edge of wing broadens to include most of outer 5 primaries, inner margin and tips of outer primaries unbroken black. Legs and bill deep red, eyes brown. Immature: mantle uneven brown, some brownish grey on wing coverts and back of head, subterminal blackish brown band on tail. Flight buoyant for gull, tramples in shallow water or wet mud to bring up food; small crustaceans, molluscs, worms and fish; also picked from surface of water; will take insects on wing. Call: harsh *kwup*, strident *kwarr* and almost dove-like sounds. Breeds April to July in colonies on coastal sandhills, saltmarshes, *Spartina* beds, shingle and sandbanks; inland on lakesides and islands, bogs and swamps; nest loosely built of plant debris, either on vegetation or in scrape on ground; 2 or 3 eggs, pale blue or greenish to dark umber, blotched dark brown and underlying grey. Both parents incubate *c.* 22-24 days and tend young, who fly 5-6 weeks. **332**

Larus scopulinus *Laridae*
RED-BILLED GULL   *c.* 14½ ins
Australasian: New Zealand, coast and offshore islands, also larger lakes inland. Head, neck, underparts and tail white, mantle, back and wing coverts uniform pale grey; primaries black with white tips and bases, 2 outer ones broad subterminal white bands; ♂ larger than ♀. Legs and bill scarlet, eyes silvery white with red eyelids. Immature: mantle suffused pale buff, dark brownish band on wing; legs purplish brown, bill brownish black, eyes brown. Sub-antarctic race slightly darker with stouter bill. Feeds on small fish, insects, earthworms and sometimes berries, also scavenges. Call: strident, tremulous scream. Breeds October onwards in dense colonies on rock stacks and cliffs, also sandbanks and flats near mouths of rivers; sub-antarctic race nests in caves and cavities. 2, some-times 3, brownish ochre eggs with darker spots and blotches, in well formed nest of grass and other plant debris; both parents incubate *c.* 21 days.

Lathamus discolor *Psittacidae*
SWIFT PARROT   9½ ins
Australasian: Tasmania, islands of Bass Strait; migrates in numbers to SE Australia after breeding and moves locally after food. Habitat: wet and dry sclerophyll forest, savannah, orchards. Upperparts rich green, crown dark blue, red mask, yellow lores; shoulder patches, innermost coverts, underwing coverts red, undertail coverts dull red; wings blue; narrow pointed tail pale blue washed red; legs brown, bill brownish-horn, eyes pale yellow. Rapid weaving, whirring flight, darting out and back to feeding trees, where creeps through foliage; rests on topmost dead branches; seldom on ground except to drink. Call: excited chittering whistle, distinctive clinking flight notes. Food: nectar from eucalypts and other flowering trees; fruits, seeds; also insects and larvae, attacking psyllid lerps on eucalypts. Breeds September to Feb-ruary, 20 to 60 ft up in tree hole. 3 to 5 white eggs laid on decayed wood, incubated by ♀ 20 days, ♂ bear; young fly probably after 6 weeks. **394**

LEATHERHEAD see **Philemon corniculatus**

Legatus leucophaius see under **Cacicus cela**

Leiothrix argentauris *Muscicapidae : Timaliinae*
SILVER EARED MESIA   7 ins
Oriental: E from Nepal across Indo-China, SW China
to Sumatra. Breeds in broadleaved mountain forests,
also secondary growth in cleared areas, moving to
lower altitudes in winter, flocking with other species.
♂: mantle olive with red wingbar, yellow patch on
brown folded wing; crown black; throat scarlet,
blending with orange-yellow underparts; rump, undertail crimson. ♀ lacks red throat, rump; duller yellow
below. Legs yellow-brown, bill yellow, eyes red. Forms
flocks of up to 10, feeding on insects or fruit near ground.
Bold behaviour, but flies weakly. Voice: low clear
song; also noisy call *quir quir quir*. Breeds April to
August. ♀ and ♂ build cup nest of bamboo leaves, moss,
lined roots. 3 or 4 eggs indistinguishable from those of
Pekin Robin, *L. lutea*. **711**

Leiothrix lutea *Muscicapidae : Timaliinae*
PEKIN ROBIN   5 ins
E Palaearctic, Oriental: from S Himalayas across N
Indo-China, China N to Yangtze Valley. Breeds
mountain forest, moving lower in winter; most abundant below 2,000 ft in S China. Head olive green;
mantle, flanks greyer; rump more olive flecked white;
black centre to forked olive tail; crimson, yellow patches
on folded wing; throat orange-yellow merging into
orange breast; rest of underparts white; legs yellow,
bill red; eyes red-brown. Gregarious, flocking with
other species outside breeding season. Song of ♂
accompanied by wing flapping display; characteristic
call, loud *tee tee tee tee*. Diet includes seeds, insects.
Breeds April to June. Nest built near ground, suspended from vertical or lateral branch; deep cup of
leaves, grass, moss, lined fine grass. 3 to 5 pale green-
white eggs, blotched grey-brown at blunt end. **712**

Leipoa ocellata *Megapodiidae*
MALLEE FOWL   22-27 ins
S and W Australia; sedentary in arid country inland.
Back brown with black and white crossbars to feathers
giving 'ocellated' effect; tail tipped white, crown
black, neck slate-grey; throat pale brown, underparts
white with black central stripe; legs blue-grey, bill
slate-black, facial skin black and white, eyes hazel. Shy
disposition and seldom seen, but calls represented by
onomatopoeic native names *gnow* and *lowan*. Diet of
green buds in spring, later seeds, e.g. of acacias; young
feed on insects. ♂ and ♀ begin collecting material
April or May and excavate hole 15 ft across, 3 or 4 ft
deep, which they fill with dry leaves to 1 ft above
ground level, then cover with loose sand. ♀ lays 5 to 35
eggs, delicate pink when fresh, at long intervals in
central cavity; ♂ keeps mound at 92 °F, regulating heat,
which is derived at first from fermentation of leaves,
later from sun; process occupies him for 11 months.
Young dig their way out of mound, run in a few hours,
fly in a day and look after themselves entirely. **175**

Leptolophus hollandicus see **Nymphicus
hollandicus**

Leptopoecile sophiae *Muscicapidae : Sylviinae*
SEVERTGOV'S TIT WARBLER   3½ ins
Palaearctic: 4 races; resident in highlands of Sinkiang,
Kashmir, Tibet just reaching NW India and SE USSR;
moves lower down in winter. Habitat: scrub and juniper thickets from 8,000 ft to alpine zone. ♂: forehead
and 'eyebrow' whitish ochre, crown and nape reddish
brown, crest violet; mantle brownish grey; rump and
tail glossy violet blue; chin to breast reddish brown
with violet lustre, belly light ochre with golden gloss
on sides; wings olive with greyish and rufous edgings.
♀ and juvenile much duller. Legs brownish black, bill
black (paler tip), eyes red. Very active in undergrowth
but flight weak; joins flocks in autumn. Call, a thin
squeak. Food mainly insects though some seeds in
winter. Breeds mainly in May; ♂ brings material and
♀ builds nest (mainly moss, fluff, feathers) in thicket,
especially rhododendron, 2-3 ft up. 4 to 6 white eggs
with purplish-black spots, incubated by ♀ and ♂. **740**

Leptoptilus crumeniferus *Ciconiidae*
MARABOU   60 ins
Ethiopian region, except extreme S, migratory in N
of range and in S Africa. Slate-grey upperparts with
green iridescence; underparts white; head, neck and
breast with air-filled sac bare, crimson to black, with
white ruff at base; legs grey, heavy bill greyish-white,
eyes light brown. Largely commensal, but often near
lake or river; follows locusts and attracted to carrion
in open country. Vulture-like, soaring high up to
watch for feeding opportunities, to descend at speed
with rush of air through wings. Generally silent, except
for croaks and grunts at nests and bill-rattling in
mutual display. Scavenger, associating with and
driving away vultures; frogs and locusts also important
in diet and destroys *Quelea* nests. Breeding variable
throughout range; colonial in trees, cliffs, even on
buildings in towns; in W Africa often with pelicans;
rather small nest of sticks holds 2 to 3 granulated white
eggs; incubation and fledging periods apparently not
known. **73**

Leptosomus discolor *Leptosomatidae*
CUCKOO ROLLER or COUROL   *c.* 17 ins
Malagasy: confined to Madagascar and Comoro Is;
resident forest and scrub. ♂: upperparts blackish,
heavily glossed purple and green; crown and hindcrown blackish, forming slight crest; head, cheeks,
naps, underparts to breast grey, becoming paler on
underwing (tips black), under tail coverts; feathers
between base of hooked serrated black bill and dark
brown eye 'brushed' forward over upper mandible;
legs orange. ♀ and immature: upperparts dark brown
glossed green; chestnut-tipped wing coverts form patch
on closed wing; breast and face, including frontal tuft,
chestnut narrowly barred black; rest underparts buff
to pale buff spotted dark brown. 2 powderdown
patches on rump give 'bloom' to plumage. Singly or in
pairs; normally flies direct with slow wingbeats but ♂
has undulating display flight, calling repeated *quiyu
quiyu qui*; also from conspicuous bare perch, puffing out
throat. Soft whistling and bubbling calls between pair.
Food off upper branches: locusts, stick insects, beetles,
hairy larvae; chameleons; prey beaten against perch
before swallowing. Nests in hollow tree, perhaps also
hole in bank, laying 2 creamy buff eggs in bare
chamber. Young fed as adults.

Lerwa lerwa *Phasianidae*
SNOW PARTRIDGE   *c.* 15 ins
E Palaearctic, marginally Oriental: Himalayas between *c.* 10,000 and 17,000 ft, from NW Pakistan
through Nepal, Sikkim, Bhutan to Tibet and W China;
may descend below 7,500 ft in severe winters. Habitat:
alpine pastures, open hillsides with some vegetation
above tree line and up to snow line. Upperparts
narrowly barred black and white; underparts mostly
rich chestnut with pale broad streaks, especially belly
and flanks. Legs and bill bright red, eyes brownish red
or blood red. Gregarious, small family parties or
groups up to *c.* 20, tame when not persecuted; covey
scatters when alarmed with great whirring and clap-
ping of wings; flight fast and strong. Call: low alarm
whistle, shriller when strongly threatened; ♂ utters 2
to 4 subdued clucks, rising in intensity, followed by
quickly repeated high-pitched challenge. Food: lichen,
moss, seeds and plant shoots; probably some insects.
Breeds May to July; 3 to 6 pale buff to dirty grey-buff
eggs finely marked with red, in scrape in ground
under cover of rock or bush, sometimes lined with
leaves and moss.

LESSER
   BIRD OF PARADISE see under **Paradisaea
     guilielmi**
   BLACK-BACKED GULL see under **Larus
     argentatus**
   CRESTED TERN see **Sterna bengalensis**
   DOUBLE-COLLARED SUNBIRD see **Cinnyris
     chalybeus**
   FLAMINGO see **Phoeniconaias minor**
   GOLDEN PLOVER see **Pluvialis dominica**
   GREY SHRIKE see **Lanius minor**
   HONEYGUIDE see **Indicator minor**
   JACANA see **Microparra capensis**

SPOTTED WOODPECKER see **Dendrocopos minor**

Leucophoyx thula see **Egretta thula**

Leucopsar rothschildi *Sturnidae*
ROTHSCHILD'S STARLING or MYNAH   *c.* 10 ins
Oriental: confined to Bali, where local and rare in
remaining forests; *c.* 180 birds in captivity 1969. White
plumage, tips of flight and tail feathers black; long
white crest. Legs bluish grey, strong bill blue-grey and
yellow, bare facial skin blue, eyes dark brown. Little
known of habits in wild but aggressive in captivity
against both its own and other species. Has bred in
large communal aviaries and special compartments
with varying success. Most successful period May-June
in US zoos. Has built in nestboxes, hollow trunks and
rock crevice, using twigs, straws, grass and feathers.
3 or 4 eggs usual clutch, but one pair raised 9 young
from 2 broods. **971**

Leucosarcia melanoleuca *Columbidae*
WONGA DOVE   *c.* 15 ins
E Australia, E coast from N Queensland to Melbourne,
Victoria. Habitat: rain forest, also sheltered gullies in
heathlands and more open woodland. ♂: upperparts
dark slate-grey, forehead and chin white; throat slate-
grey, rest of underparts mottled black on white, broad
white band from sides of neck to white of upper breast.
♀: smaller, slightly less bluish. Legs pinkish red, bill
purplish pink or purplish red at base, darker at tip,
eyes dark brown or red, orbital skin pink with blue
grey outer edge. Wary, good walker, feeding on seeds
on ground; when flushed rises with loud wing flap but
lands quietly on branch, remaining motionless and
well camouflaged. Territorial, usually in pairs, but
more gregarious at good feeding or watering places.
Call: repeated loud and high pitched series of *coos*.
Usually breeds October to January; twig platform
fairly high up in trees or shrubs. 2 white eggs incubated
♀ and ♂. Possibly two broods. **365**

LEVAILLANT'S BARBET see **Trachyphonus
vaillantii**

LIGHT-MANTLED SOOTY ALBATROSS see
Phoebetria palpebrata

LILAC-BREASTED ROLLER see **Coracias candata**

LILY TROTTER see **Actophilornis africanus**

Limicola falcinellus *Scolopacidae*
BROAD-BILLED SANDPIPER   *c.* 6½ ins
Palaearctic: subarctic zone in Scandinavia, very
locally across N Russia and Siberia; summer visitor,
wintering muddy shores E Mediterranean, Black and
Caspian Seas, into Oriental region, Micronesia, even
Australia. Breeds wet meadows, bogs, tundra, often in
wooded areas, cf. Jack Snipe, *Lymnocryptesminimus*.
Summer: upperparts dark pattern like Jack Snipe;
head striped; wings dark brown; tail centrally brown,
edges white; throat, neck, breast streaked brown;
underparts white; legs dark, variable, flattened bill
blackish, base yellow, eyes dark brown. Much greyer
in winter with white throat and eye-stripe. Juvenile
has buff underparts. Apparently nowhere common,
usually solitary on migration and in winter. Rather
skulking, crouching when disturbed. Call a trill like
Temminck's Stint, *Calidris temminckii*, with rather
harsh trilling song in display flight. Diet: insects, earthworms, small freshwater and marine animals. Breeds
from first week June, making well hidden scrape in
moss and tall cover. 4 whitish eggs, heavily spotted red-
brown, incubated by ♀ and ♂; period and fledging
unknown. **285**

Limnocorax flavirostra *Rallidae*
AFRICAN BLACK CRAKE   *c.* 9 ins
Ethiopian; resident in swamps and lakesides. Blackish-
slate all over; legs orange-red, bill greenish-yellow,
eyes red. Immature has olive-brown upperparts. Flirts
tail like Moorhen, *Gallinula chloropus*, as it walks in open
or traverses water-lily leaves; also climbs plant stems;
runs fast but flies reluctantly like its relatives. Calls in
duet deep *churr* and high-pitched trill; also clucking

notes. Food: worms and water insects. Breeds throughout year with two peaks suggesting two broods. Large loose nest of grass, sometimes lined green leaves, in riparian cover. 2 to 6 pale stone or buff eggs, marked reddish brown and purple, incubated by ♀ and ♂ for *c.* 2 weeks; both parents tend the brood. **229**

Limnodromus griseus see under **L. scolopaceus**

Limnodromus scolopaceus *Scolopacidae*
LONG-BILLED DOWITCHER   *c.* 12 (bill 2½) ins
E Palaearctic and Nearctic: NE Siberia, N Alaska to Yukon; winters S California to Guatemala, mainly by fresh waters, estuaries and reed-fringed bays. Breeds 'muskegs': wooded swamps with quaking vegetation. Very difficult to tell from Short-billed Dowitcher, *L. griseus*, of which long considered to be western race. Summer: upperparts mottled dark brown and buff like snipe; wing tips very dark brown with white bar and trailing edge; lower back, rump white, tail barred; crown dark brown and stripe through eye on whitish cheek; breast and underparts chestnut, much richer colour than *griseus*, and more heavily barred and flecked; legs greenish black, bill blackish brown, eyes dark brown. Winter: upperparts much duller, underparts from face and throat mainly white; distinguished from *griseus* by paler, finely barred tail. Single or repeated 'thin piping note'; *griseus* has 'low mellow three-note whistle', also song flight with quivering wings. Looks compact, walking and flying with head drawn in and bill pointing downwards. Probes mud or sand deeply for worms, leeches, small molluscs; also takes insects and larvae, some seeds and roots. Breeds from June, making sparsely lined scrape, often partly sheltered by dwarf birch. 4 eggs in shades of buff, marked dark brown and grey, incubated by ♀ and ♂ *c.* 3 weeks. ♂ sometimes cares for the brood. **286**

Limosa haemastica see under **L. limosa**

Limosa limosa *Scolopacidae*
BLACK-TAILED GODWIT   15-17 (bill 3¾-4¾) ins
Palaearctic, including Iceland; otherwise mainly N temperate from Britain across Eurasia to Kamtchatka; replaced in Nearctic by Hudsonian Godwit, *L. haemastica*, regarded by some as conspecific. Winters from Britain S to subtropics, tropics and beyond: Africa, Oriental region to Australia, Tasmania, on muddy freshwaters, estuaries and sea shores. Breeds meadows, often grazed, swampy heaths and moors, lakesides, forest clearings. Summer: crown and upperparts dark brown with pale feather edges; face to breast light chestnut, barred lower down; black wing tips and trailing edge below broad white bar; dark rump, tail white with broad black terminal band; underparts white, sparsely barred; very long legs blackish-green, long almost straight bill flesh pink, tip brown, eyes dark brown. Winter: grey-brown above, face, breast lighter, underparts light grey. Stately walk with head well up, flies with neck slightly bent and legs well beyond tail. Call: *wicker wicker wicker*; *kwee-yet* like Lapwing, *Vanellus vanellus*, on breeding ground; sings in display flight, which goes up to 200 ft. Also courtship on ground. Probes for small animals in soil or mud, and wades deeply; also takes insects and molluscs from plant stems. Breeds from end March in S of range; scrape, sometimes well lined and with stems interlaced over it, in thick cover, holds 4 blue green to dark brown eggs, spotted and blotched darker brown and grey; incubated by ♀ and ♂ 22-24 days; both tend young, who fly 4-5 weeks. **287**

LIMPKIN see **Aramus guarauna**

LINNET see **Acanthis cannabina**

Lissotis hartlaubii *Otididae*
HARTLAUB'S BUSTARD   24 ins
Ethiopian: Sudan, Somalia, E Africa; resident in open country at varying elevations. ♂: similar to Black-bellied Bustard, *L. melanogaster*, but lower back and rump black and back of neck grey. ♀: generally darker above, neck spotted and streaked light fawn with whitish streak in front; black crescents on breast; lower

back and rump not entirely black. Legs yellowish brown, bill yellow, eyes very light brown. Shy and difficult to tell from Black-bellied Bustard, so little known of habits, which may be assumed to be similar. Feeds on beetles, locusts and other insects. Breeding season probably May and June in Somalia. Lays probably 2 eggs, sandy brown, marked brown and grey, on bare ground. Incubation and parental care as other bustards.

Lissotis melanogaster or Eupodotis melanogaster *Otididae*
BLACK-BELLIED BUSTARD   26 ins
Ethiopian: across Africa from about Lat. 16°N to Zambia and Angola in suitable habitat, which is open grassland or cultivated areas for feeding, with cover nearby. Local movements in search of food. ♂: mantle and scapulars tawny with black shaft-stripes; rump and tail vermiculated black and fawn; upper wing coverts mainly white, flight feathers black and white; head, cheeks, nape buff with short crest, throat silver grey; white line down side of neck leads to white patch on side of breast, while black of underparts extends in thin black line up centre of neck to throat. ♀: neck buff, barred blackish, upper wing coverts light fawn, belly white and no black line down neck. Legs yellowish brown, bill yellow, eyes light brown. White on wings very conspicuous in flight. Usually in pairs in moist areas, squatting when danger threatens and hard to flush. Like other small bustards ♂ makes display flights, dropping to ground with wings held high. Rather silent, with soft whistle and barking *or-buk or-buk* in breeding season, which varies throughout range. Feeds mainly on insects, especially locusts and grasshoppers. Lays 1 or 2 glossy, buff eggs, boldly marked chestnut brown and grey, on bare ground. Incubation and parental care as other smaller bustards. **245**

LITTLE
BEE-EATER see **Melittophagus pusillus**
BLUE HERON see **Florida caerulea**
BLUE PENGUIN see **Eudyptes minor**
BUSTARD see **Otis tetrax**
GREBE see **Tachybaptus ruficollis**
GREEN BEE-EATER see **Merops orientalis**
GULL see **Larus minutus**
LORIKEET see **Glossopsitta pusilla**
OWL see **Athene noctua**
SPIDERHUNTER see **Arachnothera longirostris**
STINT see under **Calidris temminckii**
TERN see **Sterna albifrons**
WATTLEBIRD see **Anthochaera chrysoptera**

LIVINGSTONE'S TOURACO see **Tauraco livingstonii**

Lobibyx novaehollandiae *Charadriidae*
AUSTRALIAN SPUR-WINGED PLOVER   15 ins
SE Australia and Tasmania; colonised South Island, New Zealand since *c.* 1940. Resident on edge of swamps, lagoons and streams; on crop fields and shores in NZ. Upperparts brown, crown and shoulders black; underparts and rump white, black tip to tail; bony yellow spur at 'wrist' of wing which is white below with dark trailing edge; legs reddish, bill and facial wattles yellow, eyes yellow. Described as more like small heron than plover, flying low with slow beats of rounded wings. Walks sedately but can run fast; shy and hard to approach. Alarm or aggressive call grating rattle *kerrick kerrick*. Food mainly animal: insects and small crustaceans, some plant material. Breeds July to January, making scrape often on dry or stony ground but not far from water. 4 light olive eggs, marked brownish black and dull grey; incubation and fledging probably as Lapwing, *Vanellus vanellus*. **264**

Lobipes lobatus see **Phalaropus lobatus**

Lochmias nematura *Furnariidae*
SHARP-TAILED STREAMCREEPER   6¼ ins
Neotropical: locally distributed from E Panama throughout S America to NE Argentina; mountain watercourses from 5,000 to 8,500 ft. Fairly uniform dark umber or chestnut brown according to race; rather short black tail; underparts spotted white; one race has white 'eyebrow'; bill rather slender, slightly

curved. Unobtrusive; haunts sewage effluents in Brazil, searching for insects.

Locustella fasciolata *Muscicapidae: Sylviinae*
GRAY'S GRASSHOPPER WARBLER   7 ins
Palaearctic: breeds in narrow belt of NE Asia from River Ob to Japan (Hokkaido) and Sakhalin; winters Philippines, Moluccas, Sundas and W New Guinea. Habitat: grassy thickets often near streams and in clearings. Upperparts dark brown, olive tinge on head and russet on tail coverts; 'eyebrow' ashy-grey; underparts whitish, breast and neck scaly grey, flanks olive-brown; wings and tail reddish brown, latter rounded. Juvenile darker. Legs flesh brown, bill dark brown, eyes nut brown. Very secretive, moving about in grass cover; very difficult to flush from nest. Call: distinctive *tokkok-trook*. Song brief, loud and flutelike, of 10 notes (2 slow ones in middle). ♂ starts to sing on ground, runs up twig, then down again; often sings at night. Food insects. Breeds mainly June; builds quite large deep nest of fallen leaves and grass on damp ground in dense vegetation. 4 dirty white eggs with few large dark spots over dense but faint lilac spots. **741**

Locustella naevia *Muscicapidae: Sylviinae*
GRASSHOPPER WARBLER   5 ins
Palaearctic: several races; breeds in band between 40°N and 60°N from W Europe to 95°E; winters S Europe, N Africa and in Asia from Caspian Sea to W India. Habitat: rank grass with scattered bushes or young trees, marshy or dry. Upperparts yellowish olive brown, each feather with dark centre; underparts white or buffish, sometimes with spots and streaks on throat and flanks; wings dark, tail reddish brown and rounded. Legs pale yellowish brown, bill dark brown, eyes brown. Very secretive. Displaying ♂ walks along stems with tail spread and flapping wings. Call: hard *tchick*; song, rapid, uniform, ventriloquial, high pitched trill like angler's reel. Often at night. Food: insects and larvae. Breeds May to July; builds grass nest, typically hidden in tussock of grass, rushes or other thick low cover, sometimes a foot up, entrance often by run. Usually 6 creamy eggs with dense brownish red spots and generally a dark hair-streak; incubation both sexes 14 days. Young, fed by ♂ and ♀, fledge 10-12 days. 2 broods in S of range. **742**

LOGRUNNER, NORTHERN see **Orthonyx spaldingi**

Lonchura castaneothorax or Donacola castaneothorax *Estrildidae*
CHESTNUT-BREASTED FINCH   4½ ins
Australasian: tropical continental N Australia to New South Wales; New Guinea; introduced other islands. Resident reedbeds, grasslands in coastal districts, swamps with wild rice *Oryza sativa*, cultivated areas. Meets competition from introduced Asian Spice Finch, *L. punctulata*. ♂: upperparts dark cinnamon, wings greyish-brown; rump, upper tail coverts, central tail feathers yellowish, rest of tail darker; crown, hind-neck greyish-brown; lores, cheeks, throat black; breast pale chestnut with black band and borders; underparts white streaked cinnamon and black at sides; flanks, under tail coverts black. ♀ very similar, slightly paler. Legs grey, bill bluish-grey, eyes brown. Immature generally shades of brown. Single birds have undulating flight, large flocks (sometimes of juveniles) fly rapidly with quick turns. Call: single *tit*; song, high-pitched, lasts 12 seconds; duets and trios between birds. Feeds largely grass seeds, perching on stalks to hold several together with feet; flocks damage crops autumn, winter; takes termites on wing in spring. Complex and variable mutual courtship display with bodily contact. Breeds colonially second half wet season in N, ♀ and ♂ building small domed nest of green grass, usually woven round living stems, softly lined; sometimes 1 to 3 ft up in shrub, bamboos. 5 or 6 white eggs incubated ♀ and ♂ 12-13 days; both feed young from throat; fledging *c.* 3 weeks. 2 or 3 broods. **939**

Lonchura punctulata see under **L. castaneothorax**

LONG-BILLED
DOWITCHER see **Limnodromus scolopaceus**

Lophoaetus occipitalis *Accipitridae*

LONG-CRESTED HAWK EAGLE   22½ ins

Ethiopian: Senegal to Ethiopia, and S to Cape of Good Hope; resident well wooded and cultivated areas, moister savannahs and riverine tree belts, but not dense rain forest. Very dark brown or black, except for white patches above and below 'wrist' of wing; white bars on tail, white under wing coverts spotted black; shanks greyish brown, feet and cere yellow, bill-tip dark, eyes golden or reddish brown. Immature more mottled. Pair usually near together, rests in dense tree during heat of day; hunts from conspicuous perch, taking principally small mammals, also reptiles, large insects (*Orthoptera*). Noisy display flight, uttering loud, ringing *keee-ee-ay*; also repeated *kik kik kik kik keee*. Breeds probably annually, March onwards in N, August to December in S of range; pair builds stick nest 20 to 60 ft up, often in wild fig or introduced eucalypt; usually 2 dull white eggs, clouded brown, grey, lilac, sometimes spotted brown, incubated by ♀, fed by ♂; she sits tight, sometimes on empty nest. First ♂, then ♀ brings food to young (usually only one survives), who fledges *c.* 55 days. **156**

Lopholaimus antarcticus *Columbidae*

TOPKNOT PIGEON   *c.* 17½ ins

Australia E coast from Cape York to NW Victoria. Habitat: rain forest and adjacent ridges or eucalyptus forest, seen in open country flying between patches of suitable forest. ♂: grey, much paler below; feathers have silky-white down-like bases; wings and back pale slate grey, lighter on lower back, rump and upper tail coverts, primaries black; long black tail with band of silver and grey at base. Distinctive double crest: one on forehead grey, other on crown chestnut, bordered black. Thick bill rose-red with greenish lead base, legs purplish red, eyes orange with red orbital skin. ♀: similar but smaller, eyes yellower. Gregarious, sometimes large numbers at good feeding places; roosts tall trees on high ridges, descending into forest in daytime to feed on fruits and berries off branches. Call: low *coo*. Large nest of sticks high up in tall trees; single white egg. **366**

Lophonetta specularoides *Anatidae*

ANDEAN and PATAGONIAN
CRESTED DUCK   24 ins

Neotropical: Andean race, *L.s. alticola*, in high valleys and plateaux Andes of S Peru, Bolivia, N Chile and Argentina; Patagonian Crested Duck, *specularoides*, breeds on inland freshwaters S Chile N to Santiago, Patagonia and W Argentina N to Mendoza, Tierra del Fuego and Falkland Is; winters near seashore and salt water. Habitat (*alticola*): mountain lakes between 10,000 and 15,000 ft or higher. Forehead, face and neck pale grey-brown; crest, hind crown and band behind eyes darker; mantle, breast and flanks mottled grey-brown and brown; back, rump. upper tail coverts and belly mottled dark and pale brown; tail and under tail coverts black, wings earthy brown with pink speculum. Patagonian race similar, but smaller, greyer and more spotted underparts. Legs and bill dark grey, eyes orange-yellow. Isolated pairs or families; pair strongly territorial, even attacking other species. Call: deep repeated quack, ♀ long series of short grumbling notes. Feeds on shores, flats and in shallow water, taking small animals and some plant matter. Breeding season variable, usually September to November; lays 5 to 9 cream eggs in holes or in dense grass lined with down, young immediately led to water. **117**

Lophortyx californicus *Phasianidae*

CALIFORNIA QUAIL   10½ ins

Nearctic: originally W coast N America from Oregon to Lower California; now introduced more widely in Canada and USA, also Chile, Hawaii, New Zealand; local movements seasonally in native range. Habitats with low trees and shrubs, open spaces with low cover: from oak woods and chaparral-sagebrush to city parks and gardens, up to 5,000 ft in S of range in summer. ♂: complex plumage pattern with dark brown upperparts, black cheeks and throat bordered white; breast and 'scaly' nape grey-blue; flanks barred black and white, belly scaled black on white with chestnut patch; curved head plume shared with Gambel's Quail, *L. gambelii*. ♀ has similar but much duller pattern, with dark-spotted white face and throat. Legs, bill and eyes dark. Gregarious up to 50 birds, except when courting and nesting. Covey runs if approached, splits up in flight if pursued. Roosts in trees. Assembly call: *come right* or *come right here*; ♂ crows loud *kah-ah* in spring. Food mainly vegetable, soft leaves and buds in spring; seeds, fruits rest of year; some insects, spiders and snails, especially during first week of life. Breeds in spring, lining scrape with grass or leaves, usually hidden by shrubs, log or other cover. 10 to 17 buffish eggs, marked dull brown, incubated by ♀ and ♂ 21-23 days. **202**

Lophortyx gambelii see under **L. californicus**

Lophura leucomelana see **L. lophura**

Lophura lophura or Lophura leucomelana *Phasianidae*

KALEEJ PHEASANT   20-27 ins

Oriental: several races widespread over region; hybridises with and sometimes regarded as one species with Silver Pheasant, *L. nycthemerus*. Resident in denser forests than Red Jungle Fowl, *Gallus gallus*, especially in gullies with watercourses or near cultivation. ♂: races differ considerably; black-breasted *L.l. lathami* predominantly dark purple on head and body, dark green on curved tail with white-scaled rump; crest and wingtips dark brown; spurred legs grey-brown, bill light yellow, facial skin red, eyes reddish. ♀: brown above, chestnut brown below, scaled and feathershafted white; crown and crest chestnut brown. Secretive, chiefly revealed by harsh crow of ♂, who drums by vibrating wings against body; guttural cooing and rapidly repeated *whoop keet keet* of alarm; low clucking notes. Food: young leaves and stems, grain and bamboo seeds, fallen figs; some insects and their larvae, especially termites, leaping after them in air. Breeding peaks March to May, July to August. 6 to 9 white or buff to reddish buff eggs laid in scrape on ground and incubated by ♀ 20-21 days. ♂, successively polygamous, may help last mate with young; 2 broods.

Lophura nycthemerus see under **L. lophura**

Lorius pectoralis see **L. roratus**

Lorius roratus or L. pectoralis *Psittacidae*

ECLECTUS PARROT   20 ins

Oriental (Lesser Sunda Islands), Australasian: Moluccas, New Guinea and offshore islands, Bismarck and Solomons, extreme N Queensland; feeds humid scrub, nests and roosts rain forest. Discovered 1913, outstanding example of sexual dimorphism; ♂: generally dark green, red on flanks and underwings; wings edged blue; legs flesh-grey, bill: upper red, lower dark; eyes yellow. ♀: generally red, purplish blue hindneck, belly; wings edged blue; undertail and terminal band yellow; blue round eye; legs pale flesh-grey, bill dark brown, eyes yellow. Noisy and conspicuous even in tree tops, small flocks revealed by clicking note of ♀♀ and falling seeds. Flies high above canopy with raucous *kurrah* or *kar kar kar* and slow flapping action. ♀ also has mellow whistle. Food: various nuts and seeds; large flocks collect for eucalypt nectar. Breeds October to December in tree hole up to 70 ft on edge of forest, by clearing or near water. 2 white eggs incubated by ♀ *c.* 30 days. ♂ feeds ♀ who feeds young; they leave nest 8-9 weeks, full grown 3-3½ months.

Loxia curvirostra *Fringillidae*

COMMON OR RED CROSSBILL   6 ins

Holarctic, Oriental, Neotropical: from Iberia, Britain across Eurasia roughly between 40° and 60°N to near Pacific at 130°E, but many scattered populations in mountains, e.g. N Africa, Tibet-China, Japan, and tropically in S Annam, Philippines (N Luzon). In America breeds right down W coast from Alaska to Panama and E along 50°N to Newfoundland, with outliers N Georgia, S Honduras, N Nicaragua; altogether 21 races recognised. Type habitat spruce *Picea* forests, lowland and montane; often in pines; in spruce, larch and fir up to 13,500 ft in Asia. Resident but liable to mass eruptions away from breeding areas, from which outlying groups probably established. ♂: variable brick red shading to dark brown on wings (with pale bar), short forked tail and cheeks; palest on underparts. ♀ yellowish green, streaked on upperparts, brightest on rump, breast. Juvenile browner, heavily striated. Immature ♂ orange-red. Legs, cross-tipped bill, eyes dark brown. Seldom on ground except to drink. Rapid undulating flight with loud *chup chup* calls, which change slightly when party lands on tree to feed, working cones in parrotlike postures. Song rendered *tik tik tik tukai tukai tukai*, interspersed with long drawn *tukao*. Flocks break up after noisy 'parties', flapping and gliding flights by ♂♂. Diet primarily conifer seeds, extracted by tongue after scale levered or split by mandibles; also takes pips from fleshy fruits, some seeds and variety of insects. Breeds variably, January to July. ♀, partly assisted ♂, makes foundation of twigs for cup of grass, wool, moss, hair, lichen, softly lined; usually near end of lateral branch or at very top of conifer, sometimes near trunk, 20 to 60 ft up. 3 or 4 eggs indistinguishable from Greenfinch, *Carduelis chloris*, incubated ♀ 13-16 days; both parents feed young from throat, they fly 18-22 days. **926**

Loxops parva see under **L. virens**

Loxops virens or Chlorodrepanis virens *Drepanidae*
AMAKIHI *c.* 4½ (bill *c.* ½) ins
Confined Hawaiian Islands, separate races on 6 main islands, as opposed to *L. parva*, confined to Kauai. Resident native forest above *c.* 1,500 ft Hawaiian race *virens*, ♂: upperparts yellowish olive, tinged orange especially on rump; flight and tail feathers brownish, edged olive; lores and line over forehead blackish; underparts olive-yellow. ♀ duller, upperparts tinged ashy, underparts paler. Legs and curved bill blackish, eyes very dark brown. Juvenile much as ♀. Forms small parties outside breeding season. Strong on wings and legs, dashing into cover at speed. ♂'s song 'slow, level trill' (P. H. Baldwin), also component in more complex song used in fighting and defence of territories, held October to June, after which song not heard. Searches for insects in trees, probing bark (especially strong-billed Kauai race *L.v. stejneri*), opening folded leaves, taking scale insects sometimes in quantity; attacks blossoms of koa and ohia *Metrosideros* trees, pierces corollas of lobelias to get at nectar, insects; also takes berries. Breeds probably March onwards, building open cup nest in dense twigs of small ohia tree several feet up, of sticks, grass, spider egg-cases, lined rootlets, plant fibres, lichen. 2 or 3 creamy white eggs freckled pale lilac and smoke grey in cap at big end, incubated ♀, but both parents probably feed young.

Lullula arborea *Alaudidae*
WOOD LARK 6 ins
Palaearctic; 2 races; *L.a. arborea* breeds Britain, Scandinavia to 60°N, east to Urals south to Spain and N Italy; winters S England and Europe to N Africa. *L.a. pallida* breeds N Africa, Mediterranean Islands, Asia Minor to Iran; recorded wintering in Egypt. Habitat: wood edges, hillsides with few trees, heaths, other bare areas, winters in fields. Upperparts brown with darker streaks; short crest, prominent buffish 'eyebrow'; black and white 'flash' (alula) shows on closed wing; underparts white to buffish with dark spots on breast; short tail; legs brownish flesh; bill, upper: dark brown, lower: paler; eyes umber. Call liquid *titloo-eet*; song musical and mellow with characteristic *lu-lu-lu* phrase, usually from tree and often at night. Nomadic in winter, usually in family parties. Feeds mainly on small insects. Breeding season end March to July; quite substantial grass nest on ground in a depression. 3 or 4 greyish-white, finely freckled, eggs. Incubation 13-15 days by ♀, ♂ in attendance. Young leave nest 11-12 days before flying a week later. Usually 2 broods. **607**

Luscinia calliope *Muscicapidae: Turdinae*
SIBERIAN RUBYTHROAT 5½ ins
E Palaearctic: large area Central Asia between 50° and 65°N, extending W of River Ob at 60°; E to Kamtchatka, Sakhalin, Hokkaido; isolated population mountains NW China; winters S Asia E to Philippines. Habitat typically taiga: dark coniferous or mixed forests with fallen trees, mosses, lichens, especially damp valleys. Upperparts dark brown; white 'brow' stripe cuts eye; thin white and black moustachial stripes; chin, throat ruby red; upper breast greyish, underparts shading to whitish. ♀ has throat white, head stripes fainter. Legs, bill brown, eyes dark brown. Juvenile mottled. Skulks in cover both summer and winter, though occasionally seen gardens in Burma (B. E. Smythies). Call ventriloquial *twee twee*, rattling churr of alarm; loud, often nocturnal song of nightingale type, but less sustained, often starts with mimicry. Food: insects, earthworms, snails. Nesting habits much as Bluethroat, *L. svecica*; open cup-shaped nest of local plant materials, on ground among grasses and tall herbs or low bushes. 4 to 6 greenish-grey eggs, marked red-brown at big end; incubation and fledging probably much as *L. svecica*. **685**

Luscinia luscinia *Muscicapidae: Turdinae*
THRUSH NIGHTINGALE 6½ ins
Palaearctic: across Eurasia from Denmark, S Sweden into headwaters of Ob system between 50° and 60°N, extending southward E and W of Black Sea; winters Ethiopian region mainly S of Equator in E Africa. Habitat rather open riverine or lakeside forest with thick undergrowth and ground cover especially of nettles *Urtica*; wooded steppes, shrub-clad swamps in cultivated land; occasionally parks, gardens. Upperparts uniform olivaceous brown; upper tail coverts, tail slightly rufous; underparts pale greyish brown, lightly spotted on breast, whitish on throat, belly; legs pale brown, bill mainly dark brown, eyes dark brown. Juvenile mottled above, 'scaly' below. Resembles Robin, *Erithacus rubecula*, but more skulking, though carriage more upright. Takes long hops on ground where spends much time. Call *whit*, sharper than Nightingale, *L. megarhynchos*, and song more powerful, with 'marvellously pure bell-like notes' (B. W. Tucker) replacing the flutelike *piuu*. Food small insects, worms, snails taken from litter layer; berries, small fruits in season. Breeds from early May to June, ♀ building foundation dead leaves, cup of grasses, stalks, lined finer material; usually on ground among nettles. 4 or 5 pale whitish eggs, covered with dense olive brown markings, incubated by ♀ 13 days; both parents feed young, who leave nest *c.* 11 days, fully fledged 3 weeks. **686**

Luscinia megarhynchos see under **L. luscinia**

Luscinia svecica *Muscicapidae: Turdinae*
BLUETHROAT 5½ ins
Palaearctic, marginally Nearctic: most of N Eurasia from Rhine and Danube to Bering Straits, with isolated groups N Alaska: also very local Iberia, France and Caucasus to S Caspian; winters N Africa, S Asia. Habitat dense scrub on borders lakes and rivers, extending into marginal aquatic zone; also marshy grassland with scattered bushes; willow and birch swamps on tundra; subalpine scrub round marshy meadows to 9,600 ft; winters mainly in dense riparian cover. ♂: upperparts dark brown with pale 'eyebrow'; rufous base to tail; blue gorget separated from white underparts by narrow black, white and chestnut bands. Red spot on gorget of northern and eastern races, white spot on southern race, virtually unspotted race *magna* from SE. ♀ has whitish gorget bordered streaky dark brown; underparts pale brown. ♂ autumn resembles ♀ with traces blue and chestnut. Legs yellow-brown, bill, eyes dark brown. Juvenile like Robin, *Erithacus rubecula*. Secretive, Robin-like when in open but carriage more upright; flirts and spreads tail. Call *tacc tacc* and plaintive *hweet*; song rich, nightingale-like but imitative, with metallic *ting ting ting*. Food small insects, worms, snails from thick cover and ground; berries in autumn. Breeds from mid June Scandinavia, early May in S. ♀ builds nest of dry grass with finer lining, well hidden in bank, under tussocks, dead reeds, low vegetation. 4 to 7 greenish to reddish-cream eggs, spotted red-brown in zone, incubated by ♀ 13-14 days; both parents feed young, who leave nest *c.* 14 days. **687**

LUZON BLEEDING HEART see **Gallicolumba luzonica**

Lybius leucomelas or Tricholaema leucomelas *Capitonidae*
PIED BARBET 6½ ins
Ethiopian: throughout southern Africa, in woodland of all types, especially thorn bush. Upperparts black, spotted white and yellow, flight and tail feathers blackish, edged yellow-white; forehead red; black mask and gorget; 'eyebrow', underparts whitish; legs and powerful bill black, eyes dark brown. Active, flight fast and direct, usually singly or in pairs. Often calls nasal *tnhar tnhar* from treetop; hollow, hoopoe-like *poop poop* in breeding season, which varies over range. Food mainly berries and fruit. Nests in hole of tree-trunk or bough, occasionally old tubular swallows' nests; lays 3 or 4 white eggs in bare chamber. **526**

Lybius torquatus *Capitonidae*
BLACK-COLLARED BARBET 6 ins
Ethiopian: most of Africa S of Equator, in coastal forest, savannah or park-like country with large fruiting trees, especially figs. Most races have conspicuous crimson face, throat, breast; black crown, nape, chest-band; stippled black and grey upperparts; yellow belly, edges of secondaries. Crimson replaced by pink in Malawi race, by white-spotted black in Tanzania, Mozambique. Call a loud repeated whistle, *kor kooroo*. Food mainly fruit, some insects. 3 white eggs laid in tree-hole, sometimes old woodpecker's. Often parasitised by Lesser Honeyguide, *Indicator minor*. **527**

Lymnocryptes minimus *Scolopacidae*
JACK SNIPE *c.* 7½ (bill 1½) ins
N Palaearctic: temperate and subarctic zones from Scandinavia and Baltic to NE Siberia; winters from temperate Eurasia S to Africa, India, Ceylon, in marshes, often by small stream or spring. Breeds usually large swamps with sedge and cotton grass. Upperparts and rather rounded wings mottled dark brown with greenish sheen, pale feather edges making two light bars on back; crown very dark brown, face striped, breast brown; underparts white; legs greenish-grey, bill yellowish flesh to grey, eyes dark brown. Usually solitary, springing up to pitch again not far off. Spring call hollow sound resembling distant horse cantering, uttered in display flight or on ground as bird planes down with whir rather like African and Common Snipe, *Gallinago nigripennis* and *G. gallinago*; then 'bounces' in air as if on invisible string. Probes in mud for small molluscs, insects; also some seeds. Breeds from early June; scrape, sometimes lined, in moss or hummock, hold 4 cream to olive brown eggs, marked rich dark browns, incubated by ♀ *c.* 24 days.

LYREBIRD,
PRINCE ALBERT'S see under **Menura novaehollandiae**
SUPERB see **Menura novaehollandiae**

Lyrurus tetrix *Tetraonidae*
BLACK GROUSE 16-17 (♀) – 20-22 (♂) ins
Palaearctic: N Temperate from Britain across Eurasia to NE Siberia and E China; resident in swampy heaths, moors and bogs, usually along forest edge, sea level to 6,000 ft. ♂: glossy blue-black, including lyre-shaped tail, with white wing bar and under tail coverts; brownish eclipse plumage in autumn. ♀: mottled brown and black with white wing-bar and forked tail. Legs feathered, toes and eyes brown, with red wattles above, bill brown-black. Families pack in autumn up to several hundred birds, sometimes ♂♂ together. Perches freely in trees, roosting in them or on ground. Typical gamebird flight of wing-beats and glides. Usually silent away from 'lek' (forest clearing or grassy area of open ground) where ♂♂, watched by ♀♀, congregate in spring and autumn to display like turkeys, with jumping runs, 'rookooing' calls but few actual fights. Diet exclusively vegetable from ground or trees: shoots, especially conifers, leaves, flowers and berries; also gleans crop fields. ♂♂ polygamous, take no part in rearing brood. ♀ lines scrape in fairly thick cover, laying 6 to 10 yellowish-white sparsely marked eggs which she incubates 24-29 days; young can fly 15-20 days. **186**

Macgregoria pulchra *Paradisaeidae*
MOLUCCAN BIRD OF PARADISE ♂: 13-15 ins
Australasian: resident mountains W and SE New Guinea, 8,900 to 12,800 ft in montane Podocarpus (pine) forests. ♂: generally velvet black; black-tipped primaries pale cinnamon; orange wattles round eyes and over earcoverts, narrow in front of eyes, broad and lappet-like above and behind. ♀ similar but smaller. Juvenile dusky black. Legs bluish-grey, bill black, eyes red or reddish brown. In pairs or small parties. Display (A. L. Rand): 2 or more birds chase each other through forest near tree limit, hopping along branches and flying, sometimes gliding, over gaps, air whistling through extended primaries, also calling *chic chic chic chic*. Food: tree fruits. Strong pair bond; breeding probably begins August when ♀, accompanied by ♂, builds bulky nest of plant stems and moss, lined finer stems, leaves *c.* 50 ft up in large pine. Probably single egg, earthy pink spotted brown, incubated ♀ in short spells. Both parents feed young one, ♂ perhaps taking major share.

MACARONI PENGUIN see **Eudyptes chrysolophus**

MACAW,
BLUE AND YELLOW see **Ara ararauna**
HYACINTHINE see **Anodorhynchus hyacinthinus**

Machaeropterus regulus *Pipridae*

STRIPED MANAKIN $3\frac{1}{2}$ ins

Neotropical: Venezuela, Colombia, E Ecuador, NE Peru, W and Central Brazil; resident in forests from sea level to 4,000 ft. ♂: upperparts green, including sides of head and neck; inner flight feathers with white inner webs; tail, short, greyish-brown, feathers broad and stiff; crown and nape crimson; throat dull white; underparts pinkish chestnut, striped white and suffused scarlet on breast; legs, bill greyish, eyes red. ♀: upperparts olive-green; underparts whitish with brownish breast band. Display by ♂ includes 'sharp, buzzing sound' with bill wide open, followed by rapidly revolving both over and under slender twig, holding on by feet (A. F. Skutch). Breeding habits resemble *Manacus manacus*. **588**

Macrodipteryx vexillarius or Semeiophorus vexillarius *Caprimulgidae*

PENNANT-WINGED NIGHTJAR (excluding 'pennants') 11 ins

Ethiopian: breeds from 4°S except extreme S Africa; southern populations migrate N over Equator after breeding. Habitat varied, including thick bush, nesting on rocky timbered ground. ♂ (non-breeding) and ♀: dark brown, upperparts mottled buff; dark rufous collar on hind neck; primaries blackish, barred rufous, secondaries tipped white; small white patches on breast; throat and breast mottled brown and grey; belly whitish, sparsely barred black. In breeding season ♂'s two inner primaries elongated, one with white base, lighter inner and dark outer web. Rests lengthwise on branch. Often flies by day. Sailing courtship flight by ♂ with fluttering pennants and bat-like twittering pipe; also call rendered *kuwhoop kuwhoop kuwhoop . . churr*. ♂ may break off pennants after courtship. Food: insects hawked on wing. Drinks at dusk before hunting. Breeds August to January or longer, according to area, laying 2 rich pink or pinkish brown eggs, marbled and blotched red, brown and purple in bare place on ground.

Macronectes giganteus *Procellariidae*

GIANT PETREL 32-38 ins

Southern oceans from 30° to 65°S, moving northward after breeding almost to Equator, found increasingly offshore near human food sources. Generally dull brown, paler on face and neck and becoming mottled through pigment fading; legs brown to black, heavy bill (larger in ♂) horn to greenish, eyes brown-flecked or grey white. Immature more uniform dark brown; white plumage phase occurs. Less agile on wing than albatrosses but better on land than relatives and may feed there. Mutual displays with mewing calls at breeding sites; also hoarse croaking. Scavenging flocks at ports, but natural diet squids and crustaceans, also carrion, penguin eggs and chicks. One white egg laid August to October in vestigial to substantial nest mound on high ground of bare islands; incubated at least 6 weeks by ♀ and ♂, who eventually leave chick to fledge in 102-117 days. **29**

Macronyx ameliae *Motacillidae*

ROSY-BREASTED LONGCLAW 8 ins

Ethiopian: Kenya, Tanzania, S to Natal; resident grassy plains, often edges of marshes. ♂: upperparts black, feathers tawny-edged; underparts rich salmon pink with black band across breast, curving upward to gape. ♀: underparts buffish-brown, pink paler, confined mainly to belly; black streaks not band across breast. Legs brown (hind claw very long and curved), bill, eyes dark. Shy, but conspicuous when soaring, uttering plaintive song, then hovering, legs hanging downwards, before landing. Runs fast; does not perch in trees. Call: sharp *chuit chuit*. Eats mainly insects, with small molluscs, seeds. Breeding season varies with range; builds grass nest, lined rootlets, in or under tussock, often on wet ground. 3 or 4 very pale green eggs, mottled brown and lilac. **628**

Macronyx capensis *Motacillidae*

ORANGE-THROATED LONGCLAW 8 ins

Ethiopian: resident E Southern Africa, reaching to coast in S. Habitat: open grassland, often near permanent water source or beside sea. ♂: upperparts

dull brown; wing edged bright orange yellow, flight feathers edged pale yellow; outer tail feathers tipped white; yellow crown heavily streaked blackish-brown, 'eyebrow' orange; chin, throat bright orange, bordered black; underparts ochre to orange, flanks brown. ♀ paler on chin and throat. Legs (long hind claw) pale brown, bill darker, eyes brown. Ground-living but conspicuous, usually in pairs. Flies heavily with whirring wings when flushed, soon landing, often uttering mewing call. Sings on wing lively *chwirri chwirri chwirri chwee*. Insectivorous. Breeding as genus. **629**

Macronyx croceus *Motacillidae*

YELLOW-THROATED LONGCLAW 8 ins

Ethiopian: Senegal and Angola to Natal, not Congo forests; resident open, e.g. *Brachystegia*, woodlands, bush-clad grassland; swamps, cultivated land, near coast in S Africa. Closely resembles *M. capensis* but edge of wing, 'eyebrow', chin and throat bright not orange yellow; edges of flight and tail feathers yellower; underparts rich yellow, buff on flanks slightly streaked darker brown. Legs etc as relatives, hind toe nearly 2 ins. This species, in which sexes alike, show most striking resemblance to Nearctic meadowlarks *Sturnella*. Few 'lark-like flaps' when flushed; also slow flapping courtship flight with spread tail and song. Ordinary call repeated whistling *tuewhee*. Insectivorous. Breeding varies with range; builds well-hidden nest of grass and rootlets under tuft or in tall grass. 3 whitish or pale green eggs, spotted brown over purple-grey mottling, often at big end. **630**

Macropygia phasianella *Columbidae* c. 14 ins

LARGE BROWN CUCKOO DOVE or BROWN PIGEON

Australasian, Oriental: races distributed across E Australia, Kangean I., Java, Sumatra, Lombok, Klagger I., Sumbawa, Flores, Engaro, Mentawi Is, Simalur I., Batan Is, Botel Tobago, Calayan I., N Borneo and Philippines. Habitat: forests; prefers glades and small openings. ♂: Australian form: head, neck and breast reddish brown, tinged pink on upper breast, shading to golden brown on lower breast; throat and underparts (neck downwards) speckled blackish grey; mantle and hindneck purple and green gloss; long tail. ♀: smaller, with rich rufous crown, lacks pink tinge and speckling more prominent. Legs and bill black or dark brown, eyes white or bluish, often with red outer ring. Most other races richer red-brown colour with more or less conspicuous blackish and rufous speckling on neck and underparts of ♀. Call: loud three syllable coo. Long tail used as support while feeding in trees or shrubs on fruits and berries; also feeds on ground. Breeds November to January in Australia; scanty twig platform usually low down in trees or shrubs, single creamy white egg. **367**

MADAGASCAR NUTHATCH see **Hypositta coralirostris**

MAGELLAN GOOSE see **Chloephaga picta**

MAGELLANIC PLOVER see **Pluvianellus socialis**

MAGNIFICENT FRIGATE BIRD see **Fregata magnificens**

MAGNOLIA WARBLER see **Dendroica magnoliae**

MAGPIE see **Pica pica**

MAGPIE,
AUSTRALIAN see **Gymnorhina tibicen**
AZURE-WINGED see **Cyanopica cyanus**
WESTERN see under **Gymnorhina tibicen**

MAGPIE GOOSE see **Anseranas semipalmata**

MAGPIE LARK see **Grallina cyanoleuca**

MAGPIE ROBIN, SEYCHELLES see **Copsychus sechellarum**

MALACHITE
KINGFISHER see **Corythornis cristata**

SUNBIRD see **Nectarinia famosa**

Malaconotus zeylonus *Laniidae*

BOKMAKIERIE SHRIKE 9 ins

Ethiopian: SW Southern Africa; resident open savannah and bush, plantations of introduced trees, gardens. Upperparts green; flight feathers dusky, green-edged; central tail feathers blackish, tinged green and faintly barred, outer feathers black with broad yellow tips; crown, hindneck, cheeks, earcoverts ashy grey; 'eyebrow' yellow, lores and line down side neck black, linking with broad band across bright yellow underparts; flanks washed grey. Legs lead-grey, bill black, eyes brown. Usually in pairs, often on ground near trees, hunting insects. Low flight, when black and yellow tail conspicuous. Birds duet in sight of each other on high perches; renderings: *bokmakierie*, *ko-koveet*; alarm calls: *tok tok tok*; *kwirr kirr kirr*. Breeds July to October, Cape, mainly September to December, Transvaal, ♀ and ♂ building large compact nest of twigs, grass, roots, lined fibres, rootlets; usually in thick bush a few feet up. Usually 3 or 4 greenish blue eggs, which are spotted and speckled reddish brown, incubated mainly ♀ c. 12 days; young fly c. 15 days. **655**

Malacoptila panamensis *Bucconidae* 7 ins

WHITE-WHISKERED PUFFBIRD or SOFTWING

Neotropical: S Mexico through Central America to Colombia and W Ecuador; resident at intermediate levels in lowland rain forest up to 4,500 ft. Stout, large-headed, short-tailed, ♂: upperparts from head to tail rich chestnut brown or bright cinnamon, spotted and streaked tawny and buff; throat, breast and flanks cinnamon or tawny buff (feathers edged darker), underparts shade to whitish; white tufts on cheeks 'like walrus tusks' (A. F. Skutch), smaller one on forehead. ♀: less rufous, more olive and grey. Legs pale grey, bill: upper blackish, lower bluish horn; large eyes dull red. Solitary, pairs or family parties, usually 15 to 20 ft up, flying from burrows straight to trees and often staying immobile until darts from perch to seize prey with loud clack of bill; mainly large insects and their larvae; moths, Orthoptera, also spiders, lizards. Sometimes forages in clearings early, late or in wet weather. Jerks tail when alarmed. Usually silent but utters soft, variable *peep* whistle and *tzee* call; ♂ has low twittering song. Breeds March to July Costa Rica (A. F. Skutch), ♀ and ♂ excavating $1\frac{1}{2}$ to 2 ft descending tunnel in slightly sloping ground; ring of sticks and leaf fragments masks entrance; nest chamber lined leaves. ♂ takes major share incubating usually 2 blunt white eggs for at least 14 days, and broods young for first 6 days of 20 day fledging period. ♀ brings food at first to entrance and young scramble up to it; when brooding at night ceases, they screen themselves with leaves. **524**

MALAYSIAN
BROWN WOOD OWL see **Strix leptogrammica**
FISH OWL see **Bubo ketupu**
RAIL BABBLER see **Eupectes macrocerus**

MALEO see **Macrocephalon maleo**

MALLARD see **Anas platyrhynchos**

MALLEE FOWL see **Leipoa ocellata**

Malurus assimilis *Muscicapidae: Malurinae*

PURPLE-BACKED WREN c. $5\frac{1}{4}$ ins

Australia: E of continent (W of Great Dividing Range) N to Gulf of Carpentaria and S to NW Victoria, through central and South Australia to Western Australia (apart from southern part); frequents dry scrubland. ♂: crown and sides of head purplish blue; cobalt round eye and ear coverts; mantle and upper back purplish blue; throat, chest, collar and lower back black, belly white; wings brown with chestnut shoulder patches; tail dull blue tipped white save 2 central feathers. ♀ as ♀ Variegated Wren, *M. lamberti*. Legs brown, bill black, eyes brown. Behaviour and feeding like Blue Wren, *M. cyaneus*. Breeds September to December; domed nest of grass and plant stalks

Oreoica gutturalis *Muscicapidae: Pachycephalinae*
AUSTRALIAN CRESTED BELLBIRD   9 ins
Australian: generally distributed, mainly inland, in dry mulga scrub, mallee woodlands. Upperparts khaki brown, including wings (grey edges to secondaries), tail; nape to hindcrown light grey, rising to thin black crest on forecrown, whence black stripe down through eye becomes broad black gorget round white face, throat; underparts white tinged light buff; legs blackish, rather short bill black. ♀ brown where ♂ black and white, throat pale. Juvenile much as ♀. Singly or in pairs. Call: *chuc a chuc chuc*; song rendered *Dick, Dick, the devil*, repeated; bell-like note at end, ventriloquial; ♀ may follow up with single note or repeat last 3. Food: insects and grass-feeding larvae on ground, where hops with upright posture. Breeds generally September to December, ♀ and ♂ building cup nest of bark, twigs, leaves, even cloth, lined grasses, bark rootlets, in thick fork or hollowed stump 2 to c. 10 ft up; rim often 'decorated' semi-paralysed larvae. Usually 3 white eggs, marked sepia and black, incubated ♀ and ♂; both also tend young.

ORIENTAL GREENFINCH see under **Carduelis chloris**

ORIOLE,
    AFRICAN BLACK-HEADED see **Oriolus larvatus**
    BALTIMORE see **Icterus galbula**
    BLACK-HEADED FOREST see under **Oriolus larvatus**
    BLACK-WINGED see under **Oriolus larvatus**
    GOLDEN see **Oriolus oriolus**
    OLIVE-BACKED see **Oriolus sagittatus**
    ORCHARD see under **Icterus galbula**
    WESTERN BLACK-HEADED see under **Oriolus larvatus**

ORIOLE BLACKBIRD see **Gymnomystax mexicanus**

Oriolus brachyrhynchus see under **O. larvatus**

Oriolus larvatus *Oriolidae*
AFRICAN BLACK-HEADED ORIOLE   9 ins
Ethiopian: Sudan, Ethiopia, E Africa, SE Congo, Angola, S Africa; local migrant forests, inland and coastal scrub and bush, other wooded areas including parks, gardens. Upperparts greenish yellow; head, nape, upper breast black; wing coverts black, tipped white, edged yellow-green; flight feathers blackish, edged white; central tail feathers greenish-yellow, rest black, tipped golden yellow; hindneck, underparts golden yellow; legs grey-blue, bill pinkish brown, eyes red. Immature's head, nape flecked yellow, ear-coverts blackish, chin to upper breast streaked black, bill blackish. Black-headed Forest Oriole, *O. monacha* (Eritrea, Ethiopia), Western Black-headed Oriole, *O. brachyrhynchus* (Sierra Leone to Uganda), Black-winged Oriole, *O. nigripennis* (Sierra Leone to Sudan, Uganda, N Angola) all very similar in plumage and what is known of habits. Usually in pairs but flocks when fruit ripe; haunts canopy, sitting motionless for long periods. Call: 2 or 3-syllabled *we-er-ou* (A. W. Vincent); harsh repeated *kweer* of alarm; some mimicry. Diet: caterpillars; seeds and fruit, doing some damage to crops. Breeding season varies within range; builds basket nest of grass, moss or tendrils, blended with surroundings and suspended from slender fork at end of lateral branch, usually high up tree. 2 to 4 white, cream or pink eggs, spotted reddish-brown or sepia over lavender, generally in zone. Incubation and fledging much as Golden Oriole, *O. oriolus*. **976**

Oriolus
    monacha see under **O. larvatus**
    nigripennis see under **O. larvatus**

Oriolus oriolus *Oriolidae*
GOLDEN ORIOLE   c. 9½ ins
Palaearctic, Oriental: from extreme NW Africa and Iberia throughout continental Europe to 60°N and E to headwaters of R Yenisei at about 90°E; southwards limits N Mediterranean area, Asia Minor, Iran to Indian subcontinent, with apparent gap from between Caspian and Lake Balkash S to Persian Gulf. Only

Asian population resident, rest winter tropical Africa. Habitat: open broadleaved woodland and riverine strips; parks, orchards, tree clumps in cultivated areas, tropical gardens; up to 4,300 ft Alps, 7,000 ft Himalayan valleys; winters forest canopy. ♂: brilliant yellow head and body; yellow primary coverts make patch on black wing when closed; tail black, outer feathers tipped yellow. ♀: upperparts golden green to greenish yellow; wings brown, tail as ♂ but browner; lores greyish black; underparts greyish-white to yellowish, streaked dark brown; underwing, under tail coverts yellow. Legs dark grey, bill dark pink, eyes dark red. Juvenile much as ♀ but ♂ brighter. Normally arboreal, hopping when on ground; very secretive in canopy, heard more often than seen. Undulating, rather laboured flight, sweeping upward to perch. Bathes freely. Spring call, musical fluting *ori-ole*; various harsh, cat-like notes, rattling *chrrr* of alarm. ♂ pursues ♀ closely in courtship chases.. Diet: insects from canopy in spring: beetles, flies, bees and larvae; spiders, small molluscs; fruit and berries in autumn. Breeds from end April; hammock-like nest, built mainly ♀ of grass, fibres, wool, bark, paper, lined grassheads and woven round fork or between twigs, usually at some height up tree. 3 to 5 glossy white eggs, spotted black mainly at big end, incubated ♀ and ♂ 14-15 days. Young, fed ♀ and ♂, fly 14-15 days. **977**

Oriolus sagittatus *Oriolidae*
OLIVE-BACKED ORIOLE   11 ins
Australasian: mainly coastal from W Australia (Kimberley area) across N, down E coasts and as far W as Adelaide; inland some parts New South Wales. Regular migrant some areas, nomadic in others, dependent on fruiting of trees. Habitat: rain forests in N; riverine woodland with open country; occasionally mallee scrub New South Wales. Upperparts dusky green, streaked black; flight feathers and upper surface tail dark grey; upper wing coverts tinged buff; underparts white streaked black; undertail dark grey, feathers tipped white; legs blackish blue, bill orange brown, eyes orange. Tree-living in thick cover like other orioles; swift, silent undulating flight in open. Call: monotonous whistle of 3 notes; squeaks and chattering while feeding on fruit, e.g. wild figs, camphor laurel; takes insects in areas where fruit not available. Breeds November to January SE Australia; deep cup nest of bark, leaves, cocoons, lichens, lined fine grass; suspended at end of drooping branch of eucalypt or casuarina tree, usually near edge of dense forest. 3 or 4 creamy eggs, spotted brown, chestnut over grey; incubation and fledging much as relatives. **978**

ORPHEAN WARBLER see **Sylvia hortensis**

Ortalis ruficauda *Cracidae*
COCRICO, RED-TAILED GUAN or
RUFOUS-VENTED CHACALACA   18-21 ins
Neotropical: N Colombia, Venezuela to Orinoco, Tobago; resident in secondary forest and scrub. Upperparts and breast olive green, lower back browner; underparts grey-brown, flanks rufous; forehead black, crown and head grey; tail coverts rufous, tail bronze-green, tipped white, wings tipped chestnut; legs and bill dark blue, facial skin red, eyes dark blue. Lives mainly in trees, small flocks moving from branch to branch, then gliding for c. 100 yards. Dust bathes in . clearings. Territorial confrontations as breeding season approaches. 'Sings' in mornings; native name Guacharaca onomatopoeic; ♂'s voice lower owing to looped windpipe; sound 'resounds through forest for up to 2 hours' (Helen Lapham); also cluckings and other notes. Diet of fruit, including palm nuts, and leaves. Breeds from April (rainy season) to July; colonial, partly polygamous. Builds nest of sticks and dry grass, apparently from ground to 50-80 ft in trees. 2 to 4 whitish eggs incubated by ♀ with ♂ near, c. 24-26 days. Young soon leave nest. **179**

Ortalis vetula *Cracidae*
PLAIN CHACALACA   20-24 ins
S Nearctic (Texas) to Neotropical (Nicaragua); resident in scrubby woodland and its edge, also cultivated land. Upperparts dark olive-brown with green-

ish gloss, tail tipped white; underparts brown; legs and bill black, ♂'s facial skin red in spring, eyes dark brown. Dust bathes in open; when surprised, flies into cover, running along branches, waving wings. Loud, raucous *cha-cha-la-ca* gives name, often in concerted chorus from tree-tops. Courtship on ground, ♂ strutting in front of ♀ with head erect and low-pitched calls due to curved windpipe. Diet of plant stems, fallen fruit, insects and worms; sometimes leaves from trees. Breeds from March and April, building loose nest of twigs and leaves up to 10 ft in trees or bushes. 3 or 4 granulated white eggs incubated c. 3 weeks; young leave nest after a day and soon fly. **180**

Orthonyx spaldingi *Muscicapidae: Cinclosomatinae*
NORTHERN LOGRUNNER   9 ins
Australasian: rain forest along coastal range of N Queensland, Cairns to Rockingham Bay. Almost black above, including wings, short tail; flanks, mantle washed olive brown; pale orbits, underparts white; throat, breast chestnut in ♀; legs grey, bill black, eyes brown. Forms small flocks; runs, walks on ground. Loud calls include series of notes *chow chilla chow chow*; occasionally mimics other species. Feeds, using splayed spiny tail quills as prop, scratching ground with alternate feet. Diet mainly insects, some berries. Breeds May to August. Builds domed nest with side entrance, of leaves, moss on ground, in vines, ferns or tree stump up to 10 ft. 2 white eggs. **719**

Orthorhamphus magnirostris see **Esacus magnirostris**

Orthostomus sutorius *Muscicapidae: Sylviinae*
COMMON TAILORBIRD   5 ins
Oriental: widespread throughout region, including Ceylon, S China; resident undergrowth of forests, scrub jungle, gardens, even in towns; up to 5,000 ft Himalayas. Upperparts from neck to long, graduated tail olive to yellowish green; wings light brown edged greenish; tail feathers (2 central ones elongated) tipped whitish; forehead, crown rufous; narrow eye-stripe on whitish face; underparts to under tail coverts white, tinged buff; legs pinkish flesh, thin pointed bill dark grey, eyes light brown to red. Active, searching creepers, other plants for insects, their eggs and larvae; also takes some nectar. Long tail flicked over back in flight (B. E. Smythies). Loud call: *chw-ee chw-ee* or *chip chip*, repeated 25 times in 10 seconds. Breeds April onwards, usually within 6 ft of ground in low bush or hanging branch; soft cup of plant down, lined hairs, grasses, built in cradle formed by one (folded), 2 or more large leaves sewn together with threads of spider's web, cocoon silk, wool, cotton. Bill pierces hole in leaf, pulls thread through; leaves kept together by friction with threads; each stitch separate. 3 or 4 pointed eggs, shades from white to pale blue, sparsely freckled brown and black, mainly at big end, incubated ♀ and ♂; both also tend young.

ORTOLAN see **Emberiza hortulana**

Ortygospiza atricollis *Estrildidae*
QUAIL FINCH   4 ins
Ethiopian: from Senegal, Gambia across to E Africa; also Eritrea, Ethiopia; S through N Malawi, Zambia, Rhodesia to S Africa; resident open grassland, especially round shallow pools and swamps. ♂: upperparts mottled grey and brown; narrow white edges to brown flight feathers, white tip to short blackish tail; forehead, cheeks, throat black; chin, circle round eyes white; underparts barred black and white with chestnut band lower breast; belly white, under tail coverts brown and black. ♀ paler, brown for black on head. Legs light brown, bill red, eyes brown. Immature much as ♀ but bill blackish. Ground-living in small flocks after breeding; flies up steeply, wings whirring like quail, then drops to cover again. Incessant bell-like call *tirrilink tirrilink* on wing; subdued warbling song on ground. ♂ towers in courtship flight, then falls 'like stone' with clicking noise. Diet: mainly grass seeds; attacks crops. Breeding season varies within range; builds rough pear-shaped nest of grass, often with 'porch', lined finer stems, feathers; near ground in tussock. 2 to 4 white eggs.

Ortyxelos meiffrenii *Turnicidae*

LARK QUAIL or QUAIL PLOVER *c.* 5 ins
Ethiopian: ranges in broad band S of Equator from Senegal, Ghana, N Nigeria to Ethiopia, Sudan, N Kenya and N Uganda. Habitat: arid scrub with burr-bearing heskanit grass. *Cenchrus catharticus*, probably its main food. Upperparts tawny, vermiculated and streaked black and white; flight feathers black with broad white tips, tawny band on primaries; 'shoulder' and outer coverts white; breast tawny; underparts white; legs pale flesh, bill yellowish, culmen blue, eyes brown. Lark-like on wing when whites show up, flies strongly but jerkily; runs and squats on ground. Call: soft, low whistle. Breeds December and January, laying 2 creamy or stone coloured eggs, marked black, brown and grey, in lightly lined scrape on bare ground.

OSPREY see **Pandion haliaetus**

OSTRICH see **Struthio camelus**

Otis tarda *Otididae*

GREAT BUSTARD   ♀: 30-33; ♂: *c.* 40 ins
Palaearctic: reduced and interrupted range through temperate zone from Portugal and Morocco, Central Europe, Asia Minor to Central and E China. Mainly resident, some movement S of northern and eastern birds in winter, e.g. to Mediterranean, Japan and India. Inhabits steppe grasslands and arid hills, also cultivated land, especially large cornfields in Europe. ♂: upperparts sandy, barred black, wings mainly white with black primaries; head and neck grey-mauve, with bristly white 'moustaches'; breast and base of neck chestnut marked black; underparts white. ♀: smaller, slimmer, no moustache or chestnut on breast; young ♂ like ♀. Legs brown, bill yellowish, tip darker, eyes hazel. Shy, taking cover when alarmed or to flight, when white on wings shows up, with rapid beats. Normal walk deliberate. Parties and flocks, mainly of ♀♀ form after breeding, and non-breeding ♂♂ remain gregarious. Remarkable ♂ display by turning over wing coverts and tail feathers to show white, head sunk, throat sac distended. Rather silent: bark of aggression and *kraang* of anxiety; young whistle when alarmed. Eats leaves, buds and seeds, and animals, especially beetles and voles. Breeding season from end April in S Europe, later in N. ♀ flattens area in cover, lays 2 to 4 greenish or olive-brown eggs, streaked liver brown, incubating them 25-28 days. Young fed insects by ♀ at first, fledge in about 5 weeks. ♂ does not assist. **246**

Otis tetrax *Otididae*

LITTLE BUSTARD   *c.* 17 ins
Palaearctic: temperate zone from Iberia, N Africa, France to S Russia and W Asia; sedentary and migratory, eastern population moving south in winter. Inhabits stony hill country, steppes and deserts, heaths, cultivations especially in Europe. ♂: crown and upperparts mottled sandy-brown with fine black vermiculations; most of wing white with partly black primaries: (summer) cheeks and throat slate-blue bordered white V; rest of neck black with white band; underparts white. ♂ (winter), ♀ and young have front of neck and breast buffish, streaked black, legs greyish yellow, bill black and grey, eyes pale yellow. Shy, taking to flight with rattling call and becoming almost whiter from below; flies with rapid wingbeats and hiss, action like partridge. Will also crouch and run when disturbed. Flocks in autumn. Calls *dahg* when alarmed; ♂ utters abrupt *ptrrr* in display, when, tail fanned and wings drooped, he jerks head, leaps and stamps in descent. Food vegetable and animal, especially locusts and grasshoppers. Breeding season from end April in SW Europe. ♀ makes scrape in cover, lays 3-4 greenish to olive brown eggs, streaked brown, and incubates them *c.* 3 weeks with ♂ in attendance. ♀ feeds young at first. Possibly double-brooded. **247**

Otus asio *Strigidae*

SCREECH OWL   6½-10 ins
Nearctic, marginally Neotropical: SE Alaska and Canada to Florida Keys and Central Mexico. Resident, with some winter dispersal, in woodlands, wooded canyons, orchards, gardens. Variable: 'red' phase has upperparts rufous brown with pale bars on wings and back; prominent 'horns' and crown black-streaked, facial disc and throat roughly fringed black; underparts pale, flecked rufous and black; legs feathered, bill dark horn, eyes yellow. In 'grey' and 'brown' phases these colours replace rufous brown. Nocturnal; mournful wailing hoot usually runs down scale; also series of short calls. Diet: mice, meadow voles, small birds; insects, including cutworms, locusts. Breeds April-May, in tree cavities or old woodpecker holes, buildings, nestboxes, laying 4 to 8 white eggs. **446**

Otus gurneyi *Strigidae*

GREAT SCOPS OWL   12 ins
Confined to Philippines: Mindanao and Marieduque, considered to be rare but numbers unknown. Generally rufous; wings darker, mottled brown, striped blackish; buff edges to scapulars show as stripe down back; tail tawny rufous; as are forehead, prominent ear tufts; crown darker; facial disc bright rufous; chin, throat (with white patch) tawny; underparts striped dark brown; legs fully feathered, feet pale grey; bill greyish white; eyes brown. Habits apparently not studied.

Otus insularis *Strigidae*

BARE-LEGGED SCOPS OWL   *c.* 7½ ins
Seychelles (Indian Ocean); confined to main island of Mahè, in mountain forests. Generally russet brown with black shaft streaks, most prominent on underparts; legs long, eyes yellow. Calls: *toc toc* (?♂), 're-peated sawing noise' (?♀) (R. Gaymer, M. Penny). Food includes lizards, grasshoppers, but little known of habits. Decrease attributed partly to competition from introduced Barn Owl, *Tyto alba*.

Otus leucotis *Strigidae*

WHITE-FACED OWL   10 ins
Ethiopian: 2 races cover most of region except Congo Forests, extreme S Africa. Resident in woodland, thorn bush, long grass, especially in hot, low-lying areas. Upperparts, wings and tail finely vermiculated brownish grey, narrowly barred darker grey; mantle streaked black and large white markings outer edges of scapulars; crown to nape black, forehead grey; face white, disc fringed black, 'horns' tipped black; underparts less closely vermiculated, black streaks most pronounced; under wing coverts white; bill bluish, with bristles, eyes orange. Juvenile lacks black on head. Nocturnal, roosting in trees along watercourses, but but sometimes hunts by day, especially after grass fires, for insects and mice. ♂'s call: *cuc-coo;* ♀ replies with stammering *wh-h-h-roo;* bill clicked in anger. Breeding season variable, usually uses old nests of other birds, occasionally shallow hole or fork in tree, laying 2 to 4 white eggs. Incubation and fledging probably as *O. scops*. **447**

Otus scops *Strigidae*

SCOPS OWL   *c.* 7½ ins
All Old World regions: from N Mediterranean area and NW Africa E to Central Asia, SE to Indian sub-continent and Ceylon. SE Asia to Celebes, Moluccas, N to Luzon, Manchuria, Japan. Separate range includes S Arabia, most of Ethiopian region except Congo Forests, SW Africa. Resident except in Palae-arctic whence migrates to tropical Africa and Asia. Habitat: arid and lightly forested areas, riverine forests, open oak woods, orchards, cultivated land with trees, towns and suburbs. Variable: upperparts gen-erally brownish grey to rufous brown with black shaft streaks, white streaks and fine vermiculation; head and 'horns' appear speckled; partial facial disc finely barred, dark fringed; underparts vermiculated with black vertical streaks; legs feathered, feet grey, bill bluish-black, eyes lemon yellow. Much greyer plum-age phase occurs. Mainly nocturnal, sitting upright by day against trunk, in bushes or creepers: very hard to see. Generally solitary; parties in winter areas. ♂'s 'song': monotonous but musical, whistling *kiu* repeated at 2 second intervals, from dusk through night; ♀'s reply higher-pitched, 2 or 3 syllables. Takes mainly large insects: moths, beetles, locusts; lizards, small mammals and birds. Breeds from end April, in hollow trees, cavities and crevices in rocks, old wood-pecker holes, occasionally old nests. ♀ lays 4 or 5 white eggs, incubating them 24-25 days. ♂ brings food to her for young, who leave nest 3 weeks, before fully fledged. **448**

Oxyruncus cristatus *Tyrannidae*

SHARPBILL   6½-7 ins
Neotropical: Costa Rica and Panama S through E South America to Paraguay; resident in tree tops of humid tropical forests, up to 4,000 ft in Amazonian Brazil. Upperparts predominantly olive green, very dark brown on relatively long wings and tail and a crown which is crested, yellow and scarlet, bordered black; underparts pale yellow to white, heavily spotted dark brown; rather short, strong-toed legs pale, strong pointed bill dark, eyes light brown. Said to be solitary and strong flier with diet of fruit. Nest and breeding habits unknown. **583**

Oxyura australis *Anatidae*

BLUE-BILLED DUCK   *c.* 16 ins
Australasian: southern Australia in deep, densely vegetated swamps; gathers in large flocks in winter on extensive open fresh waters. ♂: head and neck glossy black; foreneck, upper breast, flanks and back chest-nut; rest of underparts brown flecked black; tail black; wings dark brown. Eclipse throughout winter much greyer. ♀: upperparts blackish brown, chin and throat brown speckled black; foreneck, breast, belly mottled light brown and black. Legs, ♂ grey, ♀ grey-brown; bill, ♂ blue, ♀ grey-brown; eyes brown. Shy, swims swiftly and low in water, almost helpless on land; seldom flies but after laborious take-off moves swiftly. Call: virtually silent, ♂ low rattling note in display, ♀ weak quack of alarm. Dabbles on surface or dives deeply for small aquatic animals, chiefly insects, and plant matter. Builds nest September to November in dense vegetation, occasionally on ground, of plant debris on trampled down platform of herbage, often

covered by dome of reeds. Usually 5 or 6 light green eggs, incubated *c.* 26-28 days; young leave nest after day and feed themselves, guarded by ♀. **124**

OYSTERCATCHER see **Haematopus ostralegus**

OYSTERCATCHER, AFRICAN BLACK see **Haematopus moquini**

Pachycephala pectoralis *Muscicapidae*: *Pachycephalinae*
GOLDEN WHISTLER   *c.* 7 ins
Oriental, Australasian: 3 main areas of distribution, each with many island races: Indonesia E from Java to Celebes, Moluccas; Bismarck Arch. to Fiji; mainly coastal E, S and SW continental Australia with Tasmania. Replaced in New Guinea and much of N Australia by Grey-headed, *P. simplex*. Nomadic in winter in open forests; closed canopy in summer, from mallee scrub of S Australia, eucalypts of SE to dense rain forests. ♂: upperparts generally olive green with yellow band on neck; flight feathers black, tinged orange-green secondaries; tail black; head black, chin, throat white, banded black on breast; underparts yellow. ♀: upperparts generally greyish brown, tinged olive, wings, tail coverts; throat mottled greyish-white, breast grey, underparts whitish. Legs slate grey, bill black, eyes red. Juvenile rufous, flight feathers grey; resembles ♀ at 1 year old, ♂ plumage not full until *c.* 3 years old; absent altogether some races. Great variation in ♂'s head plumage and bill within each population group: black breast bar from broad to nearly absent; bill short stubby (Tasmania), powerful, shrike-like (Tannibar Is.). Dipping flight from tree to tree; ♂ unwilling to expose himself above, often visible from ground. Song loud, slurred, liquid whistles, accelerating to whip-crack; may be set off by human voice. Searches foliage for insects, especially beetles, larvae; some berries. Breeding season varies within range; ♀ and ♂ build nest of fine twigs, bark, lined rootlets, grass, green in bush or small tree up to 15 ft. 2 or 3 smooth creamy or buff eggs, freckled brown and grey, incubated by ♀ and ♂, both feed young. **800**

Pachycephala simplex see under **P. pectoralis**

Pachyptila belcheri see under **P. desolata**

Pachyptila desolata *Procellariidae*
ANTARCTIC PRION   10½ ins
Subantarctic and antarctic zones; breeds islands and antarctic coast, most southerly birds moving N after nesting. Upperparts mainly grey-blue, darker on crown and blackish behind and below eyes; dark areas show in flight as inverted W across wings; tail feathers broadly tipped black; underparts light pearly grey. Bill: upper mandible steel grey, side of lower mandible bluish; distinguished from other prions by moderate width of bill (i.e. about half its length), while lamellae or thin plates not usually visible when bill closed; they are much better developed on Broad-billed *P. vittata* and Narrow-billed *P. belcheri*. Flies singly, in groups or flocks, turning rapidly side to side, showing now lighter now darker. Comes ashore to burrows mainly by night, crooning and moaning above them and from inside. Plankton 'krill' scooped up by bill from surface and just below as bird 'hydroplanes' with wings raised, breast touching water and feet propelling it; can also dive well; does not follow ships. Breeds southern summer in large colonies in clefts or burrows, to which it can dig in snow, and caves. Laying of single white egg follows temporary exodus of ♀♀, ♂♂ guarding nests. Incubation ♀ and ♂ 45 days; young, fed ♀ and ♂ from throat, leave nest *c.* 50 days. **30**

Pachyptila vittata see under **P. desolata**

Pachyrhamphus marginatus *Cotingidae*
BLACK-CAPPED BECARD   5 ins
Neotropical: Guyanas, N Venezuela, E Colombia, E Ecuador, E Peru to N Bolivia; Amazonia and other provinces Brazil; resident forests, forest edge, clearings, sea level to 4,500 ft. ♂: upperparts grey (mixed black on mantle), tail black, tipped white; crown

black, feathers tipped iridescent blue; underparts pale grey. ♀: crown rufous to blackish; upperparts, including cheeks and breast, olive; wings with tawny margins; central tail feathers olive-brown, outer black, all tipped fawn; underparts mainly pale yellow. Legs brown, bill dark horn, eyes dark brown. Insectivorous: grasshoppers, small beetles, lepidopterous larvae. Closely related White-winged Becard. *P. polychopterus*, of wider distribution (Guatemala to Argentina, Trinidad and Tobago) breeds during rainy seasons, ♀ making untidy domed nest of grasses, ♂ standing by, at end of high lateral branch, often near wasp nest; clutch 2 white eggs, heavily marked dark brown. **592**

Pachyrhamphus polychopterus see under **P. marginata**

PACIFIC
    GOLDEN PLOVER see **Pluvialis dominica**
    GULL see **Larus pacificus**

Padda oryzivora *Estrildidae*
JAVA SPARROW   5-5½ ins
Oriental (Ethiopian): Indonesia; introduced Malaysia, Borneo, St Helena, Seychelles, Tanzania (Zanzibar area); round habitations where introduced; mangroves in Malaysia; rice fields. Generally grey; crown, throat, band behind ear coverts, upper tail coverts, tail black; cheeks, under tail coverts white; lower flanks, belly wine red. Legs brown, large bill pink, eyes dark brown. Juvenile much browner. White form occurs commonly. Rather sedentary. Call: sharp *chyup;* soft metallic whistling song ending in trill. Diet: seeds, rice, cultivated grain. Breeds colonially; domed nest of grass in tree, bush, under eaves of building. 4 to 7 white eggs. **941**

PAGODA STARLING see **Temenuchus pagodarum**

Pagodroma nivea *Procellariidae*
SNOW PETREL   12 ins
Southern oceans from Antarctic to 50°S, moving north after breeding. Almost entirely white except for black spot by eye; legs dark blue-grey, bill black, eyes brown. Juveniles show grey vermiculations on back. Found in highly co-ordinated flocks, active far into night, but scatter for breeding. Unable to stand or walk. Loud caws on breeding areas, also 'linnet-like twittering' and 'half-whistling, half-shrieking call'. Food mainly crustaceans, but also some fish and even carrion. One white egg laid end November or December in cavity or niche in rocks, sometimes more than 50 miles from sea in scattered colonies on hill tops. Incubation and fledging duties shared by ♀ and ♂.

PAINTED
    BUNTING see **Passerina ciris**
    QUAIL see **Turnix varia**
    SNIPE see **Rostratula benghalensis**
    STORK see **Ibis leucocephalus**

PALAWAN PEACOCK PHEASANT see **Polyplectron emphanum**

PALE
    CHANTING GOSHAWK see **Melierax canorus**
    CRIMSON FINCH see **Neochmia phaeton**
    FLYCATCHER see **Bradornis pallidus**
    WHITE-EYE see **Zosterops pallidus**

PALE-WINGED STARLING see **Onychognathus nabouroup**

PALLAS'S SANDGROUSE see **Syrrhaptes paradoxus**

PALLID CUCKOO see **Cuculus pallidus**

PALM CHAT see **Dulus dominicus**

PALM-NUT VULTURE see **Gypohierax angolensis**

Pandion haliaetus *Accipitridae*
OSPREY   20-23 ins
Almost throughout northern hemisphere, migrating

south in autumn; also breeds Australasia and South Africa. Vicinity of rivers, lakes or sea coasts. Upperparts mainly dark brown, underparts white with brown band across breast; head and neck mainly white with brown stripe through eye; outer primaries blackish, tail brown, barred; legs greenish white, bill dark with blue cere, eyes yellow. Spends much time perched then flies over water, splash-diving with feet forward to grip fish. Usual call a triple whistle, also alarm and nesting calls. Diet mainly fish, occasionally birds. Breeding season variable, from April in North temperate zone. Nesting colonial or solitary, on tree, crag, rock, ruin, artificial substrate, even ground. Builds large structure of sticks and debris, with finer lining; usually 3 eggs, white heavily marked brown and grey. Incubated mainly by ♀ 32-38 days. ♂ feeds young via ♀, fledged at 52-54 days. **160**

Panurus biarmicus *Muscicapidae: Paradoxornithinae*
BEARDED TIT or REEDLING   6½ (tail 3) ins
Palaearctic: main range N and S of Black Sea E to headwaters River Ob; small separate populations W to England, Iberia; larger area Manchuria, possibly elsewhere E Asia. Mainly resident extensive reed beds in freshwater or brackish marshes; disperses in winter, suffering heavy mortality in severe weather. ♂: head lavender grey with broad tapering black 'moustaches'; rest of upperparts tawny; long graduated tail edged white; wings striped white, tawny, black; underparts white, flanks more buff; under tail coverts black. ♀ has tawny head, lacks black 'moustaches', under tail. Juvenile similar but more black on wings, tail. Legs black; bill yellow; eyes pale yellow. Moves jerkily up and down reeds, often straddling two stems. Flies with whirring wings, 'loose' tail jerked rhythmically. Distinctive call: nasal *ping ping;* also twittering flight call in winter flocks of 40 to 50. Diet: mainly insects picked off reed stems; eats seeds of reed mace, reeds in winter. Breeds end April to July; ♂ takes larger share building nest of dead reeds, sedges, lined reed 'flowers', low in swampy vegetation. 5 to 7 white eggs, with numerous spots, streaks, scrawls liver brown, incubated ♀ and ♂ 12-13 days; both parents feed young, who leave nest 9-12 days. 2, sometimes 3 broods. **721**

PAPUAN HORNBILL see **Aceros plicatus**

Paradisaea apoda *Paradisaeidae*
GREATER BIRD
OF PARADISE   ♂: 17-18 (normal tail 6-7) ins
Australasian: S New Guinea, Arus Is, introduced Little Tobago (Caribbean); resident inland tropical forest on plains and hills up to 3,000 ft. ♂: upperparts, including wings, tail, maroon; central tail feathers wire-like, blackish brown, up to 30 ins long; head, neck orange-yellow; forehead, lores, chin, black glossed green; throat to upper neck iridescent oil-green; upper breast brownish black to dark maroon according to race; underparts maroon; huge tufts lacy plumes on each side breast up to 23 ins long, basal ⅔ yellow to orange, outer ⅓ pale cinnamon; legs pale brown, bill light grey-blue, pale tipped, eyes lemon yellow. ♀: generally maroon, darker head and round neck; upper breast, underparts paler; legs pale brown, bill bluish grey, eyes lemon yellow. Immature ♂ progresses from ♀-like plumage over 5 years. Active, noisy, ♂ calling *wawk wawk wawk, wok wok wok wok* (A. R. Wallace). Feeds chiefly tree fruits, probably also insects. Display: dancing parties 12 to 20 ♂♂ in large tree with spreading branches fly excitedly with elevated plumes, expanded to form 'two magnificent golden fans' while head is bent, wings raised over back, tail bent forward under perch. When ♀ appears, ♂♂ freeze on perches, arranged in hierarchy, dominant ♂ in centre (E. T. Gilliard). Breeds December to January Aru Is, nest of sticks lined rootlets in tree. 2 brownish eggs marked longitudinally red- and blackish-brown, incubated by ♀, who also raises young as no pair bond formed.

Paradisaea guilielmi *Paradisaeidae*
EMPEROR BIRD OF PARADISE   ♂: 12½-13 ins
Australasian: mountains of Huon Peninsula, New Guinea; resident mountain forests *c.* 2,200 to 4,000 ft, occasionally higher. ♂: upperparts, including lesser

wing coverts, sides of breast, glossy straw yellow; central tail feathers wire-like, up to 27½ ins long; crown, cheeks, throat to upper breast metallic oil-green; otherwise deep maroon tinged grey with light patch each side lower breast; huge tufts each side breast up to 14½ ins long, basal half usually ivory white tinged yellow, outer half lacy, tends to decompose; legs flesh brown, bill blue grey, eyes reddish brown, ♀ resembles ♂ without ornamental plumes; eyes yellow. Immature ♂ progresses from ♀-like to ♂ plumage. Call (captive): soft clear *poop poop poop;* loud piercing cry. Display (captive): preliminary bobbing, wing-flicking, then after loud call ♂ turns under perch, body remaining close to it, wings, tail widely spread, 'wires' reaching far above; lacy plumes erected to make complete circle round inverted belly; plumes waved as body moved side to side; sustained several minutes. Food chiefly fruits of forest trees. Single or 2 creamy to rose-cinnamon eggs, streaked brown and grey, incubated ♀. Hybrids known in wild with *Paradisaea raggiana* and Lesser Bird of Paradise, *P. minor.*

Paradisaea minor see under **P. guilielmi**

Paradisaea raggiana *Paradisaeidae*
COUNT RAGGI'S BIRD
OF PARADISE ♂: 13-14 (normal tail 6-7) ins
Australasian: S New Guinea; resident forest and forest edge, often near ravines, sea level to 5,000 ft; tree clumps in rocky grasslands; native gardens. ♂: back yellow to brown, according to race; wings, tail, pale to dark wine brown; central tail feathers wire-like up to 19 ins long; head, neck orange yellow; forehead, lores, chin, black glossed green; collar, greater wing coverts yellow; cheeks, gorget oil-green; upper breast blackish; underparts pale to dark wine-brown; lacy tufts on side breast up to 21 ins long, basal ⅔ red to apricot outer ⅓ pale rosy cinnamon; legs grey-brown, bill blue grey, eyes yellow. ♀: upperparts including wings maroon to yellow; tail maroon; forehead, 'face' blackish brown; hind crown to neck dull yellow; gorget blackish brown to black, sometimes traces yellow; underparts greyish wine-brown; legs light brown, bill chalky blue, eyes bright yellow. Immature ♂ progresses from ♀-like to ♂ plumage 5 years. ♀♀ and immature ♂♂ feed on fruits in parties 15 to 20 ft up, usually middle and upper branches. ♂ near display area calls high-pitched *kiing,* followed by resonant *kiii kiii kiii,* becoming louder, ending explosive *waw woow.* ♂♂, probably in parties 3 to 6, occupy own spaces on sloping limbs in tree clump. ♂ bends forward nearly to perch, raises wings upward and forward to meet 'back to back' even over top of head. Wings clapped rapidly, flank plumes raised nearly straight up and expanded. Dominance hierarchy as *P. apoda.* Nest of vines, dead leaves, lined leaf fibres *c.* 15 ft in fork of slender sapling on forest edge (E.T. Gilliard). Single or 2 pinkish cream eggs, marked longitudinally reddish brown over violet, incubated (captive) ♀ 13-15 days; young, fed ♀ with insects from throat, fledged *c.* 28 days. **992**

PARADISE
FLYCATCHER, AFRICAN see **Terpsiphone viridis**
FLYCATCHER, SEYCHELLES see **Terpsiphone corvina**
WHYDAH, BROAD-TAILED see under **Steganura paradisaea**
WHYDAH, SHARP-TAILED see **Steganura paradisaea**

PARAKEET
INDIAN RING-NECKED see **Psittacula krameri**
PILEATED see **Purpureicephalus spurius**
QUAKER see **Myiopsitta monacha**
RAINBOW see **Trichoglossus haematodus**
RED-CROWNED see **Cyanoramphus novaeselandiae**
ROSE-RINGED see **Psittacula krameri**

PARDALOTE,
BLACK-HEADED see **Pardalotus melanocephalus**
SPOTTED see **Pardalotus punctatus**

YELLOW-TUFTED see **Pardalotus striatus**

Pardalotus melanocephalus *Dicaeidae*
BLACK-HEADED PARDALOTE *c.* 4 ins
Australasian: Mid-Western continental Australia to N Queensland, and S to New South Wales; resident forests. Upperparts predominantly greenish brown, becoming yellowish upper tail coverts; crown, wings black (with white or pale feather edges and red at alula); lower tail black, tipped white; eyestripe black between white 'eyebrow' and cheek; underparts from chin whitish, suffused more or less yellow; legs grey; short, broad bill dark; eyes brown. Behaviour much as relatives. Food insects and their larvae. Breeds June to January in different parts of range, building domed nest of bark in chamber at end of hollowed-out tunnel, generally in bank or hole left by stump, 1½ to 2 ft long. Usually 4 white eggs. **816**

Pardalotus punctatus *Dicaeidae*
SPOTTED PARDALOTE *c.* 3½ ins
Australasian: E continental Australia, (except Cape York), Victoria, S to W Australia; Tasmania. Resident forests, upland birds probably moving to coast in winter. ♂: upperparts blackish (crown) to greyish brown (back), heavily spotted white; base upper tail chestnut brown to crimson; prominent white 'eyebrow', cheeks vermiculated grey, throat, base of undertail yellow; rest underparts buff-brown. ♀: generally darker, spots on head bright yellow; underparts buff-white. Legs flesh brown, bill black, eyes grey. Juvenile like ♀ but duller. Usually in pairs or flocks on outer foliage eucalyptus, searching leaves slowly for insects and their larvae; after covering one tree, birds flit one by one to next, calling incessantly, but territorial when breeding. Call loud, monotonous, ventriloquial: *slee-p* (high-pitched) *ba-bee* (much lower); also soft *pee-too.* ♂ takes pair-forming initiative in breeding season (August to January in different parts of range), may choose site, often used several years, of tunnel excavated by ♀ and ♂ for 1½ to 2 ft in stream bank or cliff, rarely tree; domed nest of bark, grass in chamber at end. Usually 4 white eggs incubated by ♀ and ♂ 14-16 days. **817**

Pardalotus striatus *Dicaeidae*
YELLOW-TIPPED PARDALOTE 3½-4 ins
Australasian: Tasmania, wintering S continental Australia, where occasionally breeds. Habitat forest treetops. Upperparts olive-grey to brownish lower back; tail black, slightly tipped white; wings black, small yellow spot near shoulder, narrow white bar; 'eyebrow' yellow to white; ear coverts black streaked white; cheeks white; chin, throat yellow; underparts buff and white; legs blackish-brown, bill black, eyes brownish olive. Very like *P. melanocephalus* but crown streaked white, cheeks vermiculated grey, flanks paler. Usually in pairs, behaving much as *P. punctatus.* Calls: *pick-it-up; chip chip:* soft *cheeoo;* long trill. Takes great variety insects captured in eucalypt leaves; some spiders. Breeds August to December Tasmania, building domed nest of bark, grass, sometimes feathers, in small hollow, hole of tree, even up to 50 ft or more; occasionally tunnels hole in bank of creek like *P. punctatus.* Usually 4 white eggs. **818**

Parisoma subcaeruleum *Muscicapidae: Timaliinae*
COMMON TIT BABBLER 5¾ ins
Ethiopian: southern third Africa; resident in light thorn bush and acacia scrub, especially along watercourses. Upperparts bluish grey, darker around eye; throat white, streaked black; breast and flanks pearl grey; rest underparts white; brick red under tail coverts contrast with black tail, tipped white; bill and legs black, eyes blackish brown. Searches foliage actively for small insects, spiders; also eats fruit. Rattling call: *cherik tik tik;* warbling song includes mimicry. Breeding season very variable: September to February, later in SE. Neat, thin-walled nest cup of fibres, covered with spider's silk, in fork near ground. 2 or 3, usually white eggs, blotched darker. **713**

Paroaria coronata see **P. cucullata**

Paroaria cucullata or P. coronata *Emberizidae: Pyrrhuloxiinae*
RED-CRESTED CARDINAL 7½ ins
Neotropical: S Brazil, Uruguay, Paraguay, SE Bolivia, Argentina to Buenos Aires, La Pampa; resident wet scrub, bushy woodland. Upperparts grey, tail black; crested head, throat to centre upper breast scarlet; underparts white; legs grey, bill horn brown, eyes dark brown. Hardy in captivity. Loud song with repetitive phrases, warbling and harsher notes. Food: seeds; insects, especially for young. Breeding much as Cardinal, *Pyrrhuloxia cardinalis;* solid nest of plant material fairly low in bush; 3 or 4 whitish eggs, spotted greyish green, heavily marked olive-buff and brown. Closely related to Red-capped, *P. gularis,* of E Brazil and Red-cowled, *P. dominicana,* of northern S America. **869**

Paroaria
dominicana see under **P. cucullata**
gularis see under **P. cucullata**

PARROT,
AFRICAN GREY see **Psittacus erithacus**
BLUE-CHEEKED AMAZON see **Amazonia brasiliensis**
BLUE-HEADED AMAZON see **Amazonia brasiliensis**
BROWN see **Poicephalus meyeri**
CRIMSON-WINGED see under **Aprosmictus scapularis**
ECLECTUS see **Lorius roratus**
ELEGANT GRASS see **Neophema elegans**
GREATER VASA see **Coracopsis vasa**
GROUND see **Pezoporus wallicus**
HISPANIOLA see **Amazonia ventralis**
KING see **Aprosmictus scapularis**
MEYER'S see **Poicephalus meyeri**
ORANGE-CHEEKED see under **Gypopsitta vulturina**
RED-BACKED see **Psephotus haematonotus**
RED-BILLED see **Pionus sordidus**
RED-BROWED FIG see **Opopsitta leadbeateri**
RING-NECKED see **Barnardius barnardi**
SWIFT see **Lathamus discolor**
VULTURINE see **Gypositta vulturina**

PARROTBILL, GREAT see **Conostoma oemodium**

PARTRIDGE,
BARBARY see under **Alectoris rufa**
BUFF-CROWNED WOOD see **Dendrortyx leucophrys**
FERRUGINOUS WOOD see **Caloperdix oculea**
GREEN WOOD see **Rollulus roulroul**
GREY see **Perdix perdix**
RED-LEGGED see **Alectoris rufa**
SNOW see **Lerwa lerwa**

Parula americana see under **Dendroica dominica**

PARULA WARBLER see under **Dendroica dominica**

Parus atricapillus *Paridae*
BLACK-CAPPED CHICKADEE 5¼ ins
Nearctic: breeds from Newfoundland, Central Quebec, Ontario, Mackenzie, Alaska S to N New Jersey, mountains N Carolina, Indiana, S Missouri, New Mexico, NW California; winters to Maryland, Central Texas. Resident or summer visitor woodland, orchards, tree lines. Closely resembles Willow Tit, *P. montanus,* and Marsh Tit, *P. palustris.* Crown glossy black, large black gorget gradually merging into white breast, pale, striated appearance of closed wing. Behaviour as other *Parus* tits; joins foraging flocks of several species. Call rapid *chick-a-dee, dee* repeated up to 10 times; also softly whistled *dee-dee,* both very different from Willow Tit notes. Food chiefly insects, especially larvae in summer; wild berries, fruits, seeds; frequently at bird tables. Breeds end April onwards New England; nest of moss, lined plant down, fur, feathers, in hole excavated in rotten pine, birch, 1 to 10 ft up; natural holes and nestboxes up to 50 ft. 6 to 8 or more white eggs, lightly speckled red-brown; incubation and fledging as relatives. **802**

Parus caeruleus *Paridae*

BLUE TIT *c.* 4½ ins

W Palaearctic: Europe, except N Scandinavia and including NW Africa, Canaries (only tit), Asia Minor, to Caucasus, Iran; replaced in E by very similar but White-headed Azure Tit, *P. cyaneus*, with which hybridises. Resident rather open broadleaved forests, lowland, riverine, montane; also conifers where few or no competitors; cork oak woods, olive groves, palm oases; cultivated land, parks, gardens well into cities; also reed beds in winter. General impression blue, from cobalt crown, wings (white bar), tail, yellowish green mantle; forehead, border of crown, cheeks, nape patch white; black eyestripe, back of head, bib; underparts sulphur yellow; legs dark slate blue, bill mainly black, eyes dark brown. Juvenile suffused yellow. Active, acrobatic like other *Parus* tits; short flights direct, longer ones undulating. Most of year works woods in parties with other tits; creeps along trunks, often feeds in litter. Roosts in cavities. Calls: *tsee tsee tsee tsit;* sibilant hiss; churring scold. Song rapid liquid trill. ♂ and ♀ raise crests, shiver wings in display; also slow butterfly flight by ♂, who feeds ♀ courtship onwards. Food: minute insects, their pupae, larvae, eggs; spiders; mainly from twigs and shrubs; also buds, flowers, soft fruits, some seeds; common at bird tables. Breeds end March to July Britain, ♀ and ♂ building nest of moss, grass, plant fibres, lined hair, wool, feathers; in hole of tree, stump, wall, occasionally behind bark, in old nests bigger birds; nestboxes, many artefacts readily taken. 7 to 16 or more white eggs, lightly freckled red-brown, incubated by ♀ *c.* 14 days; ♀ and ♂ feed young, who fly *c.* 19 days. **803**

Parus cristatus *Paridae*

CRESTED TIT *c.* 4½ ins

W Palaearctic: Europe, except NE, SE, Ireland, most of Britain (distinct race N Scotland), Mediterranean area; but extending to W Siberia between 50° and 60°N. Resident almost exclusively coniferous forest, especially pines, spruces, lowland to subalpine zones. Upperparts brown, wings, tail darker; pointed crest whitish with black feather centres; cheeks off-white with black crescents, separated by black gorget, continued as narrow collar; underparts whitish, suffused buff on flanks; legs olive grey, bill black, eyes red-brown. Behaves much as Blue Tit but feeds more on tree trunks. Calls: distinctive purring trill also thin *zee zee zee*. Trill becomes song as ♂ flutters round tree-tops or chases ♀, whom he feeds with crest erect and raised wings as she quivers on branch. Food: insects and their larvae, also conifer seeds (which it hides) and berries. Breeds mid April to mid June; ♀ excavates or enlarges hole, builds nest of moss, lined thickly felted hair, fur, feathers, in dead wood, usually conifer, occasionally mouse hole, old nest, nestbox; ground level to 10 ft. 5 to 8 or more white eggs, spotted dark red often in zone, incubated by ♀ 13-15 days; young, fed mainly by ♀, fly 16-20 days. Exceptionally 2 broods. **804**

Parus
cyaneus see under **P. caeruleus**
leucomelas see under **P. niger**

Parus major *Paridae*

GREAT TIT *c.* 5½ ins

Palaearctic, Oriental: Europe except NE, Asia S of 60°N, except some southern areas but including much of Indonesia; in this huge range potentially distinct species occur. Resident broadleaved woodland of many types: oaks, olive groves, tropical forests, mangroves, bamboos, also pines in Asia; up to 13,700 ft Yunnan; and cultivated lands, parks, gardens. Upperparts yellowish green to blue grey with white bar, pale feather edges on wings; white outer tail feathers; crown, nape glossy blue-black extending round white cheeks to join gorget and central stripe (broader and expanding on belly in ♂) down sulphur yellow underparts; legs lead blue, bill mainly black, eyes brown-black. Juvenile suffused yellowish. Behaves as other *Parus* tits but perhaps more aggressive and frequently hammers nut on branch with powerful bill. Feeds much on beech mast on ground when available; common at bird tables. Roosts in cavities. Call ringing *tink tink tink* only best known of extensive vocabulary; song *tee-cher tee-cher tee-cher,* amphasis on first syallable. ♂ postures to ♀ and chases her. Mainly insectivorous, especially moth larvae in spring; spiders, small molluscs, worms; fruit, nuts, peas, buds. Breeds end March to July in Britain; ♀ and ♂ build foundation, often substantial, of moss and grass, usually lined hair, in hole of tree or stump up to 15 ft or higher, sometimes in rock crevices, walls, behind bark, old nests; nestboxes and many artefacts. 5 to 12 white eggs, marked red brown, incubated by ♀ 12-16 days; young, fed by ♀ and ♂, fly *c.* 19 days. Occasionally 2 broods. **805**

Parus montanus *Paridae*

WILLOW TIT *c.* 4½ ins

Palaearctic: broad band across Eurasia, mainly between 50° and 65°N from Britain to E Siberia, Kamtchatka, Sakhalin, Japan. Very similar to Marsh Tit, *P. palustris,* and Black-capped Chickadee, *P. atricapillus,* for long regarded as conspecific; *P. songarus* of Central Asian mountains also closely related. Resident damp coniferous forests, dominated by spruce and, higher up, *Abies* firs; also subarctic birch zone and montane shrubs up to 7,300 ft; broadleaved woodlands, dry and damp, in W Europe, Britain. Very like juvenile Marsh Tit with dark smoky brown not glossy black crown; looks generally more unkempt than Marsh Tit; light patch on secondaries also guide. Usually solitary or in pairs, seldom joining other tits or visiting bird tables; often dives deeply into cover from which it calls distinctive *zit zit zit*, harsh 'squeezed-out' *chichit-tchay-tchay*. Ordinary song repeated *piu*, but has rich warbling song, not carrying far, resembling *Carduelis* finch. Food mainly insects and their larvae, spiders; also seeds which it may hide. Breeds early May to mid June Britain, ♀ building rather slight pad of moss, grass, lined fur, hair, feathers, plant debris; hole excavated (oval entrance) in rotten branch, stem of bush, occasionally bank; has taken nestbox when material to be 'excavated' provided. 6 to 9 white eggs, marked red-brown, incubated by ♀ *c.* 13 days; young, fed by ♀ and ♂, fly *c.* 18 days. **806**

Parus niger *Paridae*

SOUTHERN BLACK TIT 6 ins

Ethiopian: parts Zambia, Malawi, Portuguese E Africa, eastern S Africa. Replaced to N by Black Tit, *P. leucomelas,* with all-glossy plumage except for large pale wing patch and very similar habits. Resident thick dry bush and scrub. ♂: generally glossy blue-black; conspicuous white shoulder patch; edges flight feathers, outer webs outer tail feathers and tips of all, white; breast to belly rather slaty; lower belly, under tail coverts black and white. ♀: duller, paler above, dark grey below. Legs, bill black, eyes brown. Juvenile like ♀ but white on wings tinged cream. Pairs or small parties always on move and calling, like other *Parus* tits; ♂ often calls from exposed perch shrill harsh *twiddy,* followed by *zeet zeet zeet;* also loud buzzing *zeu zeu zeu twit*. Mainly insectivorous. Breeding season varies within range, September to January; nest of plant materials softly lined, in hole of tree. 3 or 4 creamy white eggs, well spotted bright red-brown; apart from small clutch, breeding details much as other *Parus* tits. **807**

Parus palustris *Paridae*

MARSH TIT *c.* 4½ ins

Palaearctic: Europe except peripheral areas; Caucasus; separate population E Asia westward along 50°N to 85°E, Sakhalin, Hokkaido, Korea. Resident mixed broadleaved woodland usually with dense undergrowth, riverine forests, orchards, parks, gardens, up to 4,300 ft (Alps). Upperparts, including wings, tail, brown; crown glossy black, cheeks white; underparts dull white, flanks suffused buff; legs blue-grey, bill black, eyes dark brown. Habits as other tits but spends more time in undergrowth, woodland glades. Usual calls *pitchu* or *pitchit-chuu;* thin *tzee tzee tzee;* nasal repeated *tchaa,* less emphatic than Willow Tit, *P. montanus: chickabeebee* may be lengthened form of this; usual songs repeated *tschuppi* and *pitchaweeo*. Food mainly insects, also seeds from thistles to beech, often stored individually, berries; regular at bird tables. Breeds early April to end June Britain; ♀ builds foundation of moss with felted cup of hair, fur, plant down; in cavity or crack of tree, wall, often with very small hole. 6 to 8 or more white eggs, lightly spotted red-brown, incubated by ♀ *c.* 13 days; ♀ and ♂ feed young, who fly 16-18 days. **808**

Parus songarus see under **P. montanus**

Passer domesticus *Ploceidae*

HOUSE OR ENGLISH SPARROW *c.* 5¾ ins

Cosmopolitan commensal: 'natural' range obscured by introductions but probably almost all Europe, parts N Africa, including Nile Valley, SW Asia, Indian subcontinent, Ceylon, Burma and across Central Asia to Manchuria, mainly between 50° and 60°N. Hybridises with Spanish Sparrow, *P. hispaniolensis,* in parts Mediterranean area. Introduced N America, where widespread from S Canada to S Mexico; W Indies, especially Cuba; temperate and subtropical S America; SE South Africa and some Mascarene Is; SE Australia, Tasmania; New Zealand. Mainly resident in cultivated areas, villages, towns, cities; Kashmir and Himalayan populations winter S Iran, NW India. ♂: upperparts rich brown streaked black; flight and tail feathers dark or blackish brown, pale-edged; narrow white bar on closed wing; crown grey bordered rich brown; cheek pattern grey and white; glossy black gorget in greyish-white underparts. ♀ generally duller, head dull grey brown; juvenile similar. Legs pale brown, bill black (summer ♂), horn-brown, base yellow (♀, winter ♂), eyes light brown. Gregarious at all times; equally at home on ground where hops with flirting tail or aloft; swift, rather whirring flight. Displays include 'sparrows' wedding' when several ♂♂ pursue ♀. Single ♂ puffs breast, droops wings towards ♀, who solicits mating with twittering. Builds winter roosting nests. Calls include *cheep, chissick,* metallic *teu teu;* chirping sometimes develops into song. Omnivorous, but takes much grain, seeds, also fruit, buds; attacks flowerheads; insects fed to young; human scraps. Breeds mainly March to September in Europe; colonial, scattered or close together. ♀ and ♂ build untidy but roughly globular nest of grass, straws, debris, lined feathers, with entrance at side, but in cavities often reduced to lined cup; in trees up to 60 ft, bushes, bottoms of large nests, mud cups of House Martin, *Delichon urbica,* nests; creepers on walls, buildings of all kinds. 3 to 6 off-white to bluish white eggs, variably marked grey, dark grey, brown, incubated mainly ♀ 9-18 days; young, fed by ♀ and ♂ from bill or crop, fly 11-18 days. Up to 4 broods. **954**

Passer hispaniolensis see under **P. domestica**

Passer melanurus *Ploceidae*

CAPE SPARROW 6 ins

Ethiopian: S and NW Southern Africa; local resident, now largely commensal with man, in native and introduced trees, especially in drier built-up areas; sometimes in quite arid conditions. ♂: upperparts uniform chestnut; flight and tail feathers blackish, edged buff; white-tipped median coverts form bar on closed wing; head, face, gorget black; broad white line from eye down neck; hindneck earth brown; underparts whitish, flanks grey; legs, eyes brown, bill black. ♀ similar but generally paler; head greyish, 'eyebrow' white. Juvenile resembles ♀. Tame and confiding, forms large flocks after breeding, builds special roosting nests. Calls harsh *chissip;* strident *chirrr chirrr* of alarm; jerky repetitive song: *chip chollop tlip tlop*. Diet: seeds, grain, soft shoots, damaging to gardens; insects fed to young. Breeds mainly September or October to March, building large untidy nests of grass, stems, debris, lined feathers; elongated entrance at side; usually in trees, so competition with introduced House Sparrow, *P. domesticus,* reduced, but also in creepers, under eaves, in old nests swallows, other weavers. 3 to 6 whitish or greenish eggs, speckled or heavily marked dark brown over grey, incubated mainly ♀, 12-14 days; young, fed both parents, fly 16-25 days. Several broods. **955**

Passer montanus *Ploceidae*

TREE SPARROW 5½ ins

Palaearctic, Oriental: most of Europe except N

Scandinavia, Adriatic coast and Balkans; Asia between 65° and 30°N, not Indian subcontinent, but extending into SE mainland and Indonesia; Japan, Taiwan. Introduced N America, some islands SE Asia, Australia, New Zealand but without devastating success of House Sparrow, *P. domesticus*. Mainly sedentary, but dispersals, perhaps regular movements, from Central and N Europe. Habitat: open country with scattered trees and small woods, cultivated areas, orchards; villages and towns, especially SE Asia, Japan. Plumage much as House Sparrow but sexes alike with chocolate crown and nape, crescentic black patch on white cheek. Legs pale brown, bill black (summer), blackish brown to yellow at base (winter, juvenile), eyes dark brown. Less obtrusive than House Sparrow even where common; associates in winter with other sparrows, finches, buntings, also large flocks on own. Calls resemble House Sparrow's but *chip* sharper and hard-sounding *tec tec* in flight distinctive; repeated chirping song. ♂ postures to ♀ in display, raising and lowering chocolate crown feathers. Takes seeds, corn, insects (e.g. beetles, larvae, aphids) and spiders; less frequent at bird tables than House Sparrow. Breeds April to September in Britain; usually colonial; ♀ and ♂ build neater version of House Sparrow nest with definite flask shape when in open in tree up to 25 ft; very commonly in tree holes, buildings, rock clefts, where reduced to cup; takes nestboxes readily; often in bottom of large nests, e.g. herons, hawks. 4 to 6 off-white eggs variably marked dark brown or grey, incubated ♀ and ♂ 12-14 days; young, fed by ♀ and ♂, fly 12-14 days. 2, sometimes 3 broods. **956**

Passerella iliaca *Emberizidae: Emberizinae*
FOX SPARROW   7¼ ins
Nearctic: from Pribilof Is, N Alaska, SW over forested Canada to Colorado, Nevada, S California; winters from Maryland, S Indiana, S Missouri, New Mexico, British Columbia, to Central Florida, Gulf Coast, Central Texas, Lower California. Habitat dense, often coniferous thickets, also riparian alders, willows, burnt-over land, meadow/woodland edges. Races vary in grey and brown tones; upperparts generally rich brown streaked grey; pale edges to coverts form narrow wingbars; rump, tail orange-brown; crown chestnut streaked darker; pale 'eyebrow', white moustachial stripe with brown above, below; large central spot on white, brown-streaked underparts. Western race especially dark. Legs light brown, bill yellowish, eyes dark brown. Rather wary and secretive but sings from exposed perch, even in winter, richest phrasing of any 'sparrow', short but clear and melodious, rising in pitch, then final cadence; call, drawn-out *stssp*. Food mainly from ground; kicks litter with both feet to expose small animals. Breeds June in N; large nest of grass, moss, roots, lined feathers, fur, holds 4 pale greenish eggs, thickly spotted reddish brown. **862**

Passerina amoena *Emberizidae: Pyrrhuloxiinae*
LAZULI BUNTING   5¼ ins
Nearctic: breeds S British Columbia, S Alberta, SE Saskatchewan, NW Dakota to NW Lower California, N New Mexico, W Texas; winters lower California, mainland Mexico. Variety of scrub habitats from coastal sage-brush of California, thickets of willow, rose, poison oak, dogwood, with open grassy spaces or areas of *Artemisia*, mustard; also newly colonised burnt-over land; occasionally up to 8,000 ft. ♂: upperparts, including head to breast, light blue (head, rump brilliant in good light, otherwise appear blackish), upper back streaked brownish; broad and narrow white wingbars; breast orange brown shading paler on flanks, underparts white. First year ♂ blue only on head. ♀: generally unstreaked brown above, paler below; wings, rump, tail tinged bluish; light wingbars. Legs dark, bill grey, eyes brown. As habitats ephemeral, tends to be nomadic, especially when population high. Call: soft *tsip;* harsher *zid'l* from night migrants; loud song 8 to 14 notes, in groups of 2 to 4 with abrupt changes in pitch. When feeding, bends slender stems to get at seeds in autumn; summer diet: grasshoppers, bugs, beetles, cicadas and larvae from herb and shrub layers. Breeds June, July; nest of green or dry grass,

stems, finer fibres, usually low in bush or hidden on ground below one. 3 or 4 bluish green eggs, occasionally dark speckled, incubated ♀ 12 days; ♀ and ♂ feed young. Sometimes 2 broods. **870**

Passerina ciris *Emberizidae: Pyrrhuloxiinae*
PAINTED BUNTING   5¼ ins
Nearctic: SE North Carolina, N Mississippi, S Kansas S to N Florida, S Louisiana, SE New Mexico; winters Central Florida, Central Mexico to Panama. Variety of scrub habitats: woodland edge, riverine strips, into well-wooded towns S USA. ♂: mantle yellow-green; wings dusky, glossed green, red; tail purplish brown; head, neck, cheeks, stripe down to side breast dark violet blue; rest of plumage bright red, also orbits. ♀ has upperparts green, wings, tail darker; underparts yellowish to amber on belly. ♂ darker autumn, young ♂ like ♀ with some blue on head. Legs dark brown, bill grey or light horn, eyes dark brown. Very shy, keeps much to cover except when ♂ sings from tree or bush top loud, clear *pew-eata pew-eata I eaty you too;* call: sharp 2- or 3-note chirp. Diet mainly seeds, e.g. foxtail grass; also insects, e.g. cotton worms, boll weevils. Breeds May to July, ♀ building deep, thin-walled cup of grass, stems, bark strips, dead leaves, lined hair, rootlets; usually in fork, well hidden in bush or tree. 3 or 4 white eggs, marked reddish brown, incubated ♀ c. 12 days; ♀ and ♂ feed young. Often 2 broods. **871**

Passerina leclancheri *Emberizidae: Pyrrhuloxiinae*
RAINBOW BUNTING   5 ins
Neotropical: SW Mexico; dry lowlands with scattered bushes and scrub. ♂: upperparts (except for greenish crown and tinge shoulders) bright blue, darker on wings, tail; underparts, including ring round eye, yellow. ♀: olive-green, tinged blue on tail; underparts yellow. Legs brown, bill horn brown, eyes brown. Searches litter of underbrush for seeds and insects. Simple song from bush-top (W. Beebe). Breeding much as other *Passerina* species. **872**

PASTOR, ROSY see **Sturnus roseus**

PATAGONIAN
   BLACK-HEADED GULL see under **Larus ridibundus**
   CRESTED DUCK see **Lophonetta specularoides**

Pavo cristatus *Phasianidae*   ♀: 38, ♂: 40-46
INDIAN PEAFOWL   (80-92 with train) ins
Oriental: Indian subcontinent and Ceylon; introduced Andaman Is. Resident lowland forests or well-wooded country up to c. 5,000 ft in Outer Himalayas and Peninsular Hills; moist and dry deciduous forest near streams; also semi-tame in villages and cultivated areas. ♂: brilliant iridescent blue neck and breast; lower back light bronze-green, scalloped black; rump black; 'train' of upper tail coverts metallic bronze green with purplish and black centred, coppery 'eyes'; scapulars and wing coverts closely barred black and buff; primaries and their coverts chestnut; face white and black, fan-shaped crest of spatulate wiry feathers. ♀: head (crested as ♂) and nape rufous brown, upperparts brown, mottled paler; primaries brown; lower neck metallic green, breast buff glossed green, belly buffy white. Legs, bill horn-grey, eyes dark brown. Immature ♂ as ♀, but primaries chestnut. Small parties of ♂ and 3 to 5 ♀♀ when nesting, but sexes segregate after breeding. Feeds and drinks in open early and late, prefaced by crowing *may-awe*, also stimulated by thunder. Scream: *ka-an ka-an* repeated 6 to 8 times with head movements; alarm *tok tok* by ♀ with neck fluffed. ♂ displays by raising train and quivering drooped wings, strutting, prancing, shivering train and presenting back view; ♀ occasionally responds. Rests during day in thickets. Runs to escape, seldom taking wing, when rockets upwards with loud flaps, to fly quite dexterously. Roosts in tall trees. Diet: seeds, grain, lentils, ground nuts, shoots, berries, figs; invertebrates, small reptiles; can be pest near villages. Breeds June to September in N, April-May in S, January to March Ceylon. Usually hides nest in thorny undergrowth, but sometimes semi-feral

birds use ruins and house tops. 4 to 8 pale cream to buff eggs, finely pitted, incubated by ♀ c. 28 days; she tends brood. ♂ successively polygamous. **203**

PEACEFUL DOVE see **Geopelia striata**

PEACOCK PHEASANT, PALAWAN see **Polyplectron emphanum**

PEAFOWL,
   AFRICAN see **Afropavo congensis**
   INDIAN see **Pavo cristatus**

PEARL-BREASTED SWALLOW see **Hirundo dimidiata**

PEARLED TREERUNNER see **Margarornis squamiger**

Pedioecetes phasianellus *Tetraonidae*
SHARP-TAILED GROUSE   19 ins
Nearctic: N America from Central Alaska to Mid-West USA, and W to Baffin Bay. Local resident in prairies and brushlands, resorting to forests in winter, when northern birds move S. Mottled yellow-brown, black and white all over, darker on wings, much lighter on underparts; sharp pointed tail; black and white stripes on cheeks, tufted crest; legs feathered, bill and eyes dark. Lives in flocks, which fly with flaps and glides when disturbed from feeding on buds and shoots, especially of northern trees; also buds and berries of junipers. Complicated courtship dances on 'leks' (see *Lyrurus tetrix*) by up to 50 ♂♂, in rounded postures, uttering booming calls from inflated sacs. Flight call: *whucker whucker whucker*. ♀ lays from April in Colorado to early May in Canada 7 to 15 fawn-brown eggs, usually marked red-brown and lilac, in lined scrape well hidden in local cover; she incubates them for c. 3 weeks; young fully grown in 6 weeks to 2 months. **187**

Pedionomus torquatus *Pedionomidae*
PLAINS WANDERER or
COLLARED HEMIPODE   ♀ 4, ♂ 5 ins
SE Australia; open grasslands and plains, making local movements within range. Reddish-brown, buff and black upperparts, underparts paler; collar of black spots on white; ♀ has chestnut breast; legs yellow, slender pointed bill and eyes brown; tail very short, wings short and rounded. Prefers to run or stand still rather than fly and has upright posture unlike true hemipodes, surveying surroundings above vegetation. Probably partly nocturnal. Diet: seeds and other vegetable matter; insects. Breeds September to January, making scrape in ground; 4 pale yellow or green eggs, spotted grey and olive, incubated by ♂; role of sexes reversed as in hemipodes (*Turnicidae*, Family 40).

PEKIN ROBIN see **Leiothrix lutea**

Pelagodroma marina *Hydrobatidae*
WHITE-FACED STORM or FRIGATE PETREL   8 ins
Southern oceans and N Atlantic; distinct race on Galapagos Islands in Pacific; northward migration after breeding. Upperparts brownish: crown, nape and cheeks smoky; tail and wings blackish brown; underparts from chin white; legs and bill black, eyes brown; rump white in one race. Only storm petrel regularly seen in coastal waters. Like relatives visits colonies at dusk, dancing over nest-holes; flight very erratic. Calls in burrows 'twittering', 'squeaky' and 'groaning'; low notes on wing. Food mainly small crustaceans, e.g. *Euphausia*, from plankton. Breeding season varies widely according to range, from March-April in N Atlantic, early November New Zealand; colonies on bare or scrub-covered islands. One white egg zoned red with violet undermarks laid in burrow c. 2 ft long. Incubation mainly by ♀ for 53-56 days; chick, fed by ♀ and ♂, fledges in 52-67 days. **36**

Pelecanoides urinatrix *Pelecanoididae*
DIVING PETREL   7½-8 ins
Subantarctic and South Temperate oceans, breeding usually remote islands and migrating over sea after-

wards. The race illustrated, *exsul,* sometimes regarded as separate species breeding Kerguelen, Crozet Is and elsewhere; range of *urinatrix* circumpolar, including Falkland Is, Tristan da Cunha, islands off New Zealand. Upperparts from crown to tail black except for white edges to new secondaries; cheeks grey; underparts white, tinged smoky under wings; race *exsul* has black bill proportionately broader at base, usually shows grey speckling on breast; legs blue, eyes dark brown. Silent at sea, but variety of wailing, mewing, cooing, chattering calls over breeding station, off which (in New Zealand area) parties collect from April onwards, nocturnally clearing out or excavating burrows in turf of island. Single white egg laid in chamber at end of burrow August, incubated ♀ and ♂ *c.* 5 weeks; chick, fed by ♀ and ♂ on paste of small crustaceans (main food of adult with small fish), fledges *c.* 7 weeks. Moult, during which birds briefly flightless, takes place at sea. **37**

Pelecanus conspicillatus *Pelecanidae*
AUSTRALIAN PELICAN *c.* 48 ins
Two races in continental Australia, Tasmania, New Guinea and Amboina; accidental New Zealand. Sedentary on mudflats, islands, estuaries, shores and islands of inland lakes. Mainly white, with black on wings and tail; legs grey-blue, bill yellow orange, eyes brown. Found in flocks, fishing in shallows or resting on shore; swims and flies well but waddles on land. Food principally fresh and saltwater crustaceans. Mainly silent but utters hoarse croak; young in nest chatter. Breeds colonially from September to March on flat ground, making scrape, surrounded by local plant material, for 2 to 3 dirty white eggs, coated with lime and stained during 4-5 week incubation by ♀; young, fed by ♀ and ♂, fledge in *c.* 2 months. **39**

Pelecanus occidentalis *Pelecanidae*
BROWN PELICAN 42-48 ins
Three races in S Nearctic and N Neotropical, including West Indies and Galapagos; N American birds winter Florida, California and farther S. Habitat coasts and lagoons with shallow shores and mangrove swamps. Dark grey-brown body with silvery upperparts; crown straw-coloured, turning white on face and neck which in summer has nape and sides brown; legs black, bill mainly grey with brown pouch, eyes light yellow. Gregarious: noted for formation flying, with heads tucked into bodies; also soars to great heights and has various displays at nest-site. Diet of fish caught by shallow plunges with wings half open. Mainly silent but young have piercing scream. Breeding season variable; builds stick nest colonially on ground or in trees, laying 2 to 3 eggs, chalky white at first. Incubation *c.* 30 days by ♀ and ♂; young fly *c.* 9 weeks, mature in 3-4 years. **40**

Pelecanus onocrotalus *Pelecanidae*
OLD WORLD WHITE PELICAN 54-72 ins
SE Palaearctic, Ethiopian and very local Oriental region; northernmost Palaearctic birds move S in autumn. Habitat margins of shallow rivers, lakes, deltas and coasts. Predominantly white, tinged pink and with crest in spring; wingtips and trailing edges black, yellow patch on breast; legs pink to orange; bill blue and pink, pouch pink or yellow, eyes dark. Manifests social behaviour by formation flying and communal fishing, driving shoreward in crescent, splashing wings and feet, to scoop up prey in shallows; also crash dives; principal food fish. Displays at colonies, with guttural calls. Breeding season varies with range; colonies on shore or in marsh, with nests of trampled local vegetation for the 1 to 2 chalky white eggs, incubated *c.* 30 days by ♀ and ♂, who feed young for *c.* 60 days. **41**

PELICAN,
AUSTRALIAN see **Pelecanus conspicillatus**
BROWN see **Pelecanus occidentalis**
OLD WORLD WHITE see **Pelecanus onocrotalus**

PENDULINE
TIT see **Remiz pendulinus**
TIT, AFRICAN see under **Eremomela icteropygialis**

PENGUIN,
ADELIE see **Pygoscelis adeliae**
EMPEROR see **Aptenodytes forsteri**
JACKASS see **Spheniscus demersus**
LITTLE BLUE see **Eudyptes minor**
MACARONI see **Eudyptes chrysolophus**
PERUVIAN see **Spheniscus humboldti**

PENNANT-WINGED NIGHTJAR see **Macrodipteryx vexillarius**

PEPPERSHRIKE, RUFOUS-BROWED see **Cyclarhis gujanensis**

Perdix perdix *Phasianidae*
COMMON or GREY PARTRIDGE *c.* 12 ins
W Palaearctic: from Scandinavia, Ireland and Spain across Europe, Asia Minor to Central Asia; introduced N America. Sedentary, typically on farm land in Europe; also rough grasslands, heaths, steppes, semi-desert, shingle and dunes. Upperparts brown with black and white streaks; crown, neck and breast grey, inverted chocolate 'horseshoe' on lower breast (fainter on ♀); flanks grey, barred chestnut; face and throat orange brown; legs grey, bill greenish horn, eyes brown, facial skin red. Spends winter in coveys of varying size, breaking up into pairs after communal displays. Walks with neck withdrawn, runs to take off into skimming flight, swerving easily; roosts on ground. Call (♂ especially) *kirric kirric;* cackling in flight. Feeds on wide range of plants; insects, especially ants, important for young. Breeds late March onwards in Europe, lining scrape in thick cover, ♀ incubating 9 to 20 olive brown eggs 23-25 days; ♂ and ♀ tend brood, which flies at 16 days. **205**

PEREGRINE see **Falco peregrinus**

Perisoreus infaustus *Corvidae*
SIBERIAN JAY *c.* 12 ins
Palaearctic: mid Scandinavia E to N Kamchatka down to N Japan; sedentary, some movement for food in hard winters. Habitat: deep in forest, rarely at margins. Upperparts olive brown with blackish brown cap and brownish cheeks; rump and long, rounded tail rufous, central tail feathers grey; wing coverts bright rufous with brown edges; throat light grey; underparts greyish brown. Legs black, short bill black and slightly curved at tip of upper mandible, eyes dark brown. Tame; tail spread out like fan in flight which is easy and quiet; generally lively and restless. Call: *kuk-kuk* or *kei-kei.* Food, similar to Eurasian Jay, *Garrulus glandarius,* includes seeds of conifers and berries (may hoard these in tree hollows). Pairs for life; breeds April and May; solid nest of twigs and plant stalks, lined lichens and feathers, 5 to 20 ft up tree in denser parts of coniferous forests. 3 or 4 eggs, greenish white or dingy greyish white, marked grey and violet-grey streaks, incubated 16-17 days; young fledge *c.* 5 weeks.

Pernis apivorus *Accipitridae*
HONEY BUZZARD *c.* 20-23 ins
W Palaearctic; summer visitor Britain, Iberia, S Scandinavia E to River Ob (W Siberia), extending SE to Caucasus, N Iran; winters tropical Africa. Closely related *P. ptilorhynchus* in E Asia, *P. celebensis* Indonesia, Philippines. Habitat wooded areas, broadleaved (especially beech) and coniferous, with glades and meadows; not cultivated land. Upperparts dark brown, sometimes marked white; crown, sides of head usually grey; underparts very variable from white to dark brown, usually white barred and marked brown; tail barred, with broad subterminal band; legs, eyes, lower part of cere yellow, rest of cere and bill blackish. Broad-winged flight with soaring and hovering, developing into diving and wing-clapping displays by ♂. Rather squeaky high-pitched flight call; several other notes described. Walks and runs with ease, feeding on ground nests of bumble bees and wasps (honey, insects and larvae) scratched out with strong feet, bird sometimes disappearing in hole; insects taken in bill and tails snipped off before eating; attacks tree nests in tropics; also other insects, worms, frogs, lizards, occasionally small mammals and birds; berries.

Breeds from end May in Europe, building nest of sticks, lined greenery, often in side branch or on old nest of other bird, 30 to 75 ft up. Usually 2 whitish eggs, richly marked red-brown to chocolate and incubated by ♀ and ♂ 30-35 days; young, fed by both parents, fly 40-44 days.

Pernis
celebensis see under **P. apivorus**
ptilorhynchus see under **P. apivorus**

PERUVIAN
COCK OF THE ROCK see **Rupicola peruviana**
PENGUIN see **Spheniscus humboldti**

PETCHARY, BLACK-BANDED see under **Cacicus cela**

PETERS FINFOOT see **Podica senegalensis**

PETREL,
BERMUDA see **Pterodroma cahow**
CAPPED see under **Pterodroma cahow**
DIVING see **Pelecanoides urinatrix**
FRIGATE see **Pelagodroma marina**
GIANT see **Macronectes giganteus**
SNOW see **Pagodroma nivea**
STORM see **Hydrobates pelagicus**
WHITE-FACED see **Pelagodroma marina**

Petroica cucullata or Melanodryas cucullata
Muscicapidae: Muscicapinae
HOODED ROBIN 6½ ins
Australasian: continental Australia except extreme N; mainly sedentary but some local movements. Habitat dry savannah and mulga scrub; edges of open forest. ♂: upperparts mainly black, hood extending down breast; white stripe from breast over shoulder; white patch on blackish wings, underparts white. ♀: upperparts brownish grey, underparts paler; lacks white on shoulder but small white markings tip of tail; legs, bill bluish, eyes dark brown. Rather unobtrusive inspite of ♂'s plumage. Call rather high-pitched and feeble, with trill on descending scale; also single unmusical note; often calls at night. Takes insects and spiders, mainly from ground. Breeds August to December, building nest of bark, grasses, bound cobwebs, in fork of lateral branch usually near ground but up to 20 ft. Usually 2 pale olive to apple green eggs, mottled rich brown, especially at big end. **786**

Petroica goodenovii *Muscicapidae: Muscicapinae*
RED-CAPPED ROBIN 5 ins
Australasian: almost all continental Australia except humid forests and deserts; resident open forests inland, with varying tree preferences in different areas. ♂: upperparts, including head, dull black to blackish brown, white markings wings, tail; throat black, sometimes tinged red; large 'cap' and breast scarlet; underparts white. ♀: dull brown above; pale buff wing markings; cap dull reddish brown; underparts white. Legs, bill black, eyes dark brown. Behaviour much as Scarlet Robin, *P. multicolor.* Call like ticking of clock; 'delicate little song' (H. J. Frith). Food mainly insects taken in flight, off trees, on ground. Breeds July to December E Australia, making nest of bark fibres, grass, bound cobwebs, lined fur, feathers, decorated lichen to blend with site in fork, upper side lateral branch, twig junctions; from 6 to 20 ft up. Usually 2 bluish white to grey-green eggs, spotted brown at big end, incubated ♀, fed by ♂, *c.* 12 days; both parents feed young. **787**

Petroica multicolor *Muscicapidae: Muscicapinae*
SCARLET ROBIN 5 ins
Australasian: E continental Australia from Darling Downs (Queensland), through New South Wales, Victoria to Flinders Ranges (S Australia); also York and Eyre's Peninsulas; Kangaroo Is, Tasmania, Bass Strait Is; separate races SW Australia, Norfolk, other SW Pacific Is. Habitat: open forests in summer, denser cover in winter. ♂: upperparts, including head, throat, black; prominent white forehead, wings, outer tail feathers; breast scarlet; underparts white. ♀: upperparts brown; buff on forehead, wings, tail;

throat greyish white, breast strongly tinged scarlet, underparts dull white to pale brown. Legs, bill black; eyes hazel. Juvenile mottled brown. Moves quietly in pairs, foraging from low vantage points, still except for occasional tail flick, then darts to ground after insects, their larvae, worms. Call low trilling whistle mainly in spring; sharp double calls and clicking notes. Breeds July to December, ♀ building nest like Red-capped Robin, *P. goodenovii*, but thicker, from 2 to 40 ft in fork, on lateral branch, behind bark, in hollow, outside decorated appropriately. Usually 3 pale green or bluish to dull brownish white eggs, densely spotted brown over purplish grey, incubated by ♀, fed by ♂, 15 days; both parents feed young, who fly 16-18 days. **788**

Petroica rodinogaster *Muscicapidae: Musiciapinae*
PINK ROBIN c. 4 ins
Australasia: S Victoria, Tasmania; winters farther N, e.g. New South Wales. Breeds damp fern gullies of wet sclerophyll forests. ♂: upperparts slaty black, tail blackish brown; small white spot on forehead; underparts rose pink, under tail coverts white. ♀: olive-brown above, tail brown, wings marked rich buff; underparts pale brown. Legs, bill black-brown, eyes blackish. Juvenile mottled. Very quiet, unobtrusive, flits from tree to tree, occasionally dropping to ground after small insects. Call quiet *tic tic;* song pleasant quiet warble; virtually silent in winter. Breeds October to January Tasmania, building small cup of moss, lichen, bound cobwebs, lined fine rootlets: in low bush or tree in gully. 3 or 4 greenish white eggs, minutely spotted brown, umber, purple in zone at big end. **789**

Petronia petronia *Ploceidae*
ROCK SPARROW 5½ ins
Palaearctic: from Canary Is, Mediterranean area, Asia Minor, Palestine to mountains and deserts of SW Asia, Tibet, China between 30° and 50°N; sedentary, forming large flocks in winter, usually near breeding sites. Habitat: warm, dry rocky slopes with grass or low scrub, olive groves, higher cultivated areas, buildings of all kinds; often commensal with man, even into towns. Upperparts dull brown with feathers paler-edged on back and wing coverts; white tips to tail feathers; pale 'eyebrow' and stripe over brown crown; ear coverts dull brown, face paler, underparts pale, faintly 'scaly'; narrow yellow breast band; legs, stout bill light brown, eyes brown. Juvenile lacks yellow on breast. Winter flocks perform evolutions before going to roost. ♂ has rolling, gliding display flight with pipit-like descent; usually near nest-site. Calls: *tut,* grating *chwee,* finch-like *pey-ee.* Food mainly from ground, probably much as House Sparrow, *Passer domesticus.* Breeds end April onwards (France) usually in colonies in rock clefts, hollow trees, old nest holes of other birds, human artefacts, including wells in deserts; untidy sparrow-like nest of plant debris and feathers. 3 to 6 off-white eggs, streaked or blotched darkly, incubated ♀, fed by ♂. Both parents feed young on insects, fledging *c.* 3 weeks. 2 broods. **957**

Petrophassa albipennis *Columbidae*
WHITE-QUILLED ROCK PIGEON *c.* 12 ins
Kimberley Division of Western Australia, adjacent areas of Northern Territory. Habitat: sandstone cliffs and scattered rocks with water nearby, rarely seen in trees. Plump, generally dark brown, except black-tipped white primaries and primary coverts; head, neck, mantle and breast paler and with dark spots. Legs brown-black, bill blackish, eyes brown. In pairs or small flocks, shy and difficult to flush; ground feeder taking chiefly seeds. Breeding season variable; 2 cream eggs in slight hollow lined with soft dead grass, in ground near tuft of spinifex or stone. **370**

Petrophassa scripta or Geophaps scripta *Columbidae*
SQUATTER PIGEON *c.* 12½ ins
Australasian: inland NE and E Australia. Habitat: open country with water available. Upperparts, short wings and black-edged tail grey-brown with pale tinge, face and throat distinctive black and white markings, lower breast and belly bluish grey with white sides; glossy green and purple patch on closed wing. Legs dull purple, bill black, eyes dark brown with pale blue orbital skin, yellow or pink at corners. Stays on ground unless threatened, when rises with loud whirring of wings, scattering to seek cover in grass; also crouches to hide, hence name. Feeds mainly on grass seed. Call: frequent low crooning notes between paired birds. Breeds usually from September to January subject to weather and food supplies; 2 cream eggs in shallow scrape in ground, lightly lined with plant debris, incubated *c.* 17 days. **371**

Peucedramus taeniatus *Parulidae*
OLIVE WARBLER 5 ins
Nearctic, Neotropical: mainly resident, from S New Mexico and White Mountains, Arizona, to Guatemala; northern birds move S in winter. Habitat open coniferous forest 8,500 to 12,000 ft. ♂: back grey to darker tail with pale feather edges; wings dark grey, with whitish edges to flight feathers and 2 white bars on coverts; head, neck to upper back and throat buff-brown with thick black mask; underparts white, greyish on sides, flanks. ♀ has greyish crown, faint mask, pale yellow face, throat; less white on wings, tail. Immature ♂ may breed in similar plumage. Often associates with flocks of Western Bluebirds, *Sialia mexicana,* after breeding; feeds from ground to canopy, slowly searching branches for insects. Usual call *peta* recalls Western Bluebird; song: series of loud, liquid notes on descending scale (R. H. Pough). Breeds June (Arizona), building nest of various plant materials, lined down, usually hidden in foliage or mistletoe near end of lateral tree branch, 30 to 80 ft in conifer. 3 or 4 grey or bluish white eggs, thickly freckled blackish.

PEWEE,
EASTERN WOOD see **Contopus virens**
TROPICAL see under **Contopus virens**

Pezoporus wallicus *Psittacidae*
GROUND PARROT 13 ins
Australasian: N Tasmania; very locally coasts of Victoria, New South Wales, southern W Australia; flat ground or hilltops on coastal heaths with scattered *Banksia* or grasstrees (blackboys); also estuarine flats, swamps, grasslands; resident or moving locally. Green upperparts, including long, graduated tail, barred and mottled brown and yellow; pale stripe on wing; underparts heavily barred yellow; undertail brown; red frontal patch; legs flesh brown, bill horn-brown, eyes pale brown or yellow. When flushed, short, swift zigzag flight, flapping and gliding, pitching after 50 or 100 yds; longer flights undulating. Runs well, climbs reeds, but cannot perch effectively. Usually single or in pairs, emits strong scent. Calls at dusk 30-40 minutes: 3 or 4 bell-like notes sometimes followed by sharper notes. Food: seeds of grasses and herbs, fallen fruits; forces seedheads to ground or passes bill along them. Breeds September-December, lining hollow in grass, sometimes in centre of tussock, concealed by outer stems. 3 or 4 white eggs incubated *c.* 21 days; young leave nest *c.* 28 days, still unable to fly. **400**

Phaethon lepturus *Phaethonidae*
YELLOW-BILLED
TROPICBIRD 30-32 (body 15-16) ins
Tropical oceans, dispersing after breeding to open sea and coastal waters. Glossy white (but race *fulvus* in Indian Ocean suffused peach or even salmon pink); broad black stripe through eye links with black on mantle and wings; black on tail of 12 feathers, central pair much elongated; legs bluish, toes black, bill orange red, eyes brown. Usually alone at sea, resting on water with tail raised; clumsy on land but graceful in flight. Most active at island colonies early morning and evening. Dives after food: squids, fish, marine crustaceans, especially crabs (see also under *Pterodroma cahow,* Bermuda Cahow). Harsh tern-like scream of alarm or in flight; softer calls at nest. Breeding season varies with range; at 5 to 10 month intervals on Ascension Island. One egg, pinkish ground richly marked in purple and brown, laid in hole, crevice or burrow of other species, on bare island or sea cliff; incubated 28 days by ♀ and ♂; they feed chick, which fledges fully in 70-85 days. **38**

Phaethornis superciliosus *Trochilidae*
LONG-TAILED HERMIT *c.* 6 (bill 1½) ins
Neotropical: S Mexico, Central America, Guyanas, Venezuela S of Orinoco, N and E Colombia, W and E Ecuador, E Peru, N Bolivia, Amazonian Brazil; resident in forests from sea level to *c.* 6,000 ft. Upperparts greyish brown, outer flight feathers with pale buff or whitish tips; rump and upper tail coverts tinged orange, elongated central tail feathers white; much of head dark brown with lighter stripes; underparts grey tinged buff, under tail coverts pale buff to white, with darker markings. Legs, long curved bill, eyes dark. ♂♂ gather, up to 100 in *c.* 250 yds, and display by wagging tails, singing squeaky song, thus attracting ♀♀; display areas may persist for years. Hovers in front of food plants, e.g. wild plantain, introduced banana flowers, to which long bill gives access. Builds typical hummingbird nest usually up to 9 ft, often beneath curled palm frond. ♀ lays 2 white eggs, incubates them *c.* 17 days, feeds young by regurgitation until they fly *c.* 3½ weeks. **474**

PHAINOPEPLA see **Phainopepla nitens**

Phainopepla nitens *Bombycillidae*
PHAINOPEPLA 7½ ins
Nearctic; marginally Neotropical: breeds from Central California, S Utah and mid W Texas to Central Mexico; winters from S California, S Arizona southward. Habitat: riparian trees, often mesquites in desert country. ♂: generally glossy black from tall-crested crown to long tail; large white patch on black-tipped wings; white crescents lower breast; ♀: mainly brownish-grey with black in crest; wing patch pale grey; under tail coverts white-edged. Juvenile much as ♀. Legs, bill black, eyes light red. Flocks up to 50 wander after breeding, searching for berry-bearing trees, especially parasitic mistletoes; also take insects high in air. Slow wing-beats and fluttering flight. Call: repeated whistling *quirt;* song rather uneven between pleasant and squeaky notes. Breeds July (California), making shallow nest of twigs, fibres, down, bound cobwebs, usually in fork of bush or tree up to 20 ft, in thicket or open woodland; sometimes hidden by mistletoe or other growth. Usually 3 greenish white eggs, speckled black and brown. Both parents tend young. **661**

Phainoptila melanoxantha *Bombycillidae*
BLACK AND YELLOW SILKY FLYCATCHER 7½ ins
Neotropical: Costa Rica and W Panama; resident mountain forests from *c.* 5,000 ft to timberline. ♂: upperparts from crown deep black, glossed bluish green; chin, throat, thighs, wings, tail dull sooty black; rump lemon yellow tinged olive; sides, flanks yellow; lower breast, belly grey; upper breast, under tail coverts yellowish olive. ♀: crown black, glossed bluish green; hindneck slate grey, upperparts olive green, mixed yellow on rump; cheeks olive grey, chin, throat paler; underparts as ♂. Legs dark brown, bill blackish, eyes brown. Presumably mainly insectivorous but habits not studied.

Phalacrocorax africanus *Phalacrocoracidae*
LONG-TAILED SHAG 22-24 ins
Ethiopian, marginally Palaearctic; across Africa W to R. Gambia; also Madagascar, Egypt; local movements according to season. Uniform velvety black with relatively long tail; wing coverts and scapulars hoary grey, crest and white plumes in breeding season; immatures brownish-white underparts; legs purplish black, bill dark. Gregarious in large or small flocks, on lakes and rivers whose bends they follow in flight. Roosts communally, preferably in trees. Swims and dives after fish and amphibians, e.g. *Xenopus.* Silent, except for hiss on nest; young cackle. Breeding season varies; builds nest of local plants in colonies on ground, islands or low trees, often with other species. Both sexes incubate 2 to 4 chalky blue eggs and tend the young. **47**

Phalacrocorax atriceps *Phalacrocoracidae*
BLUE-EYED SHAG 28-33 ins
One of group of closely related species in southern oceans, also occurring inland in South America,

ing areas; usually breeds December to April S Africa. Large colonies (estimated 10 million nests Lake Chad area) crowd thorn trees over several acres, but others scattered. ♂ builds purse-shaped nest of green grass with large side entrance. 2 or 3 pale greenish blue eggs incubated ♀ 12 days; young, fed by ♀ and ♂, fly 13 days. Only one brood at each site. Vultures, hawks, carnivores, even leopards, feed on fallen young in huge colonies. **962**

QUELEA, RED-BILLED see **Quelea quelea**

QUETZAL see **Pharomachrus mocinno**

Quiscalus niger *Icteridae*
GREATER ANTILLEAN GRACKLE   10-12 ins
Neotropical: Greater Antilles (W Indies); resident open settled and cultivated areas; large roosts in towns. ♂: black, glossed violet or steel blue; long tail wedge-shaped; legs, bill black, eyes light yellow. ♀ similar but duller. Harsh calls *chak chak, chin chin chi-lin*; also high-pitched *whee-see-ee* and bell-like note. Food various; specialised jaw muscles and slight keel within upper bill adapted for opening nuts; also takes fish, robs other nests. Gregarious at all times, breeding in colonies; large cup nest of sticks, soft plant materials high in trees, palms; occasionally in cat-tail (reed mace) swamps. 3 to 5 pale blue or clay-coloured eggs, spotted and scrawled dark brown; incubation and fledging as *Q. quiscala*. **912**

Quiscalus quiscala *Icteridae*
PURPLE GRACKLE   12 ins
Nearctic; breeds from Central Canada (S Mackenzie) SE over N America to S Florida, Gulf Coast, SE Texas; winters S from Maryland, Ohio Valley, Kansas. Habitat originally open woodland near water, adapted to cultivated land, pastures, parks, right into cities. ♂: very dark all over, glossed from green to blue or purple in different plumage phases. ♀ smaller, duller, glossy only head, neck breast. Legs, bill dark grey, eyes yellow. Juvenile uniform dull brown, eyes brown. Gregarious at all times, huge roosts city parks; often joins Red-winged Blackbird, *Agelaius phoeniceus*, and Starlings, *Sturnus vulgaris*. Call harsh *cack*; song: ascending squeaky, metallic notes 'like rusty iron gate'. ♂ displays plumage to ♀, depresses central tail feathers to emphasise keel effect. Food various: digs out insect grubs; wild fruits, nuts; waste, sometimes good grain; also fish taken in water, shellfish, small reptiles, mammals, birds and eggs; dunks dry bread. Breeds April onwards; colonies 25 pairs or more; bulky nest of twigs, stalks, grass, often cemented mud, lined fine grass; almost from ground level to 50 ft in tree, often evergreen, also bushes, holes in trees and buildings, other birds' nests, often near water or in clump on farmland. 5 pale blue eggs, spotted and scrawled brown or black, incubated *c.* 2 weeks; young fly *c.* 18 days. **913**

Quoyornis georgianus see **Eopsaltria georgiana**

RACKET-TAILED DRONGO, GREATER see under **Dicrurus annectans**

RAIL,
    CLAPPER see **Rallus longirostris**
    GUAM see **Rallus owstoni**
    RED-NECKED see **Rallina tricolor**
    SORA see **Porzana carolina**
    TRICOLOURED see **Rallina tricolor**

RAIL BABBLER, MALAYSIAN see **Eupetes macrocerus**

RAINBOW
    BUNTING see **Passerina leclancheri**
    PARAKEET see **Trichoglossus haematodus**

Rallina tricolor *Rallidae*
RED-NECKED RAIL or TRICOLOURED RAIL   11½ ins
Australasian: coast of N Queensland, New Guinea, Aru Islands. Migratory, arriving Queensland beginning of wet season to haunt dense tropical scrub along creeks and on slopes of rocky ridges. Back, wings and tail dull brown; head, neck, mantle and breast rufous; belly brown mottled black; legs and rather long bill greenish, eyes dark. Very shy, usually found single or in pairs. Calls a repeated *kare*, also sharp *tok tok tok*. Feeds on insects and freshwater animals. Breeds January to April in Queensland, lining scrape on ground, often at base of tree, with dead leaves. 4 or 5 white eggs, marked red-brown and purple, incubated by ♀ and ♂ *c.* 2½ weeks; both probably also tend young. **235**

Rallus longirostris *Rallidae*
CLAPPER RAIL   14-16 (bill 2) ins
Nearctic and Neotropical: down E and W coasts USA, to W Indies, Central America, S Brazil and NW Peru; northern birds move S in winter. Race illustrated is western *R.l. levipes*. Habitat: salt marshes, mangrove swamps. Upperparts predominantly grey or grey brown, as on wings, shading from head (throat whitish, short white 'eyebrow') to buff breast and flanks; white belly barred grey-brown from legs to under tail coverts; legs yellowish, bill orange, tip dark; eyes light brown. Behaves much as relatives but swims frequently. Call a clattering *kek kek kek*, ending lower and slower. Breeds April to December Trinidad, building nest of local plants, hidden in tall grass or attached to rushes or to mangrove roots in swamps. Lays 3 to 13 eggs according to latitude, buff spotted brown and grey; often 2 broods. **236**

Rallus owstoni *Rallidae*
GUAM RAIL   11 ins
Confined to Guam in Marianas Islands, Micronesia; sedentary in long grass and ferns on damp ground at woodland edges. Upperparts brown; underparts and part of wings barred black and white; throat and stripe over eye grey, eyestripe brown; legs grey, bill dark brown, eyes red. Relatively tame, appearing on roads where killed by cars (J. A. Tubb). Has rattling chuckling call (Tubb); young call *tsip*. 'Leathery land slug' identified in food (J. T. Marshall). Breeds probably throughout year but no details available. **237**

Ramphocaenus melanurus *Muscicapidae: Polioptilinae*
LONG-BILLED GNAT WREN   5-5½ (bill 1) ins
Neotropical: tropical SE Mexico S to N Brazil, N Peru; also Trinidad. Resident dense forest undergrowth, dry forest. Crown, nape dull reddish brown; mantle grey brown; sides of head to flanks cinnamon; underparts buffy white to pale cinnamon; throat mottled black; narrow tail black, tipped white; legs pale lead-grey; very long bill brownish-white, eyes dark, orbits greyish. Often found among branches of fallen tree or in tangle of creepers. Call: distinctive soft trilled whistle. Insectivorous. Breeds April to June (Trinidad), building deep cup nest of grass, leaves, moss, lined dark plant fibres, in upright fork of bush or sapling *c.* 1½ ft up. 2 dull white eggs, spotted and speckled shades of brown, sometimes in zone. **723**

Ramphocelus flammigerus see under **R. icteronotus**

Ramphocelus icteronotus *Emberizidae: Thraupinae*
YELLOW-RUMPED TANAGER   8 ins
Neotropical: Panama, Colombia to NW Ecuador; damp clearings in forest, sea level to 5,000 ft or more. ♂: generally velvety black; lower back, rump, upper tail coverts lemon yellow. ♀: upperparts, including head, wings, tail, brownish black; rump, underparts bright yellow. Closely resembles and hybridises with Flame-rumped Tanager, *R. flammigerus*. Roosts trees, bushes. Food: fruit, insects. Breeds often in groups, ♀ building low, open nest. Usually 2 eggs, incubated ♀ 12 to 14 days, ♂ sometimes presenting food to eggs and both parents feeding young, who fly 10-13 days. **878**

Ramphocelus nigrogularis *Emberizidae: Thraupinae*
MASKED CRIMSON TANAGER   8 ins
Neotropical: SE Colombia from Caqueta S to E Peru and W into Amazonian Brazil; forests, especially secondary growth near watercourses, sea level to *c.* 4,000 ft. ♂: crimson, with throat, mask, mantle, wings, tail, centre belly black; base of lower mandible

silvery. ♀ similar but duller. Arboreal, roosting trees, bushes. Diet: fruit, insects. Breeds often in groups, details much as *R. icteronotus*. **879**

RAVEN see **Corvus corax**

RAVEN, WHITE-NECKED see **Corvultur albicollis**

RAZORBILL see **Alca torda**

Recurvirostra avosetta *Recurvirostridae*
AVOCET   *c.* 17 (bill *c.* 3¼) ins
Mainly Palaearctic, with centre in Turkestan, extending E to Manchuria, S to Persian Gulf (isolated area Pakistan), W to scattered localities W Europe, especially North Sea coasts, Iberia; isolated areas Tunisia, Nile Delta, Lake Victoria, S Africa; local movements after breeding or to Ethiopian region, especially Rift Valley lakes; also other salt or alkaline lakes, estuaries. Breeds sand or mud shores of shallow salt and brackish waters, inland or coastal. White, patterned black on head and nape, scapulars, wing coverts and primaries; long legs blue-grey, uptilted, finely pointed bill black, eyes red-brown. Immatures black-brown and generally washed pale buff. Usually in parties or flocks at all seasons. Flies with neck partly retracted, legs well beyond tail, glides to land. Rests often on one leg or sits; walks quickly with body horizontal and neck curved. Call *klooet*, repeated rapidly in alarm. Mutual and social displays on ground. Diet: mainly small crustaceans and insects swept up when wading by scything action of bill; also swims and upends. Breeds from second half April Europe; sparsely lined scrape in open usually on low mound close to water holds 4 eggs very like lightly marked Lapwings, *Vanellus vanellus*. Incubation by ♀ and ♂ 21-22 days; they tend young at least 6 weeks. **302**

RED AND YELLOW BARBET see **Trachyphonus erythrocephalus**

RED
    BISHOP see **Euplectes orix**
    BISHOP, BLACK-WINGED see under **Euplectes orix**
    BISHOP, ZANZIBAR see under **Euplectes orix**
    GROUSE see **Lagopus lagopus**
    JUNGLEFOWL see **Gallus gallus**
    LORY, MOLUCCAS see **Eos squamata**
    PHALAROPE see **Phalaropus fulicarius**

RED-BACKED
    PARROT see **Psephotus haematonotus**
    SANDPIPER see **Calidris alpina**
    SCRUB ROBIN see **Erythropygia zambesiana**
    SHRIKE see **Lanius collurio**
    WREN see **Malurus melanocephalus**

RED-BELLIED
    TROGON see **Trogon collaris**
    WOODPECKER see **Centurus carolinus**

RED-BILLED
    GROUND CUCKOO see **Carpococcyx renauldi**
    GULL see **Larus scopulinus**
    HORNBILL see **Tockus erythrorhynchus**
    OXPECKER see **Buphagus erythrorhynchus**
    PARROT see **Pionus sordidus**
    PIGEON see **Columba flavirostris**
    QUELEA see **Quelea quelea**

RED-BREASTED NUTHATCH see **Sitta canadensis**

RED-BROWED
    FIG PARROT see **Opopsitta leadbeateri**
    FINCH see **Estrilda temporalis**

RED-CAPPED
    CARDINAL see under **Paroaria cucullata**
    ROBIN see **Petroica goodenovii**

RED-CHEEKED CORDON BLEU see **Uraeginthus bengalus**

RED-COWLED CARDINAL see **Paroaria cucullata**

RED-CRESTED CARDINAL see **Paroaria cucullata**

RED-CROWNED
 PARAKEET see **Cyanoramphus novaeselandiae**
 WOODPECKER see **Melanerpes rubricapillus**

RED-EYED
 BULBUL see **Pycnonotus nigricans**
 DOVE see **Streptopelia semitorquata**
 POCHARD see **Netta erythrophthalma**

RED-FACED
 COLY see **Urocolius indicus**
 CROMBEC see under **Sylvietta rufescens**

RED-FLANKED BLUETAIL see **Tarsiger cyanurus**

RED-FOOTED BOOBY see **Sula sula**

RED-HEADED
 BARBET see **Eubucco bourcierii**
 BUNTING see under **Emberiza melanocephalus**
 FINCH see **Amadina erythrocephala**

RED-KNOBBED COOT see **Fulica cristata**

RED-LEGGED
 PARTRIDGE see **Alectoris rufa**
 THRUSH see **Mimocichla plumbea**

RED-NECKED
 PHALAROPE see **Phalaropus lobatus**
 RAIL see **Rallina tricolor**

RED-RUMPED SWALLOW see **Hirundo daurica**

RED-SHOULDERED HAWK see **Buteo lineatus**

RED-TAILED
 CHAT see **Cercomela familiaris**
 GUAN see **Ortalis ruficauda**
 SHRIKE see **Lanius cristatus**

RED-THROATED
 BEE-EATER see **Melittophagus bulocki**
 CARACARA see **Daptrius americanus**
 DIVER see **Gavia stellata**
 PIPIT see **Anthus cervinus**

RED-VENTED BULBUL see **Pycnonotus cafer**

RED-WINGED
 BLACKBIRD see under **Quiscalus quiscala**
 PYTILIA see **Pytilia phoenicoptera**
 STARLING see under **Onychognathus nabouroup**
 WREN see under **Malurus lamberti**

REDPOLL
 ARCTIC see under **Acanthis flammea**
 MEALY see **Acanthis flammea**

REDSHANK see **Tringa totanus**

REDSHANK, SPOTTED see **Tringa erythropus**

REDSTART see **Phoenicurus phoenicurus**

REDSTART,
 AMERICAN see **Setophaga ruticilla**
 BLACK see under **Phoenicurus phoenicurus**
 GOLDEN-FRONTED see **Myioborus ornatus**
 SLATE-THROATED see **Myioborus miniatus**

REDWING see **Turdus iliacus**

REED
 BUNTING see **Emberiza schoeniclus**
 WARBLER see under **Acrocephalus palustris**
 WARBLER, CLAMOROUS see **Acrocephalus stentoreus**
 WARBLER, GREAT see **Acrocephalus arundinaceus**

REEDLING see **Panurus biarmicus**

REEF HERON see **Egretta sacra**

Regulus calendula *Muscicapidae: Sylviinae*
RUBY-CROWNED KINGLET 4 ins
Nearctic; marginally Neotropical: Alaska and arctic Canada S down Rockies and along Canada-USA border, expanding in E from Washington DC to just N of Newfoundland; one race on Guadeloupe I, Mexico; winters from N of 40°N S to Guatemala. Breeding habitat: coniferous forest, often open stands; also spruce bogs, mixed woods; winters all types woodlands. Upperparts uniform olive grey; wings, tail dusky, narrowly edged yellowish-olive; 2 whitish wingbars; no 'eyebrow' but whitish orbits; ♂ has small scarlet patch on crown, usually concealed; underparts greyish-white; legs, bill blackish, eye very dark brown. Characteristic wing-flicking. Not very gregarious outside breeding season; but may associate other species. Defends territory vigorously, ♂ displaying scarlet crown. Calls: sharp, grating *kerr,* scolding chatter; song, heard on passage, remarkably loud, starts 4 to 8 high-pitched notes, then 5 to 10 octave lower, ending with repeated ascending groups of 3 short notes. Food: mainly insects, especially ants, aphids; seeds and berries in winter. Breeds May onwards, building mossy ball nest, lined feathers and suspended near tip of conifer branch. 5 to 11 creamy white eggs, speckled reddish-brown over lavender, incubated ♀ c. 16 days; young, fed ♀ and ♂, fly 18-20 days. **746**

Regulus regulus *Muscicapidae: Sylviinae*
GOLDCREST 3½ ins
Palaearctic, marginally Oriental: very disrupted range, from Azores, N Iberia, Britain and Ireland over much of Europe NE to River Petchora; possibly separate population headwater of Rivers Ob and Yenisei; also from E coast Black Sea and N Iran to mountains of Turkestan, Himalayas, Tibet; separate population Amurland, Sakhalin, Japan. Resident conifer and mixed forests, occasionally pure broad-leaved, up to 5,000 ft Japanese Alps, over 14,000 ft E Tibet; some migration of northern populations in winter. Upperparts yellowish green; wings dark brown with some greenish edges and 2 white wingbars, one more prominent; tail dark brown, feathers edged green; forehead dusky brown, lemon yellow (to orange in ♂) crown stripe framed in black; whitish line round eye; throat pale brown, underparts whitish, tinged yellowish brown. Juvenile has upperparts all greyish brown tinged green and mottled black, especially sides of crown. Legs brown, bill black brown, eyes dark brown. Flits restlessly, generally high in trees, often in parties of titmice. ♂ shows crest mainly in display. Call: very thin, needling *zeeo zeeo zeeo;* song: thin and high-pitched repetition of almost dissyllabic note with terminal flourish. Food mainly insects at all stages. Breeds from early April to July, ♀ and ♂ building moss basket nest suspended usually from conifer branch near tip, held together with cobwebs, lined small dark feathers; also in ivy, other creepers, various bushes, 5 to 40 ft up. 7 or 8 buffish white eggs finely marked light brown usually in zone, incubated ♀ c. 16 days. Young, fed ♀ and ♂, fly 18-20 days. 2 broods. **747**

Regulus satrapa *Muscicapidae: Sylviinae*
GOLDEN-CROWNED KINGLET 3½-4 ins
Nearctic: range as Ruby-Crowned, *R. calendula,* but not so far N, only just reaching Alaska; winters from Nova Scotia and British Columbia S through USA and Mexico to Guatemala. Breeding habitat: spruce forest, often in secondary growth mixed with birch, firs; on passage in broadleaved woods, thickets and weedy tangles; in winter usually in conifers, consorting with own species, chickadees, creepers, woodpeckers. Sometimes snared on burdock burs. Upperparts sombre olive-grey; wings, with 2 yellowish bars, and tail, dusky, edged yellowish; ♂ has orange crown (♀ yellow) with conspicuous black borders and white 'eyebrow'; hindneck grey; cheeks, underparts dull greyish to buffy olive; legs, bill, eyes all dark. Juvenile has no crown patch at first. Calls: single to several high-pitched notes like those of Treecreeper, *Certhia familiaris:* song 4 to 8 high notes, then rapidly descending series. Food: insects at all stages from egg. Breeds June onwards; nest globular, of moss and *Usnea*

lichen, bound cobwebs, lined feathers, fur, woven top and bottom in twigs of conifer branch, 30 to 60 ft up, occasionally lower. 8 to 10 creamy eggs, speckled red-brown over lavender, incubated ♀ c. 16 days; young, fed ♀ and ♂, fly 18-20 days. **748**

Remiz pendulinus *Paridae*
PENDULINE TIT 4½ ins
Palaearctic: Central Europe across Eurasia mainly between 40° and 50°N with some southward extensions, e.g. S France, Italy, Iberia. Mainly resident, some dispersion: reed marshes and dense scrub by rivers, freshwater and brackish lakes with variety of trees; also wooded steppes; reed beds in winter. ♂: upperparts rusty brown; head (with broad black mask), rump grey; wings, tail blackish with pale feather edges; throat white, underparts very pale buff, streaked rust on flanks; legs, bill blackish, eyes dark brown. Some races, e.g. *R.p. macronyx,* have black heads and throats; others, e.g. *coronatus,* have pale crown with mask merging back of head. ♀, much duller; juvenile lacks mask. Feeds in summer often high in trees, taking minute insects from extremities of twigs; also searches willows, reeds, reed mace; small seeds in winter from shore vegetation and withered flowerheads. Usual call soft plaintive *seeou,* also *tseep tseep tseep* from family parties. Breeds May onwards, ♂ starts by weaving basic loop of plant fibres, ♀ joins in to build fleecy, bottle-shaped nest of down, hung from tips of willow, tamarisk, other twigs overhanging water, 5 to 20, even 60 ft up, completed c. 2 weeks. 6 to 8 rather pointed white eggs incubated ♀ c. 13 days; she mainly tends young, who fly 16-18 days. **809**

RENAULD'S GROUND CUCKOO see **Carpococcyx renauldi**

RESTLESS FLYCATCHER see **Myiagra inquieta**

Rhamphastos sulfuratus *Ramphastidae*
KEEL-BILLED TOUCAN 18-20 (bill 5½) ins
Netropical: Mexico to Venezuela, N Colombia; resident in lowland rain forest up to 2,600 ft. Predominantly black; crown and mantle dark maroon; upper tail coverts white; throat, upper breast deep yellow; under tail coverts crimson; legs blackish; bill variable: upper mandible pea green with wedge-shaped orange patch at cutting edge, tip crimson; lower, pea green at base, light blue, tip crimson; eyes brown. Loosely gregarious, small flocks, mixed with other species, straggling through forest in undulating flight. Sometimes playful 'fencing' with bills. Display not spectacular but courtship-type feeding noted. Bathes in water collected in tree crotches. Call: monotonous croaking repeated for several minutes with head jerking and swaying of body, other birds joining in. In captivity roosts with bill laid along back, tail folded forward over it, to become 'featureless ball of feathers' (A. F. Skutch). When feeding, tears piece off fruit, juggles it with tips of bill, throws head back to let it drop into gullet; similarly drinks by dipping bill into water and tilting it up; also takes cicadas and other large insects. Nests in tree holes, sometimes enlarging old woodpecker borings; height very variable; some lining of green leaves. 2 to 4 white eggs incubated by ♀ and ♂ c. 16 days; both parents feed young, born with 'heel' pads on tarsus; bill develops over several months; fledging 6-7 weeks.

Rhea americana *Rheidae*
COMMON RHEA 60 ins tall
Resident South America from NE Brazil to Central Argentina in well vegetated country rather than open grassland. Both sexes rather drab brown all over, ♂ with black base to neck; no tail feathers; legs and bill light brown, eyes dark. Wings longer than Ostrich's but useless; runs very fast with neck almost horizontal. Flocks of 20 to 30 break up in breeding season when ♂♂ fight each other and display to up to 5 ♀♀, running, jerking neck and wings and roaring, noise accentuated by inflated oesophagus. Repertory of other calls. Food mainly vegetable; some insects and small vertebrates. Nest scrape in concealed site made and lined by ♂; several ♀♀ lay 12 to 30 eggs, golden yellow at first, in

same nest, where incubated by ♂ for *c.* 6 weeks. ♂ tends brood, who grow big as adults in 4 months, mature at 2 years. **2**

RHEA, COMMON see **Rhea americana**

Rhinoptilus africanus see **Hemerodromus africanus**

Rhipidura fuliginosa *Muscicapidae: Muscicapinae*
GREY FANTAIL   6½ (tail 3-3½) ins
Australasian: all round continental Australia; Tasmania; New Zealand, New Caledonia, New Hebrides; disperses after breeding into interior Australia. Habitat forest edge and scattered trees in grassland, along streams; less often in thick forest; common cultivated areas, parks, gardens in NZ. Upperparts greyish or olive brown; 2 small white bars on wing; outer feathers of tail have white inner webs, central pair dark; white 'eyebrow' and ear coverts; throat white, narrow black band at base; underparts yellowish buff. Black form in South Island, NZ, sooty black above, chocolate brown below, sometimes small white patch behind eye. Legs dark brown, bill, eyes black. Immature duller. Wags small body side to side, tail upward and downward, fanning it; but closed when pursuing insects on wing. Follows flocks, even humans, who disturb prey. Highly territorial when breeding. Call sharp *cheet;* rasping twittering gives Maori name *piwaka-waka.* Breeds August to January, building 'tailed' nest of assorted plant materials, bound cobwebs, lined hair, in fork among twigs at end of branch, often over stream, lake, 6 to 20 ft up. 2 to 4 creamy eggs, spotted grey, brown, mainly at big end, incubated ♀ and ♂ 15 days; both feed young, who fly *c.* 15 days. 2 to 5 broods (New Zealand). **790**

Rhipidura rufifrons *Muscicapidae: Muscicapinae*
RUFOUS FANTAIL   6½ ins
Australasian: islands to Guam, including Celebes, Solomons; continental Australia from extreme NW eastward to Gulf of Carpentaria; Cape York to Otway Ranges, Victoria; southern populations migratory. Habitat humid forests, migrating through dry ones. Upperparts brown tinged rufous, becoming orange-rufous lower back, tail, of which terminal half blackish brown; throat white, lower throat black, breast feathers black edged white, rest of underparts white; legs, bill, eyes brown. Acrobatic in flight though not as masterly as Grey Fantail, *R. fuliginosa,* flies directly through dense undergrowth; tail kept fanned. Takes insects off foliage at lower levels of forest, also on wing and feeds more on ground than Grey Fantail. Breeds November to January New South Wales, building nest similar to but rather coarser than Grey Fantail, usually in thin lateral fork 3 to 30 ft up in understorey. Usually 2 stone to buff eggs, minutely spotted yellow or reddish brown at big end; incubation and fledging as *R. fuliginosa.* **791**

Rhynochetus jubatus *Rhynochetidae*
KAGU   22 ins
Australasian: confined to remoter mountain forests of New Caledonia. Upperparts of loose plumage ashy grey, tinged brownish on back and coverts of broad, rounded wings which are barred black, white and chestnut; ragged erectile crest pale grey, underparts pale buffish grey; scattered powderdown; legs, bill orange-red, eyes red. Little studied in wild. Cannot fly well; runs fast for short distances, wings partly spread. Normally on ground but can perch 3 or 4 ft up. In display pair stand erect facing each other, crests raised, wings spread; ♂ attacks ♀'s feet. Also whirling antics, holding tip of tail or wing in bill. Loud rattling call heard at night; probably nocturnal in wild. Food: molluscs, especially snail *Placostylus bavayi,* shell broken by blow of bill; worms, insects to locust size. Breeds probably August to January in wild; ♀ and ♂ in captivity build nest of stocks and leaves. Single buff egg, marked brown over grey, incubated ♀ and ♂ 36 days. Chick leaves nest after 3 days, feeds itself in 4 weeks. **239**

Rhyticeros plicatus see **Aceros plicatus**

RICHARDSON'S OWL see **Aegolius funereus**

RICHARD'S PIPIT see **Anthus novaeseelandiae**

Richmondena cardinalis see **Pyrrhuloxia cardinalis**

RIFLEMAN see **Acanthisitta chloris**

RING-BILLED GULL see under **Larus californicus**

RING-NECKED
   PARAKEET, INDIAN see **Psittacula krameri**
   PARROT, see **Barnardius barnardi**
   PHEASANT see **Phasianus colchicus**

RINGED
   PLOVER see **Charadrius hiaticula**
   TEAL see **Calonetta leucophrys**

Riparia paludicola *Hirundinidae*
AFRICAN SAND MARTIN   4½ ins
Palaearctic (marginally), Ethiopian, Oriental: 7 races; breeds W Morocco, all Africa south of French Sudan and Ethiopia (not Zaire), Madagascar, Indian subcontinent S to Bombay; Laos, Thailand, Philippines, Taiwan. Many races partially migratory within Africa. Habitat: open country, especially by streams and rivers. Upperparts mouse brown, chin to upper belly mouse brown, rest underparts white (sometimes all mouse brown); tail slightly forked; legs brownish-black, bill black, eyes brown. Often congregates in large flocks. Call a dry *svee-svee;* twittering warble in breeding season. Feeds on aerial insects preferably over water. Breeding season variable and often prolonged, especially in N. Nests colonially in holes in sandbanks (*c.* 2 ft deep). 3 or 4 white eggs. **621**

Rissa tridactyla *Laridae*
KITTIWAKE   *c.* 16 ins
Holarctic: *R. t. tridactyla,* Gulf of St Lawrence, coasts of Labrador, arctic Canada, Greenland, arctic Europe, Britain and Ireland, N France; *pollicaris,* coasts Bering Sea and N Pacific. Habitat: only truly oceanic gull, outside breeding season disperses to open sea 60°N to Tropic of Cancer. Differs from Common Gull, *Larus canus,* in lacking white patches on black wing tips. Legs brownish black, bill greenish yellow, eyes dark brown with orange-red orbital ring. Immature (tarrock): some blackish mottling above eyes and round ears, broad black collar on hindneck, black terminal band on tail, back mottled with black, diagonal blackish bar on wings. Often follows ships, picks food up from surface in flight, settles and dives, or plunges in from flight like terns; also feeds on flats at low tide; takes small fish and marine invertebrates. Breeds May to July in noisy colonies on cliffs or walls of sea caves, occasionally on building (Britain); makes neat nest on ledge, of seaweed, sometimes grass and moss, with deepish cup; 1 to 3 pale blue-grey to light brown eggs, marked darker brown and underlying ashy. Both parents incubate *c.* 21-24 days; young fly 4-5 weeks. **333**

RIVER MARTIN, ALPINE see **Pseudochelidon eurystomina**

RIVOLI'S HUMMINGBIRD see under **Lampornis clemenciae**

ROADRUNNER see **Geococcyx californianus**

ROATOLO see **Mesitornis unicolor**

ROBIN,
   AMERICAN see **Turdus migratorius**
   EUROPEAN see **Erithacus rubecula**
   HOODED see **Petroica cucullata**
   NORTHERN SCRUB see under **Dryomodus brunneipygia**
   PEKIN see **Leiothrix lutea**
   PINK see **Petroica rodinogaster**
   RED-BACKED see **Erythropygia zambesiana**
   RED-CAPPED see **Petroica goodenovii**
   SCARLET see **Petroica multicolor**

SOUTHERN SCRUB see **Dryomodus brunneipygia**
WHITE-BREASTED see **Eopsaltria georgiana**
WHITE-BROWED see **Erythropygia zambesiana**
YELLOW see **Eopsaltria australis**

ROBIN CHAT,
   CAPE see **Cossypha caffra**
   SNOWY-CROWNED see **Thamnolaea coronata**
   WHITE-THROATED see **Cossypha humeralis**

ROCK
   BUNTING see **Emberiza cia**
   DOVE see **Columba livia**
   MARTIN, AFRICAN see **Hirundo fuligula**
   NUTHATCH, EASTERN see under **Sitta neumayer**
   PIGEON, WHITE-QUILLED see **Petrophassa albipennis**
   PTARMIGAN see **Lagopus mutus**
   SANDPIPER see under **Calidris maritima**
   SPARROW see **Petronia petronia**
   THRUSH see **Monticola saxatilis**
   THRUSH, SWINHOE'S see **Monticola gularis**
   THRUSH, WHITE-THROATED see **Monticola gularis**

ROCKFOWL,
   GREY-NECKED see **Picathartes gymnocephalus**
   WHITE-NECKED see under **Picathartes gymnocephalus**

ROCKHOPPER see under **Eudyptes chrysolophus**

ROCKWREN see **Xenicus gilviventris**

ROLLER,
   ABYSSINIAN see **Coracias abyssinica**
   CUCKOO see **Leptosomus discolor**
   EUROPEAN see **Coracias garrulus**
   INDIAN see **Coracias bengalensis**
   LILAC-BREASTED see **Coracias caudata**
   LONG-TAILED GROUND see **Uratelornis chimaera**

Rollulus roulroul *Phasianidae*
GREEN WOOD PARTRIDGE   10 ins
Oriental: Malaysia, Indonesia, Borneo; sedentary in dense evergreen forest up to 4,000 ft, favouring drier and sometimes open spots, also bamboos. ♂: upperparts bright green; head, neck and underparts blue-black; graduated crest scarlet; wings dark brown with orange primaries; tail terminally black; legs red, bill black and red, eyes hazel, facial skin scarlet. ♀: lacks crest, underparts green, wings chestnut, bill black. Moves actively in small coveys, keeping to cover; later pairs keep together. Call a soft mellow whistle. Diet: seeds, fruit, plant stems; insects scratched or dug up. Builds domed nest of dead leaves and stems with side entrance; lays 4 to 6 creamy white eggs incubated by ♀; ♂ and ♀ feed brood 5-6 days; they stay with parents *c.*3 months. **207**

ROOK see **Corvus frugilegus**

ROSE-BREASTED GROSBEAK see **Pheucticus melanocephalus**

ROSE-COLOURED STARLING see **Sturnus roseus**

ROSE-RINGED PARAKEET see **Psittacula krameri**

ROSEATE
   SPOONBILL see **Ajaia ajaja**
   TERN see **Sterna dougallii**

ROSEFINCH,
   LONG-TAILED see **Uragus sibiricus**
   PRZEVALSKI'S see **Urocynchramus pylzowi**

ROSELLA,
   CRIMSON see **Platycercus elegans**
   EASTERN see under **Platycercus eximius** and **Psephotus haematodus**

ROSS'S TOURACO see **Musophaga rossae**

Rostratula benghalensis *Rostratulidae*
PAINTED SNIPE ♀: 10, ♂: 9½ ins
S and E Palaearctic (Asia Minor, Iran, S China, Japan), Ethiopian and Madagascar, Oriental (not Borneo, Celebes), Australasian (not New Guinea, New Zealand). Nomadic, haunting swamps, ponds and ricefields, coastal *Salicornia* marshes, sea level to 7,000 ft. Sex roles reversed. ♀: upperparts rich bronze-green with dark vermiculations and yellow V on back; wings spotted and barred buff; sides of head and neck chestnut brown with white 'spectacles' round eyes and black bank across breast; stripe from white underparts curls up round wing. ♂: olive-brown above glossed green with buff central stripe from bill over crown; white 'spectacles', back and wings much as ♀; throat white, mottled olive brown neck and breast crossed by black band; underparts as ♀. Legs slatey-blue, long bill purplish brown, eyes, set for binocular vision, dark brown. Secretive, most active dawn and dusk; runs and stands with lowered head, flies like rail rather than snipe. 'Song' *koht khot koht;* alarm call *kek.* Whistle from ♂, more powerful noises from ♀ in spectacular courtship: wings extended like Sun Bittern, *Eurypyga helias*, tail fanned; also as threat. Diet: large insects, e.g. crickets, molluscs and worms; some grasses. Breeding season variable, makes scrape in bush or sedge cover, laying 4 pale yellow eggs, heavily marked black and purple, incubated by ♂ *c.* 20 days; he also tends brood, feigning injury if disturbed. **252**

ROSY PASTOR see **Sturnus roseus**

ROSY-BREASTED LONGCLAW see **Macronyx ameliae**

ROTHSCHILD'S
  MYNAH see **Leucopsar rothschildi**
  STARLING see **Leucopsar rothschildi**

ROYAL TERN see under **Thalasseus elegans**

RUBY-CROWNED KINGLET see **Regulus calendula**

RUBY-THROATED HUMMINGBIRD see **Archilochus colubris**

RUBYTHROAT, SIBERIAN see **Luscinia calliope**

RUDDY QUAIL DOVE see **Geotrygon montana**

RUFF see **Philomachus pugnax**

RUFOUS
  BUSH CHAT see **Cercotrichas galactotes**
  FANTAIL see **Rhipidura rufifrons**
  FIELD WREN see **Calamanthus campestris**
  GNATEATER see **Conopophaga lineata**
  GRASS WARBLER see **Cisticola galactotes**
  HUMMINGBIRD see **Selasphorus rufus**
  JAY THRUSH, FUKEIN see **Garrulax caerulatus**
  MOTMOT see **Baryphthengus ruficapillus**
  SCRUB BIRD see **Atrichornis rufescens**
  SONGLARK see **Cinclorhamphus mathewsi**

RUFOUS-BROWED PEPPERSHRIKE see **Cyclarhis gujanensis**

RUFOUS-CROWNED WARBLER see **Basileuterus rufifrons**

RUFOUS-NAPED LARK see **Mirafra africana**

RUFOUS-SIDED TOWHEE see **Pipilo erythrophthalmus**

RUFOUS-TAILED
  JACAMAR see **Galbula ruficauda**
  PLANTCUTTER see **Phytotoma rara**

RUFOUS-VENTED CHACHALACA see **Ortalis ruficauda**

Rupicola peruviana *Cotingidae*
PERUVIAN or
ANDEAN COCK OF THE ROCK 11 ins
Neotropical: NW Venezuela, Colombian Andes to E and W Ecuador, E and S Peru, N Bolivia; resident steep ravines above watercourses, 4,000 to 7,500 ft. ♂: generally brilliant orange, surmounted by narrow, bushy crest from base of bill to top of nape; wings and tail black, inner flight feathers pearly grey. Legs yellow, small bill, almost hidden by fringe of crest, orange yellow; eyes yellow, rimmed black and yellow. ♀: generally, including small crest and tail, orange brown to dull red; inner flight feathers greyish brown. Ground living, unlike most of family, with strong legs. ♂♂ have social displays, rather like leks of grouse; each clearing small area and performing rather static dances, holding a posture for several minutes. ♀♀ gather and watch. Also nests socially, ♀ building shallow mud cup, strengthened with leaves and twigs and attached to rock face; several quite close together, 2 eggs incubated by ♀ only. **595**

RUPPELL'S VULTURE see under **Gyps africanus**

RUSTY BLACKBIRD see **Euphagus carolinus**

RUSTY-BREASTED ANT PITTA see **Grallaricula ferrugineipectus**

RUSTY-CHEEKED SCIMITAR BABBLER see **Pomatorhinus erythrogenys**

Rynchops nigra *Rynchopidae*
BLACK SKIMMER 16-20 ins
Nearctic and Neotropical: from New Jersey on Atlantic coast to Buenos Aires, from Mexico on Pacific to Magallanes, Chile; has bred Lake Titicaca in Andes; winters from Mexico S to Straits of Magellan. Habitat: beaches, saltings and estuaries; grassland in S America in winter. Upperparts from crown to base of forked tail black, with white trailing edges to wings; forks of tail, underparts from forehead white, legs red, bill black, red based, lower mandible longer and larger than upper; eyes dark brown. Spends much of day resting on sandbanks and beaches, feeding mostly dawn and dusk over calm, shallow water. Skims surface, wings above body, lower bill entering water; when it strikes fish, upper bill closes; prey flipped out, swallowed, and flight proceeds without pause. Call compared to dog's bark: resonant *auw*. Breeds May onwards in USA in scattered colonies, up to 4,000 pairs, often with terns. 2 to 5 light buff eggs, marked all over black, purple and grey, incubated mainly by ♀ in scrape in sand. Mandibles of chick equal length on hatching, lower develops when nearly full grown. **342**

SABINE'S GULL see **Xema sabini**

SABREWING HUMMINGBIRD, LAZULINE see **Campylopterus falcatus**

SACRED
  IBIS see **Threskiornis aethiopicus**
  KINGFISHER see **Halcyon sancta**

SADDLEBACK see **Creadion carunculatus**

SADDLEBILL see **Ephippiorhynchus senegalensis**

SAGE GROUSE see **Centrocercus urophasianus**

Sagittarius serpentarius *Sagittariidae*
SECRETARY BIRD *c.* 48 ins
Ethiopian; sedentary. Open plains, also savannah, bushveld and cultivated land. Upperparts bluish grey with long black crest; underparts greyish white; rump black, upper tail coverts white; graduated tail with long central feathers, grey, black and white; legs flesh, bill dark grey, cere bluish, facial skin pink, eyes hazel. Walks deliberately with constant head movements; broad winged in flight with projecting legs and tail. Quick stamping steps startle prey (ground animals, including snakes) which is seized by quick thrust of head, or stamped upon if large. Roosts in

trees. Territorial when breeding, with soaring displays. Normally silent, growls in display and at nest. Breeding season variable, lays May to June in Kenya; up to 40 ft in tree or bush. Lays 2 or 3 white eggs, streaked brown, in flat nest of sticks with finer lining. Incubated by ♀ *c.* 45 days. Chicks fed by both parents, fly in 65-80 days. **174**

SAKABULA see **Euplectes progne**

SAKER see **Falco cherrug**

Salpornis spilonotus *Sittidae*
SPOTTED CREEPER 6 ins
Oriental (Indian subcontinent), Ethiopian: most of region S to Zambia, Rhodesia, N South Africa; Himalayan foothills, in Africa savannah, acacia, *Brachystegia* woodland. Generally brown: upperparts, wings liberally spotted white, and wings tipped white; soft-feathered blackish tail barred white; black eye-stripe, broad white 'eyebrow'; underparts washed buff, also spotted white and blackish; legs lead grey; slender curved bill dusky, base lower mandible whitish, eyes brown. Habits like treecreepers, *Certhia* species, climbing trunks to probe bark, flying on to base of next tree; but can also move head downwards; often with other species. Longer flights undulating. Calls: shrill, whistling *sweepy swip swip;* single *tseee;* harsh *kek kek kek.* Food: insects from bark: caterpillars, beetles, ants. Breeding season variable within African range; March and April Asia; small cup of plant material, adorned lichens, cocoons, larval faeces, woven to lateral branch, often at fork or near trunk, 25 ft or more up. 2 or 3 pale turquoise blue eggs, zoned black spots, brown and lavender markings, incubated ♀, ♂ singing nearby. Both parents brood young.

Saltator atripennis *Emberizidae*: *Pyrrhuloxiinae*
BLACK-WINGED SALTATOR 8½ ins
Neotropical: Colombian Andes, W Ecuador; open woodlands, pastures, thickets, *c.* 2,500 to 7,500 ft. Upperparts bright olive green; wings, tail black; head, neck black (crown grey in one race), long 'eyebrow', ear coverts, throat white; underparts light grey, under tail coverts cinnamon buff. Voice rather weak. Diet: berries, fruit, some flowers and seeds. Breeding: ♀, accompanied ♂, builds bulky open nest near ground in bush. Usually 2 eggs, incubated ♀ 13-14 days, ♂ in attendance; both parents tend young, who leave nest but are fed for several weeks. 2 or more broods. **874**

SALTATOR, BLACK-WINGED see **Saltator atripennis**

SANDERLING see **Calidris alba**

SAND
  MARTIN, AFRICAN see **Riparia paludicola**
  PLOVER, KITTLITZ'S see **Charadrius pecuarius**

SANDGROUSE,
  BLACK-FACED see **Eremialector decoratus**
  CHESTNUT-BELLIED see **Pterocles exustus**
  FOUR-BANDED see **Eremialector quadricinctus**
  PALLAS'S see **Syrrhaptes paradoxus**

SANDHILL CRANE see under **Grus americana**

SANDPIPER,
  BROAD-BILLED see **Limicola falcinellus**
  BUFF-BREASTED see **Tryngites subruficollis**
  COMMON see **Tringa hypoleucos**
  CURLEW see **Calidris ferruginea**
  MARSH see **Tringa stagnatilis**
  PURPLE see **Calidris maritima**
  RED-BACKED see **Calidris alpina**
  ROCK see under **Calidris maritima**
  SPOTTED see under **Tringa hypoleucos**
  STILT see **Micropalma himantopus**
  WHITE-RUMPED see **Calidris fuscicollis**
  WOOD see **Tringa glareola**

SANDPIPER PLOVER
  DIADEMED see **Phegornis mitchelli**
  MITCHELL'S see **Phegornis mitchelli**

Sarcogyps calvus or Torgos calvus *Accipitridae*
ASIAN KING VULTURE 32 ins
Oriental region: Indian subcontinent to Laos; S Yunnan. Resident in forests, sometimes dense and humid, as well as cultivated land. Generally black, with white patches above thigh and thin white line on spread wing. Ruff black, bare head and neck red to orange; legs red, bill dark horn, cere orange, eyes brown. Immature brown. Slimmer and longer winged than *Gyps bengalensis*. Rather solitary but up to 10 may gather at carcase. Soars much of day, and flies over grass fires after small carcasses. Spectacular aerial display flights with loud roaring calls; also squeaks, hisses and grunts. Feeds on carrion. Peak of laying in India February to March, in trees from 3 to 100 ft, sometimes with other vultures. ♀ and ♂ build nest of sticks and leafy branches, incubating 1 greenish white, rarely marked egg for about 45 days and then tending chick. **163**

Sarcorhamphus papa *Cathartidae*
SOUTH AMERICAN KING VULTURE *c*. 31 ins
Neotropical: Central America southward, to Argentina E of Andes and N Peru to W of them. Primary habitat rain forest, but hunts savannah and grassy areas up to 4,000 ft, coastal marshes El Salvador. Body plumage, under wing coverts creamy white; rump, tail, most of wings black; bare head and neck variable orange, red, blue, with bristly feathers on crown; legs greyish white, strongly hooked bill reddish-orange with black base, caruncles and cere orange; eyes white in reddish orbits. Immature sooty black, acquiring white with age. Rather laboured flapping flight followed by glide. Circling, wing flapping and whistling in courtship. Does not approach habitations. Not very gregarious, 3 or 4 together in air, but up to 50 at carcass, where dominates other vultures; also kills new born calves, small reptiles. Breeds from March Panama, nesting in hollow stump near ground, laying 1 to 3 white eggs, incubated ♀ and ♂ 56-58 days (captive). Young may stay with parents up to 2 years. **132**

Sarkidiornis melanotos *Anatidae*
COMB DUCK or
KNOB-BILLED GOOSE ♀: *c*. 24, ♂: 30 ins
Ethiopian, Oriental, Neotropical: Africa from Gambia and Sudan S to Cape and Madagascar; India, Ceylon, Burma and SE China; S American race from Venezuela to S Brazil, Paraguay and N Argentina. Habitat: large open waters or rivers. ♂: black with iridescent green and bronze upperparts and white underparts; head and neck white with black spots. ♀: smaller and duller. S American race similar but both sexes have darker flanks. Legs grey-black, bill black with flat knob in ♂, eyes brown. Essentially tree duck, usually in flocks; flies powerfully in V formation, with rushing sound, may travel inland to feed on cultivated areas, roosts in trees at night. Call: short hoarse whistle; loud trumpet-like calls when disturbed near nest. Feeds on aquatic plants and insects, grass and crops. Breeds all months, making large nest of reeds and rushes lined with feathers, on ground in long grass, in reeds or hollows of trees. Polygamous. Lays 4 to 8 shining yellowish white eggs. **127**

Saxicola torquata *Muscicapidae: Turdinae*
STONECHAT 5 ins
Palaearctic, Oriental, Ethiopian: most of Europe (very local NW Africa) SW of line Denmark to Crimea; Asia Minor, Caucasus connected by mountains with vast area Asia to China, Korea, Sakhalin, Japan; much of E Africa, extending W to Zaire, in small isolated mountain areas; Madagascar. Mainly sedentary, part N population moves south in winter. Habitat: variety open country, flat or hilly, with bushes, scattered trees; heaths, moors, rough grassland, subalpine meadows and scrub; to 15,300 ft W China; also cultivated land, roadsides; heath, scrub and wasteland in winter. ♂: upperparts black-brown; white wing patch and rump (more pronounced some races), dark brown tail; head, throat black, partial white collar runs into chestnut breast which shades to whitish belly; duller autumn due to brown feather margins. ♀ has upperparts mottled dark brown; face, throat brown. Legs, bill black, eyes dark brown. Juvenile resembles ♀. Flits between exposed perches, often calling and flirting tail, then drops to ground after prey. Calls: hard *tsak tsak*, becoming *hwee-tsak-tsak* of alarm; song variable but musical, sometimes delivered in display flight when ♂ rises up to 100 ft and 'dances in air'. Food mainly ground-living insects, worms, snails; small seeds and fruits. Breeds second half March to August Britain; ♀ building nest of grass and moss, lined softly with hair, fur, feathers; usually well hidden in low vegetation, sometimes 2 ft up in thick bush. 5 or 6 pale blue eggs spotted red-brown in zone, incubated by ♀ 14-15 days; both parents feed young, who fly 12-16 days. 2, sometimes 3 broods. **699**

Scenopoeetes dentirostris *Ptilinorhynchidae*
TOOTH-BILLED CATBIRD or
STAGEMAKER *c*. 10½ ins
Australasian: tropical NE Queensland between Cooktown and Mount Spec; wet montane forest a few miles inland. Upperparts, including wings, tail, brown; underparts fawn mottled brown; yellowish base to throat feathers visible when singing; legs, bill, eyes reddish brown. Toothed bill used by ♂ to saw through leaf petioles for daily decoration of 'stage' (display ground); leaves strewn pale side uppermost contrast with dark forest floor. Stage usually oval or circular, between 3 and 8 ft diameter, only seen August to December. ♂ perches on 'singing stick', uttering constant penetrating stream of melody; own notes, mainly *chuck chuck*, and mimicked calls. Food: fruit, some insects, large ground molluscs. Breeds November to January; flimsy, saucer-shaped nest of thin sticks lined finer twigs, in thick foliage 20 to 100 ft up; 2 creamy to creamy brown eggs. Young fed mainly on insects.

Scissirostrum dubium *Sturnidae*
CELEBES STARLING *c*. 9 ins
Australasian, Oriental: confined to Celebes Is, where abundant in variety of habitats. Generally slaty mouse grey; wings, tail black, coverts edged grey; rump, upper tail coverts, flanks black with long, stiff, wax-like red appendages; lores (with bristles), orbits blackish; under wing coverts slaty grey, under tail coverts smoky black; legs, bill orange, eyes red. Juvenile browner, tips of specialised feathers less waxy. Gregarious, forming large breeding colonies in dead trees. Behaves like woodpecker, using stiff tail feathers to support itself against tree trunks, both for digging out larvae and excavating nest hole. Nostrils in bony grooves open almost directly upwards, presumably as protection against 'sawdust'. Also takes grain and fruit. Breeding season irregular.

Scolopax rusticola *Scolopacidae*
EURASIAN WOODCOCK *c*. 13½ (bill *c*. 3) ins
Palaearctic: broad band mainly between 50° and 60°N, covering W Europe except Mediterranean area, and extending across Eurasia to Sakhalin and Japan; isolated areas Atlantic Islands, Corsica, Caucasus, Himalayas. Northern populations move south and some winter N Africa, Middle East, India, Ceylon, S China, usually near water and in thick cover. Breeds broadleaved and mixed forests, also open conifers, wet woodlands, scrub, even moorland edge. Upperparts, including rounded wings, complex pattern of browns, buff and black with bars on nape, dark streaks on face; tail with dark subterminal band; underparts fairly evenly barred light and dark brown; legs and long bill dull flesh, large eyes, set far back in head, black-brown. Crepuscular in habits, so usually seen when flushed, flying off rather noisily through trees, or in 'roding' display over wood early or late, when ♂ calls high-pitched *chissick* and deep croak; also courts on ground. Probes in damp earth for small animals, especially earthworms. Breeds from end March in S of range; scrape, lined dead leaves usually partly sheltered by bracken, brambles, other lightish cover, on dry ground. 4 rather round buff eggs, spotted and streaked chestnut and lilac; incubated by ♀ 20-21 days; she tends young *c*. 2½ weeks, sometimes flying with them between legs if disturbed. **293**

Scopus umbretta *Scopidae*
HAMERKOP 22-24 ins (♀ smaller than ♂)
Ethiopian: S Sudan to Cape, and west to Senegal (3 races); resident in open areas near water. All brown with 'hammer head' silhouette; legs and bill black, eyes brown. Generally seen singly or in pairs, but semi-nocturnal with owl-like flight, neck partly extended, giving curious small-bodied appearance. Courtship display elaborate, accompanied by yapping cackle; calls in flight thin and squeaking; also grunts. Feeds by shuffling in water to disturb aquatic animals, especially frogs; also scavenges roads for carrion; young fed largely on tadpoles. Breeds almost throughout year, building enormous domed nest largely of sticks in tree-fork 15 to 40 ft up, with mud-plastered entrance; 3 to 6 white eggs incubated by ♀ and ♂ for *c*. 30 days; young fly in *c*. 7 weeks. **66**

♀'s duller. Call: loud repeated *tee tee tee;* ♂'s streamers whir in flight. Diet: nectar and small insects taken on wing. Builds nest of local plant materials on sometimes sloping twig of tree or shrub; ♀ incubates 2 white eggs as other hummingbirds. **478**

Troglodytes troglodytes *Troglodytidae*
COMMON OR WINTER WREN   *c.* 3¾ ins
Holarctic: most of W Europe, including NW Africa; Asia Minor, Himalayas to E China, Japan, Sakhalin, Kurile and Aleutian Is.; broad band N America either side Lat. 50°N, with tongues S in Rockies, Mid West E Coast mountains. Resident primarily coniferous and broadleaved forests with thick undergrowth, especially along watercourses; in man-modified shrubberies, gardens in Europe; coastal in Scotland, Iceland, Aleutian Is. Generally russet brown, more buff below; upperparts including wings, short tail closely barred darker brown; pale 'eyebrow'. Legs brownish flesh; bill: upper black-brown, lower pale horn; eyes dark brown. Juvenile more mottled, less barred. Extremely active, moving in and out of thick low vegetation and making short whirring flights. Bobs up and down when perched. Hops or runs on ground. Clicking *tic tic tic* call, often repeated quickly or churred. Remarkably loud shrill song with final trill, lasting *c.* 5 secs. Diet mainly insects, spiders, other invertebrates, prised out of shelter. Breeds March to August Britain; ball nest with entrance near top, of variety of local plant materials, one of several made by ♂, chosen and lined feathers by ♀: in banks, creepers, bushes, rocks, much reduced when in walls or other crevices; in old nests of other birds. 5 to 6 white eggs, freckled red-brown often in zone, incubated by ♀ 14-15 days; ♀, sometimes with ♂, feeds young, who fly 16-17 days. 2 broods. **668**

TROGON,
    BAR-TAILED see **Trogon collaris**
    BLACK-THROATED see **Trogon rufus**
    COLLARED see **Trogon collaris**
    GREATER YELLOW-BELLIED see **Trogon viridis**
    RED-BELLIED see **Trogon collaris**
    WHITE-TAILED see **Trogon viridis**

Trogon collaris *Trogonidae*
COLLARED, RED-BELLIED or
BAR-TAILED TROGON   10½ ins
Neotropical: Central America S to N Bolivia, Brazil; W of Andes to Colombia, NW Ecuador; Trinidad and Tobago; resident in forests from sea level to *c.* 7,000 ft. ♂: upperparts and breast iridescent green; wing coverts vermiculated black and white; flight feathers dusky black with white bases showing as bar on underwing; central tail feathers glossy blue-green, tipped black; outer tail feathers barred black and white, tipped white; white bar across breast, belly crimson; legs dark, bill dull yellow, eyes dark brown. ♀: upperparts and breast sandy brown; white round eye; breast band white, belly light crimson; central tail feathers rufous, outer feathers tipped white with black subterminal bar. Upright posture on perch in forest, where revealed by various whistling, hooting and cawing calls. Diet: insects and their larvae, spiders, small lizards and tree frogs; berries and small fruit. Breeds April to July Trinidad; ♀ and ♂ excavating hole in decayed tree or old termite nest; 2 white or greenish white eggs incubated by ♀ and ♂ 17-19 days; both feed young, who fledge *c.* 2½ weeks. **482**

Trogon rufus *Trogonidae*
BLACK-THROATED TROGON   10½ ins
Neotropical: S Honduras to NE Argentina E of Andes; W of Andes to Colombia, Ecuador; resident forests up to 4,000 ft, 2,500 ft in Central America. ♂: upperparts coppery green, throat black, breast bluish-green, belly orange yellow; flight feathers black, white edged, wing coverts vermiculated black and white; central tail feathers bronzed green or gold according to race and black-tipped, outer feathers barred black and white; legs blackish, bill yellow, eyes dark brown, orbits pale blue. ♀ like ♂ *T. collaris,* but belly yellow, outer tail feathers barred black and white, white tipped; white crescents at eyes; legs dark, bill grey. Upright posture with tail straight downward like relatives; darts to pick insects off leaves while hover-

ing; also berries, small fruit. Calls: weak, mellow *cow cow cow,* churring and rattling *krrr-re-eck,* also clear modulated notes. Breeds April in Central America, excavating hole 4 to 12 ft up in slender decayed tree. 2 white eggs incubated *c.* 18 days; parents feed young on insects; fledge 14-15 days. **483**

Trogon strigilatus see **T. viridis**

Trogon viridis or T. strigilatus *Trogonidae*
GREATER YELLOW-BELLIED or
WHITE-TAILED TROGON   11½ ins
Neotropical: Panama S to NW Bolivia and Brazil; W of Andes to Colombia, Ecuador; Trinidad; resident forests and scrubby savannah up to *c.* 7,000 ft. ♂: upperparts bronze green, rump purplish blue; flight feathers blackish, show white bar below; central tail feathers greenish blue, broadly tipped black; outer feathers black, tipped white; crown, breast, purplish blue, throat black; belly orange yellow; legs, eyes dark, orbits pale blue, bill pale greenish or bluish grey. ♀: upperparts, breast and flanks dark grey; wing coverts black, finely barred white; outer tail feathers tipped and barred white; belly orange yellow. Behaves as relatives. Call loud *tok toktok tok tok tok toktok;* also squeaky double note; answers to rather similar call of Pygmy Owl, *Glaucidium brasilianum.* Diet: insects and spiders; berries and small fruit. Breeds April to July Trinidad, in holes of dead trees. 2 rough, glossy, greenish white eggs incubated by ♀ and ♂ 17-19 days; parents feed young, who fledge *c.* 3 weeks.

TROPICAL
    KINGBIRD see **Tyrannus melancholicus**
    PEWEE see under **Contopus virens**

TROPIC BIRD,
    YELLOW-BILLED see **Phaethon lepturus**
    WHITE-TAILED see **Phaethon lepturus**

TRUMPETER, WHITE-WINGED see **Psophia leucoptera**

TUFTED
    DUCK see **Aythya fuligula**
    GUINEAFOWL see **Numida meleagris**

TUI see **Prosthemadura novaeseelandiae**

Turdoides jardinei *Muscicapidae: Timaliinae*
ARROW-MARKED BABBLER   9½ ins
Ethiopian: most of region: N to 5°S in Zaire, 2 S in Kenya; forest edges, thorn scrub, rank grass, especially along watercourses. Ash-brown above, black centres to head feathers; flight feathers, tail bronze black; underparts paler grey; throat, upper breast flecked white; underwing tawny; legs, bill black; eyes orange. Small noisy flocks feed on ground, flying low between bushes. Many harsh scolding calls include rook-like *kaa, kaa.* Diet mainly insects. Breeding season very variable, almost whole year in N of range. Roots, grass-stems used to build large nest in thick bush, tree or driftwood along stream bed. 3 turquoise eggs. **716**

Turdus iliacus *Muscicapidae: Turdinae*
REDWING   8¼ ins
Palaearctic: Eurasia between 60° and 70°N to *c.* 160°E; southern range in Europe moving towards 50°N, increasing Britain; also France, Iceland; winters W, S Europe, N Africa, SW Asia. Habitat open woodland of taiga, mixed birch, willow, alder; subarctic birch zone and riverine trees; parks and gardens in Scotland; winters often cultivated land with woods and hedges. Upperparts dark brown (Song Thrush, *T. philomelos,* much lighter) with pronounced pale 'eyebrow', fainter moustachial stripe; underparts pale buff shading to white, thickly streaked dark brown; flanks and under wing coverts chestnut-red (orange in Song Thrush), rest of underwing white. Legs yellow-brown, bill black-brown and yellow, eyes dark brown. Gregarious in winter, often social when breeding. Hops or runs in bursts, then stands upright. Call in flight soft, penetrating *seeip; chittuck* or *chic* of alarm; short song phrase of 3 or 4 notes, heard some-

times from mass twittering of flock in early spring. Takes variety of insects in summer, berries in autumn and winter, also worms, molluscs from ground. Breeds late April to early August; ♀, sometimes accompanied ♂, builds nest of grass, twigs, moss, wool, with mud cup and fine inner lining; in conifer, birch, shrubs, tree roots, steep banks, buildings, up to 25 ft. 5 or 6 eggs very like small Blackbird's, *T. merula;* incubated by ♀ and ♂ *c.* 13 days; both feed young, who fly 14 days. 2 broods. **704**

Turdus libonyanus *Muscicapidae: Turdinae*
KURRICHANE THRUSH   9 ins
Ethiopia: E and S Africa S of Equator: Tanzania, E Zaire to Natal; resident acacia savannahs, open woodland, rocky hills, usually near watercourses; sometimes in gardens. Upperparts, including wings, tail, brownish slate-grey; chin and throat white with conspicuous black moustachial stripes; upper breast grey buff; underparts light tawny brown shading to whitish; legs yellowish, bill orange red, eyes brown. Juvenile has black spots on underparts. Usually feeds on ground under trees, scratching out insects, also takes fruits. Call musical, whistling *tchi chee;* squeak of alarm; quiet song in breeding season, broadly August to January throughout range. Large nest, decorated leaves and lichens on mud base, lined finer plant materials, in fork of tree or stump. Usually 3 dark bluish eggs, densely speckled brown over pale lilac. **705**

Turdus merula *Muscicapidae: Turdinae*
BLACKBIRD   10 ins
Palaearctic, marginally Oriental: almost all Europe (including NW Africa) S of 60°N (N of it in Scandinavia) with narrow extension E through Asia Minor, Caucasus, mountains of S Asia, to S China; northern populations winter southward to N Africa. Introduced New Zealand. Habitat variety of wooded country with dense undergrowth or mossy ground layer: broadleaved and mixed woods in plains to subalpine conifers towards tree limit; parks, gardens, vineyards, palm oases; cultivated land to cities in Europe; similar lowland habitats in winter. ♂: jet black with orange-yellow bill and orbits; partial albinos common. ♀: generally dark brown, throat pale, light brown breast spotted darker. Legs dark brown, bill from black to orange, less bright in ♀; eyes dark brown. Juvenile mottled rufous. Spends much time on ground, running or hopping, but often skulks, though song perches usually exposed. Flight direct except in ♂'s butterfly display. Variety of ritual postures and complicated manoeuvres on territorial boundaries, sometimes fierce fights. Call *tchook tchook;* high pitched *tsee,* scolding *tchic tchic.* Song mellow, fluting with rather feeble ending, but some performers superb. Takes great variety of insects, other invertebrates, especially worms; fruit and berries of many kinds. Breeds end February to August Britain; ♀, sometimes helped ♂, builds substantial nest of local plant material and debris, with mud cup, fine lining; in trees, bushes, e.g. brambles, woodland banks, great variety of sites on cultivated land and human artefacts, ground level to 12 ft or more. 3 to 5 greenish blue eggs, more or less heavily freckled brown or red-brown, often at big end, incubated by ♀ 12-15 days; both parents feed young, who fly 12-15 days. 2, 3 even more broods. **706**

Turdus migratorius *Muscicapidae: Turdinae*
AMERICAN ROBIN   10 ins
Nearctic and Neotropical: breeds from NW Alaska through much of Canada to W South Carolina, Central Alabama, Arkansas, Mexico, to Guatemala; winters as far N as S Maine, S Ontario, Nebraska, Wyoming, S British Columbia. Habitat open areas with scattered trees, forest edges and clearings; orchards and gardens, reaching high densities in residential areas like Blackbird, *T. merula,* its Old World counterpart (despite name). ♂: upperparts generally grey, becoming blackish on head (white patch round eye), parts of wings (flight feathers pale edged) and longish tail; throat white streaked black; underparts chestnut red, under tail coverts white. ♀ duller and paler. Legs greyish, bill yellow, eyes dark brown. Juvenile greyish above, buff below, mottled

and spotted. Large flocks on migration and in winter roosts, usually in swamp; birds feed in small parties during day on great variety of fruit and berries (palmetto in winter); also take earthworms, insects and their larvae from ground. Fights between ♂♂ for territory in spring and against image in windows, shiny surfaces. Variety of calls, including high-pitched hiss. Loud song, strongest before dawn, of 2 and 3 note phrases with pauses, each phrase varying in pitch. Breeds May to August, building bulky nest of plant stems and debris, with mud cup and fine inner lining; first nests often in evergreen or conifer, second brood nests in deciduous cover. 3 to 5 blue-green eggs incubated by ♀ c. 13 days; both parents feed young, who fledge c. 14 days. 2 broods. **707**

Turdus olivaceus *Muscicapidae: Turdinae*
OLIVE THRUSH 9½ ins
Ethiopian: several races, some very local, cover most of eastern and southern Africa. Habitat evergreen and deciduous forest, open hillsides by streams, montane heaths up to 10,000 ft Kilimanjaro; cultivated land, urban gardens. Upperparts, including cheeks, wings, tail, dark olive slate; chin, throat whitish, streaked dark brown; underparts dusky olive shading to orange-rufous on belly, flanks; under tail coverts whitish, marked dusky; legs yellow-brown, stout bill orange-yellow, eyes brown. Juvenile streaked above, spotted below. Fast, direct flight. Dominates other garden birds. In display ♂ puffs out feathers, spreads tail, shuffles round ♀ with wings trailing. Call *tsit* on take-off; low *tschuk tschuk* of alarm; simple, variable song. Scratches leaves and debris for insects and other invertebrates, including snails, cracked open against stone. Thrush habit of running forward, stopping with head cocked one side, darts forward again usually to pull out worm; also takes fruit. Breeding season varies within range; builds grassy cup, often on stout foundation of earth and plant materials, close to tree trunk in forest, on stump or in thick bush. 3 to 5 bluish green eggs, spotted fine brown or blotched rufous over purple. **708**

Turdus philomelos see under **T. iliacus**

Turdus viscivorus *Muscicapidae: Turdinae*
MISTLE THRUSH 10½ ins
Palaearctic: Europe, including NW Africa, but except N Scandinavia, most of S Russia; extending E between 50° and 60°N to meet narrow band through Asia Minor, Caucasus, mountains SW Asia; northern birds migrate to temperate and Mediterranean areas. Habitat subalpine coniferous forest (not dense spruce), also montane oak, beech, up to 11,500 ft Himalayas; lowland mixed woods, cultivated land, parks, gardens, into cities. Upperparts grey brown with pale outer tail feathers; ear coverts finely mottled; whitish underparts heavily spotted black-brown, underwing whitish; legs yellowish brown, bill dark horn and yellow; eyes brown. Juvenile 'scaly', sometimes confused with White's Thrush, *Zoothera dauma*. Upstanding carriage on ground, where spends much time. Flies with wing closures, rather undulating. Parties form autumn, causing confusion with gregarious Fieldfare, *T. pilaris*. Display by rather leisurely chases from perch to perch. Usual call, emphasised when excited, rattling chatter; also repeated *tuc tuc tuc;* song, from exposed perch, loud, less fluty than Blackbird, *T. merula*. Takes fruits and berries when available, also molluscs, earthworms, variety of insects; sometimes young birds. Breeds second half February to June Britain; ♀ building substantial foundation of moss, lichens, grasses, wool with earth cup and fine lining, often green grass; from ground level to 50 ft, typically in fork of tree or on lateral bough, conifer or broadleaved; also bushes, low rock faces, buildings. 3 to 5 creamy buff or pale blue green eggs, marked red-brown over grey or violet; incubated by ♀ 13-14 days; both parents feed young, who fly 14-16 days. 2 broods. **709**

TURKEY VULTURE see **Cathartes aura**

TURKEY, WILD see **Meleagris gallopavo**

Turnix varia *Turnicidae*
PAINTED BUTTONQUAIL c. 8 ins
Continental Australia and Tasmania; resident open forest, heathlands, tall scrub. Upperparts very dark brown with pale feather margins, mantle greenish, nape chestnut, both spotted white; crown brown, broad white 'eyebrow', throat and underparts grey, sides of breast greenish; legs orange, bill dark, eyes red-brown; ♀ brighter than ♂. Partly nocturnal, pairs or family parties scratch for grass seeds, grain, shoots, small insects; they drink with 'bibbling' action of mandible and dust frequently; if flushed, only fly short distance. ♀ conducts courtship and utters loud booming call by means of specialised vocal organ. Breeding season September to February in E Australia. Both sexes build nest in sheltered scrape on ground, but ♂ incubates the 4 buffish or white eggs, thickly marked brown and grey, 12-13 days, ♂ tends the brood, who have 3 moults in 10 weeks. **213**

TURNSTONE see **Arenaria interpres**

TURQUOISE WREN see **Malurus callainus**

TURTLE DOVE see **Streptopelia turtur**

Turtur abyssinicus *Columbidae*
BLACK-BILLED BLUE-SPOTTED
WOOD DOVE c. 7 ins
Ethiopian: Senegal across to Ethiopia and N Uganda. Habitat: dry scrub and open woodland. Plump; upperparts light brown, forehead pale grey, 2 broad black bands over rump, iridescent dark blue blotches on secondaries; underparts brownish pink, flanks pale chestnut, under tail coverts white. Legs purple, bill black or dark, eyes dark brown. (Blue-spotted Wood Dove, *Turtur afer*, almost identical but range only overlaps in S Ethiopia; slightly darker, larger greener wing patches and red base to bill.) Tame, usually in pairs; ground feeder, taking seeds and similar plant matter; flies rapidly but rarely any distance. Call: prolonged soft cooing. Breeding season variable; lays 2 dark cream eggs on small platform of twigs, sometimes on old nest of other species, in tree or shrub. **379**

Turtur afer see under **T. abyssinicus**

Turtur chalcospilos *Columbidae*
EMERALD SPOTTED WOOD DOVE 7 ins
Ethiopian: N Somalia, Ethiopia, Katanga and Angola S to Natal and Cape. Habitat: dry bush-veld and open woodland, also cultivated areas. Plump; head grey, forehead paler, narrow black line from gape to eye; upperparts light brown, 2 shining emerald green, sometimes bluish, patches on closed wing, 2 dark bands across lower back; underparts light mauve-pink with pale chin. Wing mainly chestnut but blackish primaries and outer secondaries, tail brownish with black tip. Legs purplish red, bill black with reddish purple base, eyes dark brown. Single or in pairs; feeds on ground taking small grain, seeds and some small animals. Flight usually short, rapid, often zigzag; raises tail briefly on landing. Call: prolonged melancholy cooing, running up and down scale. Breeds any month, building usual twig platform in tree or bush, rarely more than 2 or 3 yards from ground; lays 2 pale cream eggs incubated ♀ and ♂. Both parents feed young, who fly 16 days. **380**

TWO-BANDED COURSER see **Hemerodromus africanus**

Tylas eduardi *Oriolidae*
KINKIMAVO 9 ins
Madagascar: race *T.e. eduardi* in forests of humid east, occasionally secondary growth, sea level to c. 5,500 ft; *albigularis* in central western savannah. Upperparts olive-brown, crown encircled black and white; underparts, including underwing, under tail coverts deep ochre; flight feathers greyish, tail dusky; *albigularis* greyer above, whiter below. Legs, bill black, eyes yellow. Moves rather slowly along larger branches of forest mid-storey, gleaning medium-sized insects; often in mixed flocks, e.g. with Helmetbird, *Aerocharis prevostii*. Breeds August to September.

Tympanuchus cupido *Tetraonidae*
GREATER PRAIRIE CHICKEN 18 ins
Nearctic: now very local in Central to S USA, migratory in north of range. Habitat originally tall-grass prairie, now also open and scrubby grasslands and cropfields. Barred white on shades of brown, with blackish rounded tail, dark brown head and crest; ♂ has long feathers on sides of neck, orange yellow wattles above eye and air sacs; legs feathered, feet greyish, bill and eyes dark. Lives in open in winter, burrowing in snow to roost. Spring displays by ♂♂ at 'leks' (see *Lyrurus tetrix*): short run with neck feathers raised and sacs distended, giving booming sound, then cackles and leaps in air. Breeds May to June, ♀ lining scrape in thick vegetation for 11, 12 or more olive eggs speckled brown, which she incubates for 23-24 days then takes chicks away; on wing in July. **190**

Tyrannus melancholicus *Tyrannidae*
OLIVE-BACKED or TROPICAL KINGBIRD 9 ins
Nearctic and Neotropical: breeds S Texas, S Arizona through Mexico and Central America to S America W of Andes to Peru; E of Andes to Rio Negro, Argentina; Trinidad and Tobago, Grenada. Resident chaparral desert, savannah, parkland, cultivated land and gardens, borders of lakes and rivers, sea level to 8,000 ft. Upperparts greyish green; wings, forked tail blackish brown with light edges to wing coverts, inner flight and tail feathers; head and neck grey with concealed orange crest, black mask; throat and breast greyish white: underparts lemon yellow; legs, bill black, eyes dark brown. Behaviour and diet as other kingbirds; flies nearly vertically down to perch; most active in evenings. Tremulous call *pip-pree;* also staccato high-pitched ascending notes. Breeds throughout year, building bulky cup nest like other kingbirds, usually at end of lateral branch up to 40 ft in tree. 2 to 4 creamy white eggs, boldly marked reddish brown and violet grey, often in zone, incubated by ♀ c. 14 days; young, fed by both parents, fly c. 14 days. **584**

Tyrannus tyrannus *Tyrannidae*
EASTERN KINGBIRD 8½ ins
Nearctic: breeds from S Canada throughout USA (except SW) to S Florida, Gulf Coast, Texas, N New Mexico; winters from Costa Rica E to Guyanas and S through W Brazil to S Bolivia, Peru, NW Argentina. Habitat open country with trees, woodland with occasional higher trees, gardens and parks; winters on campo (open grassland with trees), savannahs. Upperparts dark grey, with white edges to coverts making narrow bars on wings; long tail, often fanned, black broadly tipped white; thin orange crest normally housed in crown; underparts from throat white; legs, bill blackish, eyes dark brown. Rapid aerobatics with quick wingbeats give quivering effect. Attacks large birds crossing territory, even landing on their backs. Spreads wings and tail in display flight. Usual call *tzi tzee;* also high-pitched strident note extended into squeaky chattering; full song reserved for dawn chorus. Watches for insects from elevated perch, taking great variety on wing, off leaves, surface of water, sometimes ground; berries and seeds in autumn. Lays second half May after ♀ and ♂ have built bulky nest of sticks and grass with finer lining, usually 20 to 25 ft up on lateral branch, but occasionally up to 80 ft and down to stumps, fence posts, low shrubs near water. 3 to 5 creamy white eggs, marked brown and grey, incubated by ♀ c. 13 days; young, fed by parents, fly c. 2 weeks. **585**

Tyrannus verticalis *Tyrannidae*
WESTERN KINGBIRD 9 ins
Nearctic, marginally Neotropical: breeds from British Columbia and Manitoba S through western half USA to N Texas and N New Mexico; winters from NW Mexico to El Salvador; occurs on autumn passage E coast USA. Habitat open country with trees, fences and wires; frequent round ranches and into towns. Upperparts grey; flight feathers dark grey to black; long tail black with white outer feathers; thin concealed orange crest; throat white, breast pale grey, underparts lemon yellow; legs, bill horn grey, eyes brown. Calls: high-pitched squeaks, chattering and

twittering, less shrill than *T. tyrannus*. Diet almost entirely of insects, especially grasshoppers. Breeds sometimes socially, several pairs in one grove, building cup nest of soft materials, typically on lateral branch 15 to 30 ft up, but may use artifact sites if no trees. 4 creamy white eggs, marked brown and grey, incubated and young tended as *T. tyrannus*. **586**

Tyto alba *Tytonidae*

BARN OWL   *c.* 13½ ins
Cosmopolitan; Palaearctic: Europe E to Black Sea, N Africa, Arabia; Oriental: Indian subcontinent, much of SE Asia, Java and islands; Australasian: continental Australia, Tasmania, E New Guinea and islands; Nearctic: S of 50°N; Neotropical: except extreme S. Resident and migratory, also dispersal of young. Habitat varied: usually lightly wooded, mainly arid and rocky, frequently in or close to habitations. Race *T. a. alba*: upperparts orange buff, finely mottled grey and white; heart-shaped facial disc and underparts white; race *guttata* greyer on back, underparts buff spotted black, as in several other of over 30 races; Asian *stertens* has grey upperparts. Long legs feathered white, feet dark brown; bill yellowish to flesh-white; eyes black. Nocturnal, spending day perched upright in cavity, but sometimes hunting in daylight and often in evening when feeding young; quarters ground with light, wavering flight. Wing-clapping by ♂ in display. Crouches with wings spread horizontally in defence. Call a loud shriek often given in flight; hissing and snoring noises, especially by young; *kee-yak* like Tawny Owl, *Strix aluco*; snaps bill when angry like other owls. Food predominantly mice and other small rodents; some small birds, insects. Breeds almost the year round, making scrape, surrounded by pellets, in large cavity in tree, rocks or building, sometimes in old nest, e.g. of Hamerkop, *Scopus umbretta*, in Africa. 4 to 7 rather pointed white eggs incubated by ♀ 32-34 days; both parents feed young, who fly 9-12 weeks; often 2 broods. **429**

Tyto tenebricosa *Tytonidae*

SOOTY OWL   15 ins (♀ larger than ♂)
Australasian: New Guinea; two areas E continental Australia; Victoria (round Melbourne) to SE Queensland; N Queensland (including Atherton Tableland); rather wet, densely forested country. Upperparts: brownish black, streaked and flecked white; underparts sooty, mottled white and closely barred; rounded facial disc greyish-white; black round eyes and rim; tail very short; legs grey, feathers pale; bill brown; very large eyes brown. Habits much as Barn Owl, *T. alba*, roosting by day usually in hollow tree, sometimes in thick vegetation. Call: whistling screech, other screaming notes. Breeds October to December in southern range, laying 2 white eggs in tree holes. **430**

Upupa epops *Upupidae*

HOOPOE   11 (bill 2-2½) ins
Palaearctic up to between 50° and 60°N; almost all Oriental region except SE islands; Ethiopian except Congo Forest; W Madagascar. Northern populations winter S Asia and Africa S of Equator in open bush, low scrub, cultivated areas. Darker African race, with broader black and white bands, sometimes regarded as separate species *U. africana*. Breeding habitat: dry open park-like country, forest clearings, grassy and wooded steppes, palm groves; gardens, orchards and vineyards. Head, with fanned black-tipped crest, upper back and breast variable pinkish-brown; scapulars and back banded cream and black; rounded wings black banded white; rump white, upper tail coverts black with some white; tail black with broad white band; flanks and belly whitish, streaked dark brown; legs slate grey, fine curved bill blackish to greyish, eyes brown. Rises from ground into fluttering flight, looking predominantly black and white. But walks and runs swiftly, probing ground for large insects and their larvae, especially mole crickets; also lizards and various invertebrates. Crest usually flat but extended when alarmed. Fond of dust baths but not known to drink. Small parties on migration. 'Song': soft *hoop hoop hoop*; also chatters when excited and has cat-like *kiaow* call. Breeds from April in Europe, August in S Africa; in holes in trees, rock faces, walls

of stone and earth, even occupied buildings, piles of stones, drainage holes, anthills. 5 to 8 off-white or yellowish olive eggs incubated by ♀ and ♂ 16-19 days; both feed young, who fly 20-27 days; sometimes 2 broods. **509**

UMBRELLABIRD see **Cephalopterus ornatus**

UMBRELLABIRD, LONG-WATTLED see under **Cephalopterus ornatus**

Upupa africana see under **U. epops**

Uraeginthus bengalus *Estrildidae*

RED-CHEEKED CORDON BLEU   *c.* 5 ins
Ethiopian: resident W Africa E to Eritrea, Ethiopia, Somalia, S to E Congo, Uganda, Kenya, N Tanzania, in thorn bush and acacia savannah, forest edge, neglected cultivations; gardens and habitations. ♂: upperparts light brown; rump, tail, underparts azure blue; crimson cheek patch; belly brown some races; under tail coverts white. ♀, immature duller, lack cheek patch. Legs, eyes brown, bill pearly pink. Tame and confiding, like many of its relatives visits bird tables. Pairs or family parties. Call: weak, squeaky; 3-note song *ts ts tseeee* repeated continuously. Food: seeds, largely taken from ground. Breeding season varies within range; nest spherical or oval, sometimes with outer network of stems, rootlets, of fine green grass, lined feathers, in bush, tree, thatched roof, old nests of weavers; some races, e.g. *U.b. schoanus* of Central Ethiopia, build near hornets' nests. 4 or 5 white eggs. **946**

Uragus sibiricus *Fringillidae*

LONG-TAILED ROSEFINCH   10-11 (tail 3½) ins
E Palaearctic: E Kazakhstan and S Siberia to Sakhalin, Kuriles, N China, N Japan, Manchuria, Mongolia; nomadic in autumn and winter. Habitat: dense riparian scrub, wooded hillsides, boggy forests of pine, birch, alder, willows; sea buckthorn thickets; to 5,500 ft in Altai. ♂: generally pink with dark feathershafts on back; wing coverts mostly blackish-brown with broad white tips; flight feathers blackish, white-tipped; central tail feathers mainly black, outer ones mainly white; forehead, throat, cheeks silvery pink. ♀: yellowish-grey where ♂ pink, except rump, upper tail coverts. Immature similar but duller. Small flocks of juveniles form after breeding. Flight fluttering, wingbeats producing peculiar trill. ♂♂ flit about during courtship with soaring song flight, gliding down to ♀. Call: melodious 3-note whistle; song 'ripples like brook of spring water' (M. D. Zverev). Food mainly seeds, pecked at while swinging on plant. Breeding season from first half May (race *U.s. ussuriensis*); nest of dry grass, stalks, plant fibres, softly lined, placed *c.* 6 ft up, close to trunk of small tree, bush. 3 to 6 rich blue-green eggs marked brown incubated by ♀ and ♂, who also feed young. **934**

Uratelornis chimaera *Coraciidae: Brachypteracinae*

LONG-TAILED GROUND ROLLER   *c.* 18 ins
Confined to SW Madagascar; resident sandy bush and desert country. Upperparts light buffish brown with dark feather shafts and pale edges; flight feathers of rather short, rounded wings dark brown, wing coverts pale blue grey; outer feathers of very long, graduated tail white; white gorget framed by black and rufous streaks and black breast band; underparts pale buff; long legs light brown, heavy bill horn brown, large eyes light brown. Runs to cover when alarmed, standing still with tail raised. Normally on ground but perches scattered bushes. Reputed to 'hibernate' in dry season. ♀ and ♂ excavate slightly ascending tunnel *c.* 4 ft long with chamber at end. 3 or 4 eggs incubated by ♀, fed by ♂.

Uria aalge *Alcidae*

COMMON GUILLEMOT or MURRE   *c.* 16½ ins
Holarctic: similar to but much less extensive than Black Guillemot, *Cepphus grylle*, mainly NE Atlantic coasts Norway to Portugal, Iceland, Newfoundland area, and both sides Pacific to N California and Kuriles; isolated stations elsewhere; replaced to N by Brünnich's Guillemot, *U. lomvia*; winters at sea.

Breeds sea cliffs and offshore stacks. Summer: northern race *U. a. aalge* very similar to Razorbill, *Alca torda*, except for straight pointed bill; southern *albionis* has upperparts brown not black. Both show 'bridled' form with narrow white ring round eye tailing off into line along side of head; bridled proportion generally increases in colonies S to N. Legs yellowish to black, bill black (yellow inside), eyes black-brown. Throat and cheeks white in winter. Social at all times, with mutual and communal head-twisting displays. Rests on shanks on ledges, but can stand if necessary. Behaviour much as Razorbill. Usual call, from ledges or sea, growling *arrr*, with various elaborations. Takes mainly fish, marine worms, small crustaceans; fish carried more or less lengthwise in bill. Breeds from end April in S, in colonies on cliff ledges, sometimes top of stack or rocky island. One egg, immensely variable from white, blue, green, brown to (rare) red, with dark brown blotches, scrawls and spots, laid on bare ledge, tapering shape causing it to rotate and not roll over in wind. Incubation by ♀ and ♂ 28-30 days, fledging as Razorbill. **346**

Uroaeetus audax see **Aquila audax**

Urocynchramus pylzowi *Fringillidae*

PRZEVALSKI'S ROSEFINCH   *c.* 8 (tail 3½) ins
E Palaearctic: W China and Mongolia; thick low scrub, e.g. dwarf willows, rhododendrons, *Potentilla tenuifolia*, usually near water; vertical migration downhill in winter. ♂: upperparts from crown sandy brown, streaked black; flight feathers blackish brown edged warm buff or tawny; pale buff bar on brown coverts; central feathers of long, graduated tail blackish brown, edged white, outer ones crimson-rose; lores, 'eyebrow', cheeks, underparts rosy red shading to white on belly. ♀'s underparts white, faintly tinged rose on breast; throat, breast, flanks streaked black; outer tail feathers dull rosy white. Legs black, bill black and yellow, eyes dark brown. Presumably mainly seed-eating. Breeds alpine areas May, details unknown.

VAN DER DECKEN'S HORNBILL see **Tockus deckeni**

Vanellus armatus *or* Hoplopterus armatus
Charadriidae

BLACKSMITH PLOVER   *c.* 12 ins
Ethiopian: S from Kenya and Angola; resident in open country usually near fresh or brackish water. Forehead, crown, back of neck and upper tail coverts white; upper wing coverts and scapulars pale grey; cheeks, throat, nape, breast black; underparts white, also tail, but with broad terminal black band; black spur on wing; legs and bill black, eyes red. Juvenile similar but browner. Usually in pairs or small parties, sometimes larger flocks in good feeding areas, e.g. in evening on grassland where cattle have grazed; also recently burnt areas. Call: loud *klink klink klink*, like blacksmith hitting anvil. Food: insects and their larvae, small molluscs, worms. Breeds April to August in Kenya; from September in Cape Colony. Lined scrape among debris, often near water, holds 2 to 4 buffish brown eggs, marked dark brown and grey. Incubation and fledging much as other plovers (see *V. vanellus*). **268**

Vanellus coronatus *or* Stephanibyx coronatus
Charadriidae

CROWNED PLOVER   *c.* 12 ins
Ethiopian: E and S of region; resident, with local movements, on grassland in plains, sparsely wooded areas, even semi-desert, up to several thousand feet. Upperparts fawn brown, crown encircled by white above black stripe; black line between fawn breast and white underparts; flight feathers mainly black, white patch at base of wing; under wing and tail coverts and rump white; black subterminal band to tail; legs red, bill red, tip dark, eyes orange-yellow. Juvenile has buff edges to feathers of upperparts. Usually in pairs or small parties, building up to large flocks after breeding. Walks and runs with body horizontal, but stance upright. Plover-like dip forward to catch prey, mainly insects, especially beetles, grasshoppers and locusts, which it gleans from freshly burnt areas. Flight call *kree kree kree kreeip; kie-wiet* of

alarm. Communal dances at dusk and in night. Breeding mainly from July to December. Lined scrape holds usually 2 or 3 buffish brown eggs, marked dark brown and grey; incubation and fledging probably as other *Vanellus* plovers. **269**

Vanellus senegallus or Afribyx senegallus
Charadriidae
WATTLED PLOVER   14½ ins
Ethiopian: most of region except Congo forests and extreme SW; local movements seasonally. Mainly swamps but lowland grassland and cultivated areas near water. ♂: upperparts olivaceous brown; crown black but centre and forehead white; neck streaked black; outer wing coverts, inner secondaries white, other flight feathers black, wing spur small; white tail has subterminal black bar; chin, throat black; breast, upper belly pale grey brown, divided from rest of white underparts by blackish band; underwing white; legs, bill (black-tipped), eyes yellow, broad dark red and yellow wattles. ♀ has much less black on throat. Gregarious and tame; noisy in breeding season with shrill *peep peep*, intensified as alarm note (said to be sure indicator of water); also *choo-ee* call. Food: insects and grass seeds. Breeds March-April in N of range, September to December in S, making vestigial scrape, often on mound. 3 to 4 buff or olive brown eggs, marked black, sepia grey. Incubation and fledging as *V. vanellus*; sometimes 2 broods in S. **270**

Vanellus spinosus or Hoplopterus spinosus
Charadriidae
SPURWING PLOVER   10½ ins
SE Palaearctic (Greece, Turkey, Asia Minor, Middle East); Ethiopian N of Equator (has bred S Africa); some local migration by night. Habitats: alluvial and cultivated country near fresh water, e.g. Nile Valley, becoming habituated to man; marshes by sea in recent colonisation of Greece. Predominantly black and white with brown back and upper wing coverts; crown and crest black; cheeks, sides and back of neck and rump white; tail and tips of sharply spurred wings black; chin to belly black, underwing and tail coverts white; legs and bill black, eyes carmine. Juvenile duller. Noisy and aggressive, attacking intruders near nest. Hunched posture and slow flight. Often seen with crocodiles. Monotonous, plaintive call by night, also *did ye do it* in flight and sharp *trak trak trak* of alarm. Food mostly taken at waterside: beetles and other insects. Breeds mainly April-August. Scrape, often lined, on sand or mud flats, rocky islets in rivers. 3 or 4 greyish-buff eggs, marked dark brown and lilac, incubated by ♀ and ♂; details as *V. vanellus*. May have 2 broods. **271**

Vanellus tectus or Sarciphorus tectus *Charadriidae*
BLACKHEAD PLOVER   10 ins
Ethiopian: across region from Senegal, widening to include Red Sea coast, Uganda, Kenya; local migrations. Habitat dry plains and open areas in bush. Upperparts pale brown; outer wing coverts white, flight feathers dark; white tail has subterminal black bar; crown black with short, pointed crest; forehead white, extending over eye round nape; chin white, surrounded black from eye to longish plumes of breast; rest of underparts white; legs carmine, small red wattle in front of orange-brown eye. Small flocks; tame, but will mob passing birds of prey, though rather slow in flight. Shrill whistling call as birds rise in alarm; also loud hollow cry. Feeds largely by night on insects and molluscs. Breeding season variable throughout range; makes scrape on open ground, lined grass, often edged fine gravel. 2 or 3 clay or buff eggs, spotted and blotched black and purple. Incubation and fledging much as *V. vanellus*. **272**

Vanellus tricolor or Zonifer tricolor *Charadriidae*
BANDED PLOVER   *c.* 10½ ins
Continental Australia (except tropical N), Tasmania; nomadic according to local conditions. Habitat short grassland usually near water; cultivated land; mud flats, sometimes arid plains. Upperparts light brown; head and neck blackish with white stripe behind eye; throat whitish, black band from below eye downwards across breast; primaries black, outer secondaries

black and white; tail white with terminal black band; underparts white; rather short legs purplish red, bill yellow, tip black; bulbous red wattles above it; eyes yellow. Habits much as other *Vanellus* plovers. Call: melodious *a chee chee chee*. Food: insects, flushed by shuffling with foot, and their larvae; seeds of grasses. Breeds July to November, often socially. Scrape on bare ground, sometimes in cattle dung, holds usually 4 light brown eggs, marked dark brown and grey; incubation by ♀ and ♂ *c.* 28 days: feigns injury or mobs intruders near nest or brood. **273**

Vanellus vanellus *Charadriidae*
LAPWING   *c.* 12 ins
Palaearctic: broad band (S Scandinavia to Mediterranean) across temperate zone from Atlantic to Pacific; partial migrant southward from breeding areas to N Africa, Middle East, Oriental region, Japan. Habitats: open country from coastal saltings to moorlands at 3,000 ft; arable fields, wet meadows, shingle and sand dunes; winters on grassland (often when flooded) and flat coastal areas. ♂: upperparts, including crown and curved crest, metallic green; broad black band across breast; chin, cheeks, underparts white; also tail, with black terminal band; under tail coverts rufous buff. ♀: crest shorter and suffusion of buff on cheeks and back in winter, also in juvenile. Legs brownish flesh, bill black, eyes dark brown. In winter flocks feed scattered, coalesce to rest, breaking up into pairs early spring when ♂♂ give tumbling flight displays, 'singing' *peerweet weet weet . . . weet weet;* usual call *pee-weet* gives alternative name. ♂ also shows rufous under tail in scrape-forming action. Food much as Golden Plover, *Pluvialis apricaria*, 90% animal matter. Breeds, often socially, from mid March Britain. Lined scrape, sometimes quite substantial nest of dead stems, on hummock or flat in variety of situations, holds usually 4 light brown eggs, marked dark brown; incubation by ♀ and ♂ 24-31 days; both parents tend young who fly 4½-5 weeks. **274**

VANGA, LAFRESNAYE'S see **Xenopirostris xenopirostris**

VARIABLE
    SEEDEATER see **Sporophila americana**
    SUNBIRD see **Cinnyris venustus**

VARIEGATED WREN see **Malurus lamberti**

VASA PARROT, GREATER see **Coracopsis vasa**

VELVET ASITY see **Philepitta castanea**

VERDIN see **Auriparus flavus**

VERMILION-CROWNED FLYCATCHER see **Myiozetetes similis**

Vermivora celata *Parulidae*
ORANGE-CROWNED WARBLER   5 ins
Nearctic: breeds from near tree limit Alaska, NW Canada, S to S Manitoba, New Mexico, N Lower California; winters from S USA to Guatemala. Habitat open woodlands with heavy undergrowth, young secondary growth, riparian thickets and, in far N, stream bottoms with dwarf trees; chaparral scrub in California; winters live-oak woods (Florida), woodland edge, parks, gardens. Upperparts olive green, feathers grey-tipped except on rump; round orange crown patch usually concealed; underparts yellow, lightly streaked. Duskier in autumn and immature with less difference between upper and underparts. Legs brown, bill dark, eyes dark brown. Western race ('Lutescent Warbler') much yellower. Song: varied, musical trill, rising in pitch after slow beginning, then dying away; call: sharp *chip*. Insectivorous, feeding different levels of vegetation. Breeds from early April in S to June in N of range; nest of coarse grass, bark fibres, softly lined, generally well hidden on ground. Usually 5 white eggs, finely spotted red-brown, incubated ♀ *c.* 12 days; young fly after same period. **901**

VERREAUX'S
    EAGLE see **Aquila verreauxii**
    GIANT EAGLE OWL see **Bubo lacteus**

Vidua macroura *Estrildidae*
PINTAILED WHYDAH   ♀: 4½; ♂ (with tail): 12-13 ins
Ethiopian: almost throughout region; resident grasslands, open bush and scrub; cultivated areas; near habitations. ♂: crown, back, shoulders, flight feathers, tail with enormously elongated 4 central feathers, black; rest of plumage white. ♀: brown, streaked darker like sparrow, with buff stripe over crown. Non-breeding ♂ like ♀ but more white on wings. Legs black, bill red, eyes dark brown. Immature earth-brown, streaked above, buff below, bill reddish-black. In small parties, ♂♂ outnumbered by ♀♀, immatures; large flocks after breeding, roosting in trees. Jerky, erratic flight, ♂ wiggling tail; in display dances or hovers over ♀, chases other ♂♂; repeats *tseet tseet tsip* in courtship flight, quivering wings; also shrill, sustained twittering song; repeated *chitt* of alarm. Food mainly grass and other small seeds. Breeding season depends on hosts: Waxbill, *Estrilda astrild* and *Cisticola* species, sometimes laying first egg, white or pale cream, in nest; young reared with host's brood. Probably polygamous. **947**

VIOLET CUCKOO see **Chalcites xanthorhynchus**

VIOLETEAR HUMMINGBIRD, SPARKLING see **Colibri coruscans**

VIOLET-HEADED LORIKEET see **Eos squamata**

VIREO,
    CHESTNUT-SIDED SHRIKE see **Vireolanius meliophrys**
    WHITE-EYED see **Vireo griseus**

Vireo griseus *Vireonidae*
WHITE-EYED VIREO   5 ins
Nearctic, marginally Neotropical: breeds E USA from Massachusetts, Ohio, S Wisconsin, SE Nebraska, to S Florida, Gulf Coast, N Mexico; winters from SE USA to Honduras. Habitat woodland edge, dense broadleaved thickets with brambles, vines, often near water, secondary growth on hillsides, hedgerows. Upperparts greenish yellow, wing feathers dusky with pale edges and two distinct white bars, tail feathers dusky edged yellow; narrow yellow 'spectacles'; chin white shading to yellow on flanks, belly; legs brown, bill dark brown, eyes white. Immature shows yellow 'spectacles' round brown eyes. Inquisitive, can be called up by 'squeaking', otherwise hard to see. Calls: harsh mew, short tick, single loud whistle; song series of 5 to 7 distinct notes very variable but constantly repeated. Mainly insectivorous but takes fruit autumn and winter: sumac, grapes, wax myrtle. Breeds end May-June; rather cone-shaped, ragged-looking nest of leaves, moss, wasp nest 'paper', sticks woven with plant fibres and suspended but well hidden 3 to 6 ft up in thick vegetation. 4 white eggs, scattered brown dots at big end. **906**

Vireolanius melitophrys *Vireonidae*
CHESTNUT-SIDED SHRIKE VIREO   *c.* 7 ins
Neotropical: S Mexico to Guatemala; resident mainly oak forests 4,000 to 10,000 ft. Upperparts including wings, tail, olive green; crown, hindneck slate-grey bordered broad yellow 'eyebrows'; black band from lores to earcoverts, black moustachial stripe; underparts white, with chestnut breast band extending to sides and flanks. Hunts, often in pairs, high in trees, moving cautiously, sometimes hanging upside down to seize insect; larger prey held beneath one foot and tackled with strong bill. Calls include low, nasal rattle, penetrating screech. Breeding habits unknown (A. F. Skutch).

Vultur gryphus *Cathartidae*
ANDEAN CONDOR   48-52 ins
Neotropical: Andes from Venezuela to Cape Horn; commonest Central Peru to Aysén (Chile); resident mountains, above 10,000 ft N of Peru, to sea level farther S. Largest flying bird, wingspan 9-10 ft.

Generally glossy black; whitish patch upper wing coverts; white ruff; bare head and neck usually red, sometimes black; ♂ has fleshy dark red or black crest; legs grey, bill horn white, eyes brown. Main food carrion: located by eyesight from height; first bird to carcase may be followed by 10 to 20 others, planing down in spirals, final approach on foot; also takes coastal refuse in S of range, dead birds on Peruvian guano islands. Lays September-October in large nest of sticks and debris in mountain cave or cleft. Single (occasionally 2) white egg, incubated ♀ and ♂ 54-58 days; chick takes 16 months to fledge, fed ♀ and ♂, so breeding only in alternate years.

VULTURE
AFRICAN WHITE-BACK see **Gyps africanus**
ASIAN KING see **Sarcogyps calvus**
BLACK see **Coragyps atratus**
EGYPTIAN see **Neophron percnopterus**
GRIFFON see **Gyps fulvus**
INDIAN WHITE-BACKED see **Gyps bengalensis**
PALM-NUT see **Gypohierax angolensis**
RUPPELL's see under **Gyps africanus**
SOUTH AMERICAN KING see **Sarcorhamphus papa**
TURKEY see **Cathartes aura**
WHITE-BACKED see **Gyps africanus**
WHITE-HEADED see **Trigonoceps occipitalis**

VULTURINE
GUINEAFOWL see **Acryllium vulturinum**
PARROT see **Gypositta vulturina**

WAGTAIL,
AFRICAN PIED see **Motacilla aguimp**
FOREST see **Dendromanthus indicus**
GREY see **Motacilla cinerea**
PIED see **Motacilla alba**
WHITE see **Motacilla alba**
YELLOW see **Motacilla flava**

WAHLBERG'S EAGLE see **Aquila wahlbergi**

WALDRAPP see under **Geronticus calvus**

WALLCREEPER see **Tichodroma muraria**

WANDERING
ALBATROSS see **Diomedea exulans**
TATTLER see under **Tringa brevipes**

WARBLER,
AFRICAN SEDGE see **Bradypterus baboecala**
BARRED see **Sylvia nisoria**
BLACK AND WHITE see **Mniotilta varia**
BLACKPOLL see under **Mniotilta varia**
CANADA see **Wilsonia canadensis**
CETTI's see **Cettia cetti**
CHINESE BUSH see **Cettia diphone**
CLAMOROUS see **Acrocephalus stentoreus**
DESERT FANTAIL see **Cisticola aridula**
GARDEN see **Sylvia borin**
GRASSHOPPER see **Locustella naevia**
GRAY'S GRASSHOPPER see **Locustella fasciata**
GREAT REED see **Acrocephalus arundinaceus**
GREY see **Gerygone igata**
GREY-BACKED see **Cisticola subruficapilla**
KNYSNA see **Bradypterus sylvaticus**
MAGNOLIA see **Dendroica magnoliae**
MARSH see **Acrocephalus palustris**
MELODIOUS see **Hippolais polyglotta**
OLIVE see **Peucedramus taeniatus**
ORANGE-CROWNED see **Vermivora celata**
ORPHEAN see **Sylvia hortensis**
PARULA see under **Dendroica dominica**
PLAIN WILLOW see under **Phylloscopus collybita**
REED see under **Acrocephalus palustris**
RUFOUS-CROWNED see **Basileuterus rufifrons**
RUFOUS GRASS see **Cisticola galactotes**
SARDINIAN see **Sylvia melanocephala**
SEDGE see **Acrocephalus schoenbaenus**
SEVERTGOV's TIT see **Leptopoecile sophiae**
SHORT-TAILED BUSH see **Cisticola squameiceps**
SPECKLED see **Chthonicola sagittata**
SUBALPINE see **Sylvia cantillans**

SUTTON's see under **Dendroica dominica**
WHITE-THROATED see **Gerygone olivacea**
WILLOW see **Phylloscopus trochilis**
WILSON's see **Wilsonia pusilla**
WOOD see **Phylloscopus sibilatrix**
WORM-EATING see **Helmitheros vermivorus**
YELLOW see **Dendroica patechia**
YELLOW-THROATED see **Dendroica dominica**

WATER DIKKOP see **Burhinus vermiculatus**

WATTLEBIRD, LITTLE see **Anthochaera chrysoptera**

WATTLED
CRANE see **Grus carunculatus**
IBIS see **Bostrychia carunculata**
JACANA see **Jacana jacana**
PLOVER see **Vanellus senegallus**
STARLING see **Creatophora cinerea**

WAXBILL,
COMMON see **Estrilda astrild**
CRIMSON-RUMPED see under **Estrilda astrild**
SYDNEY see **Estrilda temporalis**

WAXWING,
BOHEMIAN see **Bombycilla garrulus**
CEDAR see **Bombycilla cedrorum**

WEAVER,
BLACK-HEADED see **Ploceus cucullatus**
SOCIAL see **Philetarius socius**
SPECKLED-FRONTED see **Sporopipes frontalis**
SPOTTED-BACKED see **Ploceus cucullatus**
STRIATED see **Ploceus manyar**
STRIPE-BREASTED SPARROW see **Plocepasser mahali**
WHITE-BROWED SPARROW see **Plocepasser mahali**
WHITE-HEADED BUFFALO see **Dinemellia dinemelli**

WEDGE-BILLED WOODCREEPER see **Glyphorhynchus spirurus**

WEDGE-TAILED
EAGLE see **Aquila audax**
GREEN PIGEON see **Treron sphenura**
SHEARWATER see **Puffinus pacificus**

WEEBILL, BROWN see **Smicrornis brevirostris**

WEKA see **Gallirallus australis**

WEST AFRICAN BLACK FLYCATCHER see under **Melaenornis pammelaina**

WEST INDIAN NIGHTHAWK see **Chordeiles gundlachii**

WESTERN
BLACK-HEADED ORIOLE see under **Oriolus larvatus**
BLUEBIRD see under **Peucedramus taeniatus**
GREBE see **Aechmophorus occidentalis**
KINGBIRD see **Tyrannus verticalis**
MAGPIE see under **Gymnorhina tibicen**
MEADOWLARK see **Sturnella neglecta**

WHALE HEAD see **Balaeniceps rex**

WHEATEAR see **Oenanthe oenanthe**

WHEATEAR,
BLACK-EARED see **Oenanthe hispanica**
HOODED see **Oenanthe monacha**

WHIMBREL see **Numenius phaeopus**

WHIPBIRD, EASTERN see **Psophodes olivaceus**

WHIP-POOR-WILL see **Caprimulgus vociferus**

WHISKERED TERN see **Chlidonias hybrida**

WHISTLER,
GOLDEN see **Pachycephala pectoralis**
GREY-HEADED see under **Pachycephala pectoralis**

WHISTLING EAGLE see **Haliastur sphenorus**

WHITE
BELLBIRD see under **Procnias nudicollis**
CRANE, SIBERIAN see **Grus leucogeranus**
HELMET SHRIKE see **Prionops plumata**
HERON, GREAT see **Egretta alba**
IBIS (AMERICAN) see **Eudocimus albus**
IBIS (AUSTRALIAN) see under **Threskiornis spinicollis**
PELICAN see **Pelecanus onocrotalus**
STORK see **Ciconia alba**
TERN see **Gygis alba**
WAGTAIL see **Motacilla alba**

WHITE-BACKED
VULTURE, AFRICAN see **Gyps africanus**
VULTURE, INDIAN see **Gyps bengalensis**

WHITE-BEARDED
HONEYEATER see **Meliornis novaehollandiae**
MANAKIN see **Manacus manacus**

WHITE-BELLIED
BUSTARD see **Eupodotis senegalensis**
GO-AWAY-BIRD see **Corythaixoides leucogaster**
SEEDSNIPE see **Attagis malouinus**
SUNBIRD see **Cinnyris talatala**

WHITE-BILLED DIVER see under **Gavia immer**

WHITE-BREASTED
KINGFISHER see **Halcyon smyrnensis**
ROBIN see **Eopsaltria georgiana**
SEA EAGLE see **Haliaeetus leucogaster**
SWIFTLET see **Collocalia esculenta**
WOOD SWALLOW see **Artamus leucorhynchus**

WHITE-BROWED
BABBLER see **Pomatostomus superciliosus**
COUCAL see **Centropus superciliosus**
SCRUB ROBIN see **Erythropygia zambesiana**
SCRUB WREN see **Sericornis frontalis**
SPARROW WEAVER see **Plocepasser mahli**
WOOD SWALLOW see **Artamus superciliosus**

WHITE-CHEEKED
BULBUL see under **Pycnonotus cafer**
HONEYEATER see **Meliornis niger**

WHITE-COLLARED
PIGEON see **Columba albitorquis**
PRATINCOLE see **Galachrysia nuchalis**

WHITE-CRESTED
HORNBILL, ASIAN see **Berenicornis comatus**
TOURACO see under **Tauraco livingstonii**

WHITE-CROWNED
CLIFF CHAT see **Thamnolaea coronata**
SHRIKE see **Eurocephalus anguitimens**
SPARROW see **Zonotrichia leucophrys**

WHITE-EARED HONEYEATER see **Meliphaga leucotis**

WHITE-EYE,
GREEN see under **Zosterops pallida**
GREY-BREASTED see **Zosterops lateralis**
INDIAN see **Zosterops palpebrosa**
KIKUYU see **Zosterops kikuyensis**
PALE see **Zosterops pallidus**
YELLOW see **Zosterops senegalensis**

WHITE-EYED
FOLIAGE GLEANER see **Automolus leucophthalmus**
SLATY FLYCATCHER see **Dioptrornis fischeri**
VIREO see **Vireo griseus**